GEOMETRY OF ENGINEERING DRAWING

Geometry of Engineering Drawing

DESCRIPTIVE GEOMETRY BY THE DIRECT METHOD

George J. Hood, M.E.

Professor Emeritus of Engineering Drawing
University of Kansas

Albert S. Palmerlee, A.M.

Professor of Engineering Drawing
University of Kansas

FOURTH EDITION

McGRAW-HILL BOOK COMPANY, INC.

New York   Toronto   London

1958

GEOMETRY OF ENGINEERING DRAWING

THE MAPLE PRESS COMPANY, YORK, PA.

PREFACE

Descriptive geometry is the outstanding subject for training the imagination to visualize structures and objects. It also provides training in analyzing the geometry of three-dimensional structures, and in accurately representing structures in drawings. The ever-increasing complexity of engineering designs requires increasing ability to visualize clearly and to represent accurately.

At the time of publication of the first edition of this textbook in 1926, a more descriptive name for the subject seemed advisable. From a long list of possible names, "Geometry of Engineering Drawing" was adopted. And, to distinguish the new method from the older projection method, the subtitle "Descriptive Geometry by the Direct Method," was chosen. A short history of the origin of this method is given later in this preface.

The direct method of descriptive geometry employs the practical attitude of mind, the vocabulary, and the methods used by the professional engineer to visualize and design structures and to make and read drawings. The direct method fosters habits of thought, and it develops an ability to visualize and to draw that usually exceeds the ability of the student who is taught to think in terms of projections.

By the direct method, the attention is focused on the visualized structure or object. Each view of the object is observed by looking at the object in a definite direction. In the drawings, each view is considered and spoken of as if it were an actual view of the three dimensional object. A view is never considered as two dimensional, or as projected or drawn on a plane. In agreement with engineering practice, the direct method discards projections, planes of projection, quadrants, ground lines, and traces of planes. The projection method is described in Chapter 14.

The frequent use of auxiliary and oblique views in this textbook has led some to refer to the direct method as "the auxiliary-view method." That conclusion is not justified, since no one type of view has any precedence over any other type. Auxiliary and oblique views are readily visualized and drawn by those who think in terms of the direct method.

v

And these views often are useful or necessary when designing structures and when solving problems related to the geometry of structures.

In this Fourth Edition of "Geometry of Engineering Drawing," the principal change to be noted is that now there are two authors. Professor Albert S. Palmerlee is co-author of this edition. He has provided and check-solved all of the 960 problems of the Problem Section. He also has suggested changes in the text, and has written some of the new material. From now on, Professor Palmerlee will be the active author of this book, and Professor Hood will retire.

The first four chapters have been rewritten, and the order of presenting the various items has been changed. Paragraphs regarding the relations of views have been incorporated in Chapters 2 and 3. Necessary definitions have been assembled in one article. Some new material and new illustrations appear. The importance of visualization is emphasized. Each chapter now begins with Article 1, and with Figure 1.

Concerning the order in which the material is presented, and in regard to training the constructive imagination, Professor Thomas E. French has written: "That this may be accomplished more readily by taking up solids before points and lines has been demonstrated beyond dispute."

Wall charts, 3 feet square, are available, as is explained in a statement following this Preface. These charts are enlargements of some of the basic figures of the textbook, and of some of the complicated figures. The use of the charts relieves the teacher of the need to draw accurate figures on the chalkboard, and saves for class discussion a considerable amount of time that otherwise would be required to draw the necessary figures.

The continuity of the text is maintained by assembling the problems in classified groups in the Problem Section. Each group is referred to in its logical place in the text. The problems are stated in a variety of ways in order to develop the ingenuity, resourcefulness, and self-reliance of the student, and to give him training in visualizing, in reading exactly, and in following specifications. The 960 problems offer a considerable range of choice, and are sufficient for several years' use without repetition. The problems of Group 5 are particularly useful for training and for testing the ability of the student to visualize. For examinations and tests, the problems appearing in the earlier editions of this textbook are useful.

A simple coordinate system and coordinately ruled problem sheets provide means for locating the given data of each problem quickly and accurately. The ruled paper also makes easier the work of checking the accuracy of the solutions. A convenient key for correcting problems is printed inside the back cover of this book.

The problem sheet is shown to reduced scale in the Problem Section of this textbook. The actual size of the problem space has been increased to 8 by 9 inches. Samples of printed problem sheets may be obtained from the publishers of this book who can supply the sheets in any quantity. A coordinately ruled chalkboard in the classroom is a convenience.

The use of coordinate paper permits the accurate solution of problems either with or without the use of a drawing board and T-square. The essential tools—triangles, pencil, and compass—can readily be carried by the student so that he can solve problems anywhere. If unruled paper is used for solving problems, it will be necessary for the student also to have a drawing board, T-square, and scale.

This textbook contains much more material than can be assigned for study in the time normally allowed for descriptive geometry. A comprehensive textbook, however, gives dignity to the subject, gives the student a broader realization of the many applications of geometry to engineering drawings, and aids in overcoming any doubts that the student may have regarding the practical value of descriptive geometry. The student who has become familiar with this textbook should find continued use for it as a reference book.

A short history of the origin of the direct method of descriptive geometry may be of interest. In 1902 the senior author began teaching descriptive geometry by the projection method, and in 1909 he published a small problem book for use in his classes.

During this time he read many engineering magazines and designed a number of machines. He soon began to realize that he visualized the views in drawings as three dimensional, and he began to wonder why he was teaching that views are projected on a plane as if they were two dimensional. Also, he noted that many descriptive geometry problems could be solved without reference to a ground line, and that there was no need for traces of planes in engineering drawings.

But the projection method was old and firmly established. It would be presumptuous for a young teacher to think that he could change all of this; and so he continued to teach projection.

But he also continued to make plans for teaching descriptive geometry without using projections or planes of projection. This development of new ways of thinking proceeded slowly. New methods, vocabulary, definitions, and principles were needed. Gradually he introduced these new ideas in his classes. Then came World War I, and there was no spare time.

As soon as peace was declared, the senior author began to expand and to organize his notes, and to make the many drawings that would be needed for illustrations. The result was the publication in 1926 of the first edition of his textbook on the direct method of descriptive geometry.

At first, this new method met with considerable resistance. Only a few teachers were willing to pioneer in its use. But gradually the direct method has been accepted and used by a considerable number of teachers.

We express our grateful appreciation to those teachers who were willing to pioneer in the use of the direct method; to the late Professor Thomas E. French for reviewing the preliminary manuscript and for his encouragement; to Professors Richard L. Grider, Frank E. Jones, Charles W. Kinney, and Harold B. Mummert for criticisms and/or check-solving the problems of the earlier editions; to Henry J. Hood for check-solving the problems of the third edition; for helpful suggestions given by teachers of Ohio State University, and by teachers of other schools.

Criticisms, corrections, and suggestions will be appreciated by the authors.

GEORGE J. HOOD
ALBERT S. PALMERLEE

Wall Charts for Use with
Geometry of Engineering Drawing

Enlarged illustrations of some of the figures of this textbook are available. These are in the form of blue-line prints one yard square.

The use of these charts in the classroom saves much time that otherwise would be required to draw accurate figures on the chalkboard. When mounted on wallboard and placed on the chalk trough, the figures and the lettering are clearly visible across the average-sized classroom.

A list of the Figures that are available may be obtained from the Department of Engineering Drawing, University of Kansas, Lawrence, Kansas. Sets of prints may be procured from the Department at the current commercial price for prints, plus postage.

CONTENTS

FIGURE 1. Hoover Dam and Power Plant. Illustrations of other engineering projects appear throughout this book. (*Courtesy of the U. S. Bureau of Reclamation.*)

Chapter 1

THE ENGINEER AND
ENGINEERING DRAWINGS

1. The engineer adapts the materials and controls the forces of nature for the convenience and use of mankind. He does this by designing structures of many kinds: aircraft, apparatus, bridges, buildings, dams, factories, instruments, machines, power plants, railways, roads, ships, tools, etc.

When the engineer undertakes the design of a new structure, he first visualizes the appearance of the proposed structure as clearly as he is able. Then, by means of drawings and words, he describes the structure to the draftsman who makes the assembly and detail drawings. These drawings convey to the workman the information that he needs to make the various parts of the structure and to assemble it as a whole.

The *geometry of engineering drawing* explains the application of geometrical principles to engineering drawings.

Descriptive geometry by the direct method employs the engineer's practical and direct method of thinking and talking about the drawings that he makes and reads.

2. An Engineering Design. Figure 1: Hoover Dam and Power Plant were designed and constructed through the cooperation of engineers from every field of engineering—civil, electrical, mechanical, mining, hydraulic, structural, railway, refrigeration, industrial, sanitary, chemical, geological. All these combined their knowledge and experience in the design of this great engineering project.

Hoover Dam and Power Plant were designed and constructed with the following purposes in view: flood control, river regulation, silt control, power development, irrigation, and domestic water supply.

The engineers who planned this project observed the deep canyon and its sheer walls. They visualized the dam and power plant in place while keeping in mind the several purposes these were to serve. They surveyed the many square miles of mountainous country from the ground and from the air, made the topographical maps, planned the innumerable details, and made hundreds of drawings. Only then did these engineers assemble the materials and begin to supervise the construction.

1

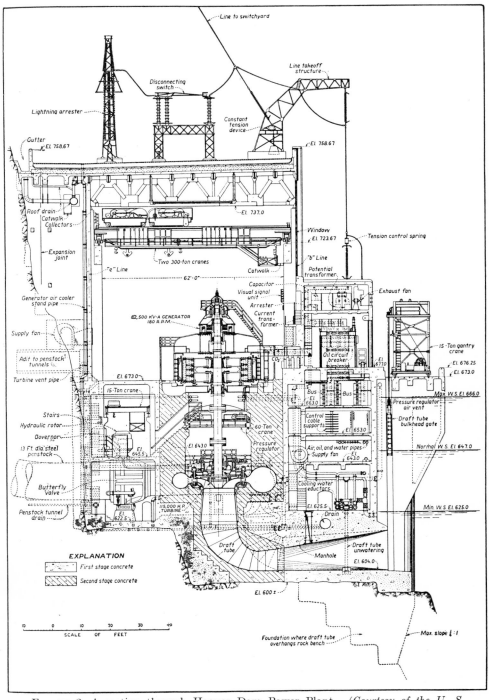

FIGURE 2. A section through Hoover Dam Power Plant. (*Courtesy of the U. S. Bureau of Reclamation.*)

2

3. An Assembly Drawing.   Figure 2 is one view of the power plant at Hoover Dam.   In this drawing some parts of the building, concrete, and machines have been sectioned, or cut away, to show more clearly interior parts that otherwise would have been hidden.

The reader of this view is looking in a horizontal direction.   He should imagine that he is looking at the actual power plant.   In this view he sees the heights and widths of the various parts, and he can measure these with the scale that is shown in the drawing.   Although the reader visualizes the view of the power plant as three-dimensional, he realizes that the front to back, or near and far, *depth* dimensions cannot be seen or measured in this view.

Every view of a drawing should be visualized as if it were an actual view of the object that is represented in the drawing.   The reader of a drawing should train himself to visualize and imagine each view as standing out from the paper on which the view is drawn.   A drawing of a three-dimensional object should never be thought of as flat, as a projection on a plane, or as lines drawn on a flat sheet of paper.   The reader of a drawing imagines that he is looking in a definite direction at the actual object.

Figures 1 and 2 should be studied in connection with the plan drawing of this project that is shown in Chapter 12.   These three figures will show that the basic plan is quite simple; that the entire design is a combination of cooperating units, machines, and structural parts; and that the total design is an assemblage of thousands of individual parts requiring hundreds of drawings to show all details.

Some of the data of the above-described engineering project are here stated:

The entire height of Hoover Dam from foundation rock to crest is 727 feet.   The length along the crest is 1,282 feet, and the thickness at the base is 660 feet.   The water surface of the Colorado River is raised 584 feet, and the area of the resulting reservoir is 229 square miles.   The water pressure at the bottom of the dam is 45,000 pounds per square foot.

The powerhouse, 19 stories high, is dwarfed by the dam.   The continuous power output is 663,000 horsepower.   The water rushes through the tunnels at a speed of 120 miles per hour.

The project required 4,400,000 cubic yards of concrete, 5,000,000 barrels of cement, and 51,000,000 pounds of steel reinforcement.   To prevent the concrete from making steam while setting, refrigerated cooling water was pumped through 582 miles of piping embedded in the blocks of concrete.   Construction began in 1931 and was completed in 1936.

The story of the design and construction of Hoover Dam illustrates that the engineer should have a broad general education, a good understanding of the various fields of engineering, and a thorough understanding of his own specialized field.   He must be able to impart his ideas to others by means of spoken and written words and by means of drawings.

4. Visualizing and Drawing Structures. The design of a structure originates in the mind of an engineer. He knows the purpose for which the structure is to be used, and the requirements of the design. He visualizes the structure as a whole, the function and the shape of each part, and the relation of each part to the adjacent parts.

The structure is then represented in drawings. The builder of the structure studies and reads the drawings, and he visualizes and builds the structure as it originally was visualized in the mind of the designing engineer.

The engineer thus transmits his ideas to others by means of a spoken and written language and by means of drawings. Adequate training in both these mediums of expression is an essential part of the education of the student of engineering. When describing even a simple structure, the spoken and written language soon becomes inadequate and resort must be had to drawings. Engineering drawing is a universal language used and understood by engineers throughout the world.

Even though an engineer may not be engaged directly in designing structures, he must know when a drawing is correct and complete, and he must have the ability to visualize any structure that is represented in a drawing. The engineer must know both how to make and how to read drawings.

New processes, new methods, and new devices for doing things hitherto impossible, and new materials having new properties, are continually being made available. Each new development opens up new possibilities in design and requires of the engineer an ever-expanding and a more definite fund of knowledge. The increasing complexity and refinement in present-day design require increasing ability to visualize thoroughly and to represent accurately.

5. Practical Applications. The geometry of engineering drawing has many practical applications. It is used in visualizing and describing structures of every possible shape, in solving problems related to the exact description of structures, in determining the geometrical elements of structures, in determining the geometrical relations between these elements, in finding the actual lengths of the parts of structures, in drawing structures of unusual shape, in showing structures in oblique position, in determining the lines of intersection between the surfaces of structures, in developing patterns for structures that are to be made of sheet plate, in drawing unusual surfaces, in making pictorial drawings and production illustrations, and in solving topographical and mining problems.

This textbook should aid the practicing engineer in solving many practical problems connected with the geometry of structures and their representation in drawings.

The subject of engineering drawing applies the methods of the geometry of engineering drawing, and, in addition, is concerned with placing dimensions, explanatory notes, and symbols on drawings.

The student should refer to his textbook in engineering drawing to learn the best methods of manipulating his triangles and other drawing instruments.   Understanding and using these professional methods will save time and will produce better drawings.

6. To the Student.   Many students find the geometry of engineering drawing quite difficult during the first few weeks.   Time, patience, and work are required to secure an understanding of the many new ideas and new techniques that are needed at the very beginning of this subject.

The solution of the problems requires a considerable amount of thinking, of ingenuity, and of resourcefulness.   Each problem should be analyzed into its simple elements.   The more complex problems are but combinations of simpler problems, involving the application of general principles and a consideration of many small details.   To solve a problem readily it is necessary to visualize the object that is to be drawn, and to understand the elementary principles that underlie the solution.   Memorizing the appearance of the solution of one problem gives little aid in solving a similar problem.   Solving a problem is an exacting job.   It is necessary to read exactly, to think exactly, and to draw exactly.   The student who thus disciplines himself soon becomes a more capable student, and he finds real enjoyment in solving the problems.   The successful engineer must solve his own problems.

Experience in reading and understanding engineering drawings is gained by studying the explanations and illustrations of this textbook.   And experience in making correct engineering drawings is gained by solving the problems.

7. Geometrical Elements of Structures.   Structures occupy space and are three-dimensional.   Every structure may be considered as a combination of various geometrical elements.   The basic geometrical elements are points, lines, and surfaces.   These basic elements are combined to form the corners, edges, and surfaces of solids.   And the solids are assembled by engineers in an infinite variety of combinations to form the parts and units of the structures that they design.

The chart of Figure 5 shows a logical classification of both the common and the unusual geometrical elements of structures.   All of these elements are useful in engineering designs.   Figures 3 and 4 show pictorial illustrations of the geometrical elements.   All three of these figures are useful for reference.

Before beginning the study of the next chapter, it is worthwhile to take a trip through this book.   Turn the pages slowly.   Note the chapter headings.   Look carefully at the illustrations and try to understand what they represent.   Read a little of the text here and there.   Such a preview is not a waste of time.   It will give some idea of what is to be expected as each new chapter is approached.

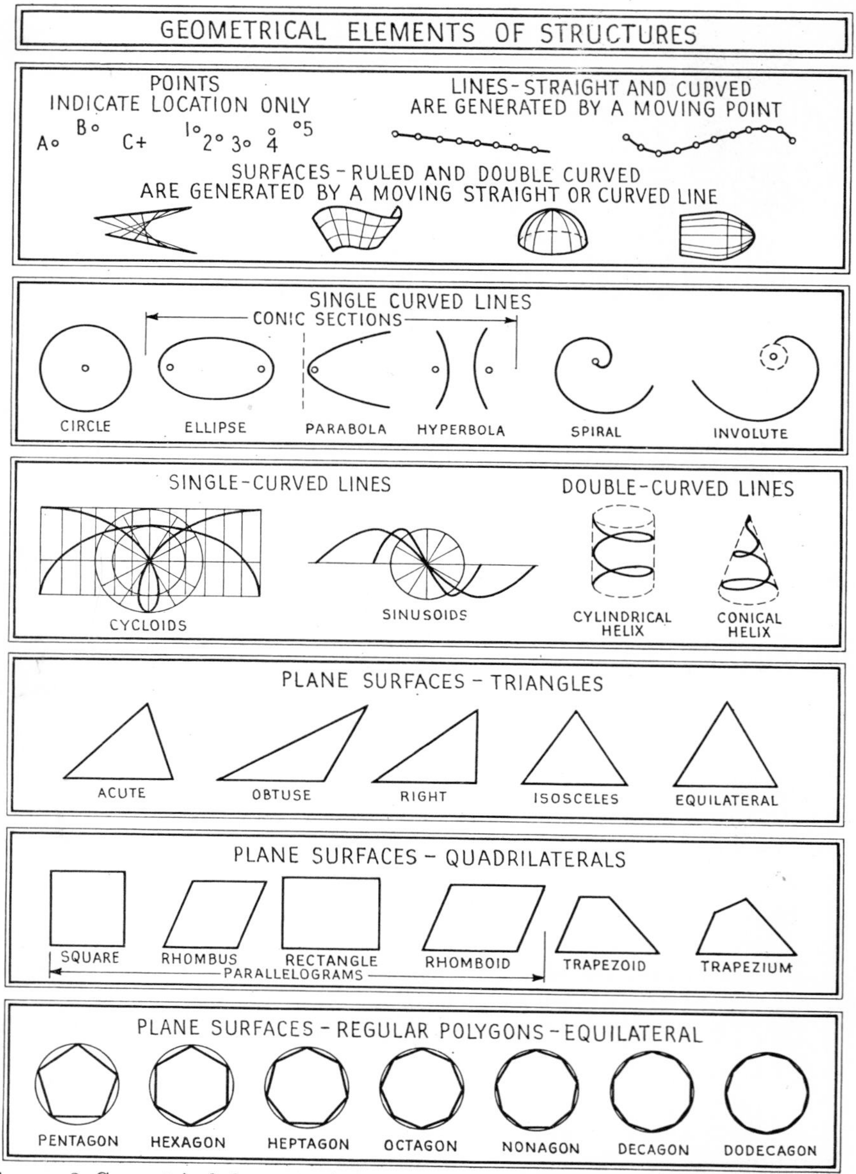

FIGURE 3. Geometrical elements of structures. (*Adapted from French and Vierck "Engineering Drawing," 8th ed., New York, McGraw-Hill Book Co., 1953.*)

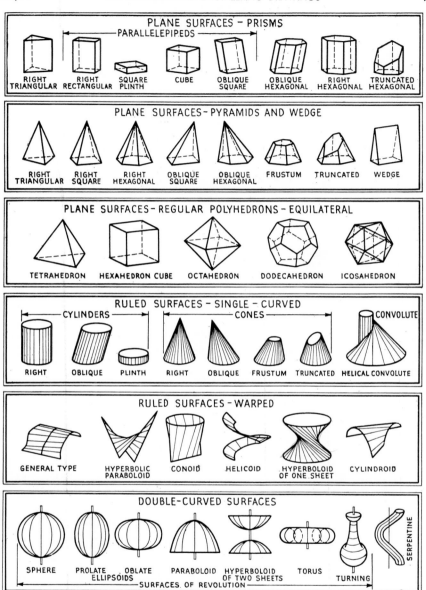

FIGURE 4. Geometrical elements of structures. (*Adapted from French and Vieuk, "Engineering Drawing," 8th ed., New York, McGraw-Hill Book Co., 1953.*)

GEOMETRICAL ELEMENTS OF STRUCTURES

- Points
- Lines
  - Straight
  - Curved
    - Single-curved
      - Circle
      - Ellipse
      - Parabola
      - Hyperbola
      - Trochoid
      - Spiral
      - Involute
      - Cycloid
      - Epicycloid
      - Hypocycloid
      - Sinusoid
    - Double-curved
      - General type
      - Helix
- Surfaces
  - Ruled
    - Plane
      - Triangle
      - Quadrilateral
      - Polygon
      - Prism
      - Wedge
      - Pyramid
      - Regular polyhedron
    - Single-curved
      - Cylinder
      - Cone
      - Convolute
    - Warped
      - General type
      - Hyperbolic paraboloid
      - Conoid
      - Helicoid
      - Hyperboloid of one sheet
      - Cylindroid
  - Doubled-curved
    - General type
    - Sphere
    - Ellipsoid
    - Paraboloid
    - Hyperboloid of two sheets
    - Torus
    - Surfaces of revolution
    - Serpentine

FIGURE 5. Geometrical elements of structures.

Chapter 2

PRINCIPAL VIEWS

1. Most structures built by man are essentially rectangular, and usually they are in such a position that the edges and faces of the structures are vertical and horizontal. In this general classification are included right cylindrical, conical, pyramidal, and similar structures in which the axis is perpendicular to the base. Structures not rectangular and structures in oblique positions attract special attention because they are unusual.

The custom of making structures rectangular is probably due to the ease and economy of building this type of structure. Also, the geometry, and hence the visualization, planning, and drawing of rectangular structures, are relatively simple.

2. Dimensions of Structures. All structures occupy space and have the three dimensions: width, height, and depth. These dimensions are measured in three mutually perpendicular directions. *Width* is measured in a horizontal, left and right, direction. *Height* is measured in a vertical, up and down, direction. *Depth*, as here used, is measured in a horizontal, front and back, direction.

It should be understood that the terms width, height, and depth are general terms, used to indicate dimensions taken in certain directions. They may be used to indicate both the extreme dimensions of the object and the dimensions of its parts.

Although it is the purpose of the geometry of engineering drawing to describe exactly the shape of structures, it is impossible to do this without considering and measuring the dimensions of structures. The actual placing of dimensions on drawings, however, is a function of engineering drawing. In the illustrations of this text a few dimensions have been added when they are needed to explain the method of representing the shape of the structure.

The generally rectangular nature of structures and the relative simplicity of considering the geometry of space as rectangular permit the use of a simple and exact method of representing all structures by means of views.

9

3. Types of Views.   There are two general types of views: perspective and orthographic.   Figure 1 illustrates the following definitions:

A perspective view of an object is observed from a fixed station point, or point of view, by means of converging rays of light that meet at the eye of the observer.

An orthographic view of an object is observed in a chosen direction by means of parallel rays of light.

Engineering drawings usually are composed of groups of orthographic views.   Each orthographic view of the structure or object is seen by the observer when he looks at the object in some definite, chosen direction.

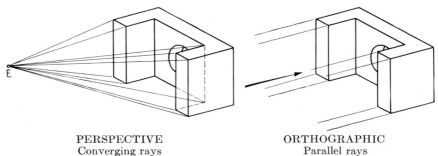

PERSPECTIVE   ORTHOGRAPHIC
Converging rays   Parallel rays
FIGURE 1. Two methods of viewing an object.

The observer sees each view by means of parallel rays of light that are reflected from all points of the object to his eye.   The rays of light are parallel to the direction in which the object is viewed.   Mathematically speaking, the observer is at an infinite distance from the object, so that the rays will be parallel.   Practical considerations make it easier to imagine that the observer is within a reasonable viewing distance of the object.   The object is regarded as stationary.   The observer moves around the object to view it in as many directions as he desires.   Usually, the object is viewed in as many directions as are needed to show all details of the object.

Orthographic views may be classified as of three types: *principal* views, *auxiliary* views, and *oblique* views.   These are described in this and the following chapters.

4. Principal Views.   It is possible to draw six principal views as here explained in connection with the rectangular object shown in Figure 2. The top view is seen by an observer who assumes a position directly above the object.   He looks down at the object in a vertical direction.   The bottom view is seen when the observer looks up at the object in a vertical direction from a position below the object.   To see the front view, the observer stations himself directly in front of the object and looks at it in a horizontal direction. The rear view is seen in the opposite horizontal direction from the rear of the object. The right-side and the left-side views are observed in opposite horizontal directions when the observer is stationed, respectively, to the right and to the left of the object.

The six principal views are thus observed in three mutually perpendicular directions. The object should be regarded as stationary. The observer *imagines* that he moves in turn to the different positions from

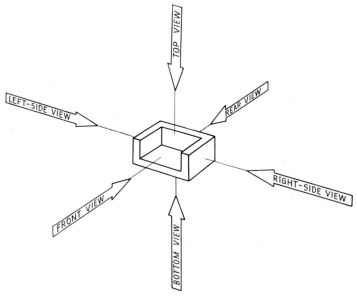

FIGURE 2. The six principal views.

which he can observe the views that are necessary to represent the object in the drawing. The observer thus orients himself in relation to the object, and also in relation to his horizontal and vertical surroundings.

5. Originating a Design. As an example of a simple engineering project, a special design is required for a *base block* having a T-slot for clamping a tool post and a tool to the slide rest of a lathe. One design of a block for holding a tool post is shown on the slide rest of a lathe in Figure 3.

The design of the structure or object has its origin in the mind of the engineer. He cannot begin to draw the views until he has a mental image of the object. The engineer sits at his drawing board, Figure 4. He knows how the block is to be used, and he has the dimensions of the machine it is to fit. But he has neither a model of the block, nor any drawings that he can copy. He must visualize the appearance of the block before he can begin to draw it.

FIGURE 3. Lathe slide rest.

FIGURE 4. The engineer begins a design.

The engineer now imagines that the block is standing on the corner of his desk, as shown in Figure 5. He visualizes as clearly as he can the general size, shape, and details of the required base block, and the method of fastening it to the slide rest of the lathe. Gradually the image of the block takes form in his mind.

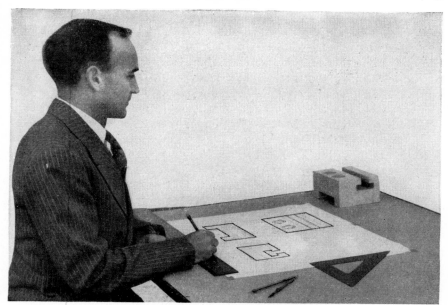

FIGURE 5. The engineer visualizes the object.

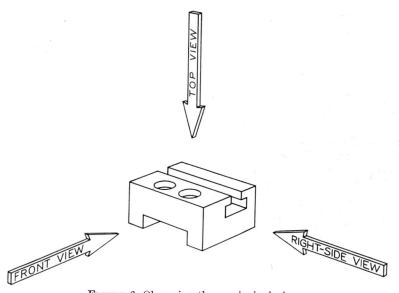

FIGURE 6. Observing three principal views.

The engineer realizes that to convey his ideas to others he must draw views that will best show the true shapes of all parts of the block and the true geometrical relations of its parts. He decides that three principal views will be needed: front, top, and right-side.

Figure 6 shows the three mutually perpendicular directions in which these views will be observed. The engineer imagines that he moves around the visualized block to positions that will enable him to view the block in the three directions indicated. Each view is now considered in turn.

6. Observing the Front View. To see the appearance of the front view of the base block, the observer imagines that he takes a position

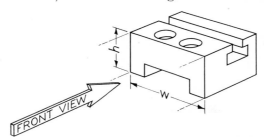

FIGURE 7. Observing the front view.

directly in front of the block so that he can look squarely at it in the horizontal direction indicated by the front-view arrow in Figure 7. This arrow is perpendicular to the front face of the block. The observer sees the block by means of the horizontal rays of light that are reflected from all parts of the block to his eye. These rays are parallel to the direction in which the view is taken, and they are indicated in the figure by means of lightweight lines parallel to the front-view arrow.

The observer of the front view sees the width and height of the block, and the true shape of the alining slot that is cut through from front to back. He sees the different levels of the corners and horizontal edges and surfaces of the block, and the locations, right and left, of the profile edges and surfaces. He imagines that he can look into the block and that he can see the hidden screw holes and the T-slot. But the observer definitely realizes that in this view he cannot see or measure depth, or the distance that one part is in front of or behind another part.

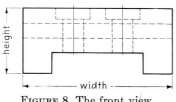

FIGURE 8. The front view.

7. The Front View. The completed front view of the base block is shown in Figure 8. It is drawn to a chosen scale so that all parts of the block will appear in correct proportion. The overall dimensions of width and height are indicated. The depth dimension cannot be seen or represented in this view.

The hidden T-slot and the screw holes are shown in broken lines. These two details are drawn in the front view only after the true shape and size of the screw holes are shown in the top view, and after the true shape of the T-slot is shown in the side view. The front view is also called a *front elevation*.

8. Visualizing the View. When the engineer draws a view, he thinks about the object itself. The points he locates are corners of the object, and the lines he draws are edges of the object. The lines bound the surfaces of the object, and the surfaces bound the solid material of which the object is made. The points and lines are never regarded as drawn or projected on a plane. Each view is visualized as if it were the actual three-dimensional object itself. The near-and-far space relations of all parts of the object are visualized in the mind of the reader of the drawing.

The front view of the base block does not completely show the rectangular shape of the block, nor does it show the shape of the screw holes. A top view is necessary.

9. Top View. In Figure 9 the pointing arrow indicates that the observer is looking down at the imagined base block in a vertical direction. From his position above the block, he sees its top view.

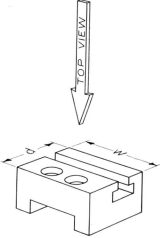

Figure 9. Observing the top view.

He sees the width, depth, and all horizontal dimensions of the block, but he cannot see its height. He notes which face of the block is to the front and which is to the rear, which face is to the left and which is to the right. He observes the circular counterbored screw holes and their location, the opening into the T-slot, and the hidden slot that is cut through the lower part of the block. He sees the true shapes of all horizontal surfaces of the object, the true lengths of all horizontal edges, the edge views of all vertical faces, and the end views of all vertical edges. During these observations he continually realizes that he is looking downward in a vertical direction.

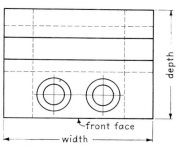

Figure 10. The top view.

The engineer visualizes the top view as described in the preceding paragraph. He then draws the top view as shown in Figure 10. The front face of the block is kept to the front as is indicated.   And the screw holes are in front of the T-slot.   The dimensions of width and depth have been indicated to show the directions in which they may be measured.   The top view often is called the *plan*.

The reader of the top view takes the place of the observer of the base block.   He visualizes its appearance from his imagined position directly above the block.   He never forgets that he is looking down at the block in a vertical direction.   He reads the drawing carefully, and he sees the details and dimensions of the block, just as they were seen by the engineer who made the drawing.   The T-slot is not drawn in either the top or the front view until its true shape and size are shown in the side view.

10. Right-side View.   The pointing arrow of Figure 11 indicates the direction in which the observer looks at the imagined base block to see

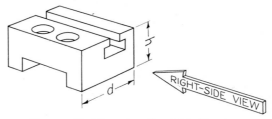

FIGURE 11. Observing the right-side view.

its right-side view.   He looks in a horizontal direction perpendicular to the profile faces of the block.   This direction also is perpendicular to the directions in which the front and top views are seen.   The observer sees the dimensions of height and depth.   He sees the true shape, size, and location of the T-slot.   And he notes the hidden screw holes and alining slot.

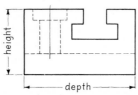

FIGURE 12. The right-side view.

The engineer determines the appearance of the right-side view by visualizing the block as described above.   He then draws this view, Figure 12.   The block is shown right side up, the front face is shown toward the front, and the T-slot toward the rear.   This is the view of the block as seen from the right.   A view taken from the left would show the view reversed. The mistake of reversing a view is best prevented by visualizing the direction in which the object is viewed, and then visualizing its appearance when so viewed.   A right-side view often is called a *right elevation*.

The reader of the right-side view first visualizes the direction in which the view is taken, and he then visualizes the appearance of the object when seen in this direction, in the same way that the engineer visualized the block before he made the drawing.

11. Grouping of Views. The different views of an object should always be grouped according to a definite, standard plan that is understood by all engineers. Figure 13 shows the three principal views of the base block correctly grouped in a single drawing. Each view is placed in a normal and natural relation to the other views of the group. When this standard grouping is observed, the direction in which each view is taken is known, the shape of the object is easily determined, all views are automatically drawn to the same scale, and mistakes are avoided. As a matter of convenience in making and reading drawings, adjacent views should be neither too close together nor too far apart.

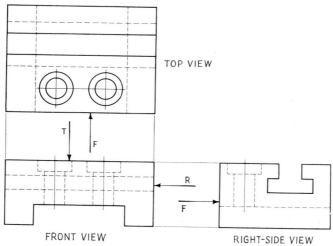

FIGURE 13. Correct grouping of views.

In Figure 13, pointing arrows F, T, and R have been added as an aid in explaining the proper location of each view in the group. Each view is visualized as representing the object itself.

To see the top view the observer imagines that he is above the object, as represented by the front view, and he looks down at the object in the direction of the vertical arrow T. The top view is then placed above the front view in the position from which it was observed. The top view is alined with the front view, and each corner is in line with the ray by which it was viewed. No point is ever located to the right or to the left of where it is seen. In the top view, the front face of the block is to the front, and the screw holes are forward of the T-slot.

In turn, to see the front view, the observer is in front of the object as represented by the top view, and he looks at the object in the direction of the horizontal arrow F. The front view is then placed in front of, and alined with, the top view. The width dimension is common to the front and top views.   The front and top views are adjacent and complementary, each to the other.

The right-side view of the block is observed by looking at the block in the direction of the horizontal arrow R that is attached to the front view. The right-side view is then placed to the right of the front view in the position from which the right-side view was observed, and it is alined with the front view.   Each corner is placed at the same level as it is seen in the front view.   The observer who looks in the direction of the arrow R notes that the front face of the block is to his left, and that the T-slot is rearward of the screw holes.   A side view never should be reversed.   It is drawn as the observer sees it.   The height dimensions may be measured in the adjacent front and right-side views.   In turn, the front view may be observed in the direction of the arrow F that is attached to the right-side view.

It is possible to group the several views of a drawing by applying a rule, or by learning to turn a view in a certain direction.   But such rules and devices are easily forgotten and often misunderstood.   It is better to place each view in its correct relation to the other views by visualizing the position of the observer and the direction in which the view is observed.

The reader of Figure 13 should be able to form a mental image of the base block which agrees in all details with the mental image originally conceived by the engineer who designed the block.   The group of three views of the base block completely represents the shape of the block. This drawing, with added finish marks, notes, and dimensions, is given to the machinist, who again visualizes the block and then makes it.

12. Right-side and Left-side Views.   In Figure 14, the right-side view is drawn to the right of the front view, and the left-side view is to the left of the front view.   Each view is placed on the side from which it was observed.   The arrows R and L attached to the top view indicate that a side view could be drawn adjacent to the top view.   And the arrows T attached to each side view indicate that the top view could be drawn adjacent to either side view.   These alternate locations for the side or top view generally should be avoided unless there is some good reason for adopting one or both.   Two side views, or a rear or bottom view are used only when needed to show some detail that cannot readily be shown in some other view.

The direction in which a right-side view or a left-side view of an object is observed is determined by the right side or the left side of the observer when he faces the front of the object.   The respective views are called right-side and left-side.

A view taken from the right is the left-side view of animate objects, men, and animals, and of vehicles in which the left side of the vehicle is determined by the left side of the passenger who is facing forward.   This is true of aircraft, automobiles, trains, ships, and some other objects.

When drawings of these objects are made, the view from the right may be labeled left-side view, or left elevation, since it is viewed from that position. The normal and natural relation between adjacent views always is maintained. Care must be taken never to reverse a view.

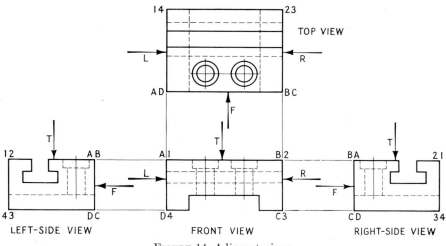

FIGURE 14. Adjacent views.

13. Definitions. The terms here defined are frequently used throughout this textbook.

A *normal view of a line* is a view that is taken in a direction perpendicular to the line. In the normal view, all points of the line are equidistant from the observer. Hence, the true length of a line is seen and may be measured in a normal view of the line.

A *normal view of a plane* is taken in a direction perpendicular to the plane. In the normal view, all points of the plane are equidistant from the observer. Hence, the normal view of a plane shows the true size and shape of any plane figure that lies in the plane.

An *end view of a straight line* is taken in a direction that is parallel to the line. Since a line is a series of points, the end view of a line is not a point and never should be regarded as a point.

An *edge view of a plane* or of a plane figure is taken in a direction that is parallel to any line of the plane. The edge view of a plane or of a plane figure is straight. But this edge view is not a line, and never should be regarded as a line. A plane may contain many straight and curved lines.

Normal, end, and edge views often are needed for solving problems.

A *horizontal line*, or *horizontal plane*, is perpendicular to the vertical direction in which a top view is observed. All points of a horizontal line or plane are at the same level, and are equidistant from the observer of the top view. The top view is a normal view of a horizontal line or plane.

The question as to whether all points of a line or plane are at the same level may be determined in the front or side view, or in any view that is taken in a horizontal direction.

A *frontal line*, or a *frontal plane*, is perpendicular to the direction in which a front view is observed. All points of a frontal line or plane are equidistant from the observer of the front view. The front view is a normal view of a frontal line or plane. No point of a frontal line or plane is in front of or behind any other point of the line or plane. The question as to whether a line or plane is frontal or not may be determined in the top or side view, or in any view that is taken in a frontal direction. A frontal line or plane is not necessarily in the front face of the object that is shown in the drawing.

A *profile line* or *profile plane* is perpendicular to the direction in which a side view is observed. A side view is a normal view of a profile line or plane. In a profile line or plane no point is to the left of, or to the right of, any other point of the line or plane. This may be determined in the top or front view, or in any view that is taken in a profile direction.

A *vertical line* is a straight line in which every point of the line is either directly above or directly below all other points of the line. A vertical line is a plumb line. The top view of a vertical line shows the end view of the line. But this view is not a point, since there are many points in a line.

A *vertical plane* is any plane which contains a vertical line. The top view shows the edge view of a vertical plane. This edge view is straight. But the edge view is not a line, since many lines may be drawn in a plane.

A single line may be horizontal-frontal, or horizontal-profile, or frontal-profile, which is vertical. An oblique line or plane is not horizontal, frontal, or profile.

14. Reading and Visualizing a Drawing. The reader of a drawing should have the same attitude of mind toward the drawing that the engineer has when he makes the drawing. The object shown in the drawing is regarded as stationary, and the reader imagines that he moves around the object to look at it, in turn, in the direction in which each view is seen. Every view should be visualized as standing out from the paper as if it were the actual object itself. A view is never thought of as flat, or as projected on a plane. The ideas here expressed are based on the practical and direct method used by the engineer when he makes and reads drawings. The older projection method is explained in Chapter 14.

The reader of a drawing imagines that he moves rapidly from one position to another as he looks first at one view and then another. In doing this he must not lose his sense of direction. He thus acquires a mental picture of the shape and proportions of the object as a whole, and by renewed observations he becomes acquainted with all details of the object.

15. Order in Which Views Are Drawn. The order in which the different views of an object are drawn depends upon the shape of the various parts of the object. No set order is possible. In general, any figure, such as a circle, hexagon, square, or rectangle, should always be drawn first in the view in which its true shape is seen. It usually is poor practice to complete a single view of an object without first drawing parts of the other views.

16. Lettering Drawings. Eight of the corners of the base block are lettered in Figure 14. The front face is lettered A B C D in regular order around the rectangle. The rear face is lettered 1 2 3 4. When corners or points are lettered or numbered, some such orderly system of lettering is advisable. Haphazard lettering takes more time and is difficult to check. Note also, when two or more corners coincide in a view, it is a good plan to letter the corners in the order of their distance from the observer. In the front view, for example, B is nearer than 2; in the top view, B is nearer than C. The illustrations of this textbook show examples of various ways of lettering views. Rectangular, rather than slanting, letters are here used since they aline with the views.

17. Design of Structures. Engineering structures are designed by combining simple geometrical elements and shapes, such as points, lines, surfaces, prisms, cylinders, pyramids, cones, and spheres. The engineer makes his complex designs by combining simple elements in various positions and in definite geometrical relations to each other.

The student of the geometry of engineering drawing cannot expect immediately to draw complicated engineering structures. The time available is too short, and the knowledge and experience of the student usually are insufficient. For these reasons, the problems of this textbook mainly specify simpler geometrical forms to be drawn in various positions and in certain geometrical relations to each other. When the student has learned to make these drawings, he is later able to draw complicated engineering structures by combining the simple basic forms. The drawings that the student makes thus form the basis for his professional designs.

18. Solving the Problems. The student should visualize the object described in the problem. In his imagination he must then move quickly from one position to another so as to view the object in the proper direction as he considers first one view and then another. Thinking and planning expedite the solution and should always precede drawing. The student who thus trains himself will soon be able to solve problems readily and will find considerable satisfaction in the accomplishment.

Before attempting to solve any of the problems in the groups listed below, it is essential that he study the preceding articles and the illustrations of the textbook. A dictionary and the index of this textbook are a considerable help to those who will make use of them.   The problems are assembled in groups in the problem section of this book.

19. Preliminary Problems.

Group 1.   Drawing Simple Objects from Descriptions.

Group 2.   Drawing Objects by Discarding Specified Parts.

Group 3.   Locating Data by Coordinates.

Group 4.   Locating Points by Measurements.

20. Visualizing.

Eminent engineers have expressed their belief that the ability to visualize is indispensable to the engineer, whether he is engaged in design, production, or administration.   The individual who trains himself to visualize clearly will find this ability useful in every situation throughout life.   Visualization and imagination are needed not only in engineering, but also in every field of human relations and endeavor.

Every structure must be visualized before it can be drawn.   And it must again be visualized by the reader of the drawing before it can be built.   The ability to visualize, to imagine, mentally to construct an object, is of particular value to the engineer.   The student of engineering should develop this power of imagery in himself as highly as possible.

The engineer who plans or designs a structure must first obtain a more or less complete mental image of the proposed structure.   When he first thinks about the structure, the image is likely to be hazy; but as the details of the structure are considered, the mental picture should become clearer until all parts of the structure, and the structure as a whole, are clearly visualized.   The image is thus gradually evolved by thinking about the function and shape of the structure.   If the engineer in his imagination sees very clearly the structure as a whole, if he sees the relation of each part to the other parts, if he sees the result of all internal or external conditions that affect the structure or its operation favorably or unfavorably—if he clearly sees all these things—then he has a complete mental image of the structure.   Few are able to visualize as thoroughly as this.   It is an ideal to strive for.   Thorough visualization saves much time and produces a structure better adapted to its purpose.

Although we are here concerned mainly with visualizing and representing the shapes of objects, it may be well to mention some other items that must be considered when designing a structure.   Complete visualization involves, among other things, the effects produced by the imagined object on all the human senses.   One should not only see the object and make it pleasing to the eye, but he should also visualize its effect upon the senses of hearing, feeling, tasting, and smelling.   Products that produce disagreeable reactions are not desirable.   The consumer is likely to use the product awkwardly and to mistreat it.   The parts must be strong enough and durable, and easily manipulated.   The effects of external and internal forces, of temperature and moisture, the need for lubrication, and many other items must be considered. The designer must anticipate as many adverse conditions as he possibly can and guard against them.

The power to visualize can best be developed by each individual for himself. Others can only suggest methods that may be used by the individual to develop this ability. As a first attempt, start with an object as simple as a cube. Imagine a cube of some definite size. Imagine yourself as moving around it and then inside it. Count its corners, edges, and faces. Think of it as solid and made from some particular material, as cast iron or wood, and then lift it to see how heavy it is. Then imagine that it is hollow, and note how much lighter it is. Note the texture of the surface. Think of it as being a certain color, and then imagine it as painted other colors. Note the play of light on the different faces. Now imagine the cube as growing smaller and smaller, until it is the size of an atom; and then let it expand until it fills the universe. The possible variations are almost infinite.

Starting with a simple object, one should be able gradually to develop the ability to visualize more complex objects, until he can obtain at least fair mental pictures of complicated structures.

21. Imagination and Visualization.   *Quotations:*

The regular detailed exercise of the imagination should take precedence over all other educational exercises.

Arnold Bennett

Our imagination is the only limit to what we can hope to have in the future.

Charles F. Kettering

Power of visualization and keenness of observation are of great importance.

Dugald C. Jackson

22. Problems.

Group 5.   Experiments in Visualization.

23. Use of Reference Planes.   When principal views are drawn, it is necessary to measure the height, width, and depth of the three-dimensional object, and of its parts. It is necessary to have a base from which each dimension can be measured. If the object were two-dimensional, then all of the measurements could be made from two base lines in the plane. But when the object to be measured is three-dimensional, its dimensions must be measured from three reference planes taken in fixed positions and mutually perpendicular to each other.

Figure 15 shows pictorial views of a rectangular object and three reference planes. At A is shown a horizontal reference plane here taken through, and coinciding with, the lower horizontal base of the object. The vertical, height distances of every corner and edge of the object are

measured from this chosen horizontal reference plane.   The observer of
the front or side view of this object will see the edge view of this reference
plane, and from it in each of these views he will be able to measure the
true height, or vertical, dimensions of the object and its parts.

   Illustration B shows a frontal reference plane here taken through the
rear face of the object.   The observer of the top or side view will see the

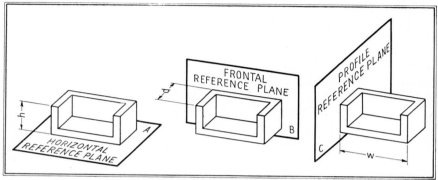

FIGURE 15. Pictorial views of reference planes.

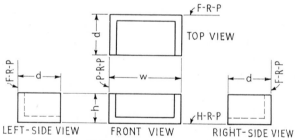

FIGURE 16. Principal views of reference planes.

edge view of this frontal reference plane, and from it as a base he can
measure the true depth, or front and back, dimensions of the object and
its parts.

   Illustration C shows a profile reference plane here taken to coincide
with the left face of the object.   The observer of the top or front view
will see the edge view of this profile reference plane, and from it as a base
he can measure the true width, or left and right, dimensions of the object
and its parts.

   Figure 16 shows four principal views of the three-dimensional rectangular object of Figure 15.   The chosen edge views of horizontal, frontal,
and profile reference planes are indicated.   Each is taken to coincide with
one of the plane faces of the object.   The over-all width, height, and
depth dimensions of the object as measured from the edge views of the

respective planes are indicated. All details are located in a similar way from the edge views of the three reference planes. Judgment should be used when fixing the location of each reference plane in relation to the object. It is helpful if the object can be oriented so that some of its principal surfaces can be selected as reference planes. For cylindrical objects the reference plane often is best taken through the axis of the cylinder. The edge views of reference planes from which measurements are made should never be considered as lines.

24. Problems.

Group 6. Reference Planes.

Chapter 3

AUXILIARY VIEWS

1. There are three types of orthographic views: principal, auxiliary, and oblique. All three are used in engineering drawings. Each type of view is observed in a direction that has certain geometrical relations to the direction in which the other two types are observed.

2. Purpose of Auxiliary Views. Auxiliary views are used to show objects in inclined or oblique positions, to describe structures having

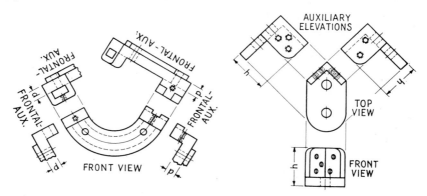

FIGURE 1. Auxiliary view examples.

inclined parts, to solve many of the problems connected with the accurate representation of structures, to draw pictorial views of objects.

Figures 1 and 2 illustrate the need for drawing auxiliary views of some machine parts. Each of the auxiliary views in these drawings is necessary to describe accurately certain details of the castings. For the skip side casting of Figure 2 nine auxiliary and part views are required to show all details so that the pattern and the casting can be made in the shop and foundry.

The object to be viewed is regarded as stationary. The observer imagines that he moves in turn to the various locations from which he can view the object in each chosen direction. The observer orients himself in relation to the object and in relation to his horizontal and vertical sur-roundings. Each orthographic view is seen by means of parallel rays of light that are reflected from every point of the object to the eye of the observer.

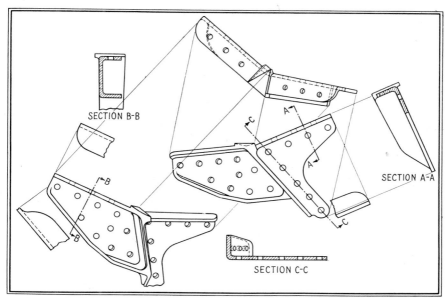

FIGURE 2. Skip side casting. (*Koehring Company.*)

3. Viewing an Object. All of the photographs in this chapter will be more realistic if viewed in a slightly downward-slanting direction and the page is held vertically. Figure 3 illustrates typical directions in which all types of views are seen. The three rings—horizontal, frontal, and profile—represent three mutually perpendicular planes. The six large arrows indicate three mutually perpendicular directions in which principal views are observed. The short arrows that lie in the three rings serve to indicate the many directions in which auxiliary views may be observed. Other short arrows could be drawn between those that are shown. A single arrow, marked oblique, indicates one of the infinite num-ber of general directions in which oblique views may be observed.

Note that each of the short auxiliary view arrows is perpendicular to only one of the directions in which principal views are observed.

An *auxiliary view* is observed in a direction that is perpendicular to only one of the directions in which a principal view is observed. Auxiliary views are unlimited in number, but partly limited in direction. Note also that, in any auxiliary view, only one of the three dimensions of width, height, and depth may be observed.

There are three types of auxiliary views: *horizontal-auxiliary, frontal-auxiliary,* and *profile-auxiliary.*

4. Horizontal-auxiliary Views. In Figure 3, the short arrows in the horizontal ring serve to indicate horizontal directions in which horizontal-auxiliary views may be seen. These arrows are perpendicular to the top-view arrow, but they are not perpendicular to either the front-view arrow

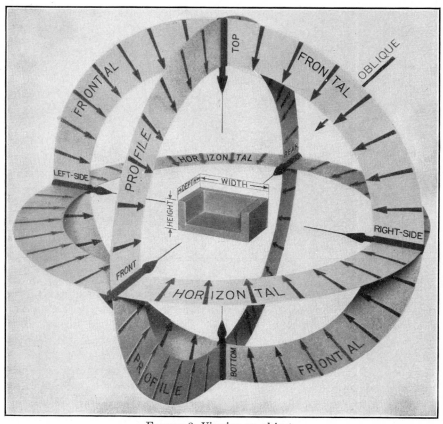

FIGURE 3. Viewing an object.

or a side-view arrow. Since the observer of a horizontal-auxiliary view looks in a horizontal direction, he sees the height dimensions of the object. Hence, these views usually are called *auxiliary elevations.*

5. Frontal-auxiliary Views. These are observed in frontal directions indicated by the short arrows in the frontal ring of Figure 3. The frontal ring and the frontal arrows are perpendicular to the direction in which a front view is seen. In each frontal-auxiliary view the depth dimensions of the object may be seen or measured.

6. Profile-auxiliary Views. These are observed in the profile directions indicated by the short profile arrows in the profile ring of Figure 3. The profile arrows and the profile ring are perpendicular to the direction in which a side view is observed. In each profile-auxiliary view the width dimensions of the object may be seen or measured.

7. Drawing Horizontal-auxiliary Views. These views usually are called *auxiliary elevations*. Figure 4 is a photograph of a cast-iron bearing

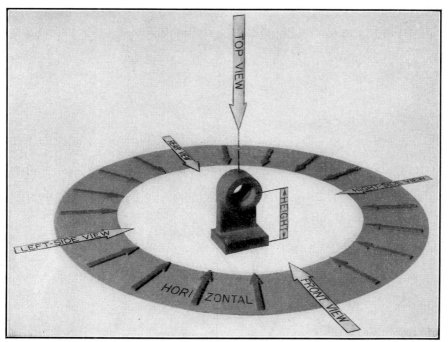

FIGURE 4. Viewing a bearing.

surrounded by a horizontal ring on which a number of pointing arrows indicate typical horizontal directions in which auxiliary elevations of the bearing may be observed. The true directions of these horizontal arrows can be seen only when the observer looks at them in the vertical direction indicated by the top-view arrow. The top view thus shows a normal view of the horizontal arrows. The observer should imagine that he moves around the object and that he looks at it in the indicated horizontal directions. He should realize that he sees the vertical height dimensions of the object, or the levels or relative elevations of its parts.

In Figure 5 the front and top views of the bearing are drawn first, and then four horizontal pointing arrows, marked H, are drawn in chosen directions. These arrows point at the top view, and they are top views of horizontal arrows. Each of these arrows indicates a direction in which an auxiliary elevation is to be observed. Rays are drawn parallel to each arrow.

Since height dimensions are to be measured in each auxiliary elevation a horizontal reference plane, H-R-P, from which different levels may be measured, is established for each auxiliary view. H-R-P is the edge view

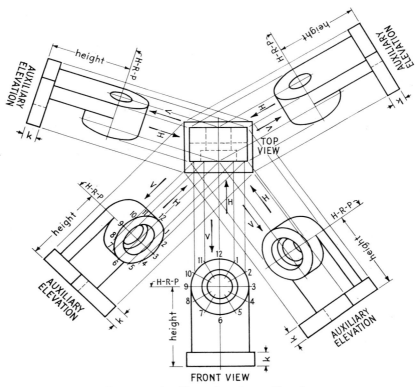

FIGURE 5. Auxiliary elevations of bearing.

of the reference plane. It is not a line. And, since the height dimensions are obtained from the front view of the bearing, the same reference plane must be shown in the front view. This reference plane could be taken at any level in the front view, but it is here best taken through the level of the central axis of the shaft hole, since it then is necessary to measure only three levels of the 12 numbered points on each circle. In Figure 5, these numbered points are shown in the front view and in one of the auxiliary elevations, where each point is on its ray and at its proper level above or below the horizontal reference plane.

The circles, which appear as ellipses, are then drawn through the 12 located points in each of the auxiliary elevations. These curves are best drawn freehand. Smooth curves can be drawn by keeping the eye ahead of the pencil, and by drawing with as few strokes as possible. The curve should not be drawn up to the end of the axis, but around the end in a single stroke, to avoid a pointed appearance of the ends of the ellipse. Imitation ellipses drawn with the compass always look like imitations. A french curve may be used for penciling or inking ellipses. The ellipses in the auxiliary elevations are views of circles, and should be visualized and considered as circles.

The levels of the base are measured from the same reference plane in each elevation view. All levels are determined from the front view, where the true shapes of the circles are shown.

Auxiliary elevations are observed in a horizontal direction and necessarily are shown adjacent to the top view. When studying an auxiliary elevation, the drawing may be turned so that the auxiliary elevation is directly in front of the top view. In this position the auxiliary elevation is right side up. The lettering is squared with each view as in Figure 5. Simple rectangular letters are better than inclined letters since the rectangular letters are alined with the rays and reference plane.

8. Reference Planes. Reference planes are useful in nearly every view of every drawing. They should be lettered in every view in which they are used. Each reference plane is represented by drawing the edge view of the plane. This edge view is never thought of as a line. The different measurements that are made from a reference plane could not be measured from a line, since the view is not flat, and since the measured distances are located at various near-and-far distances from the observer of the view.

9. Adjacent View Relations. Figure 5: The front elevation and the four auxiliary elevations are all adjacent to the top view. In turn, the top view is adjacent to each of the five elevation views. The single top view may be observed by looking in the direction of the vertical V arrows at any, or all, of the five elevation views. The five V arrows thus indicate one and the same vertical direction in which the top view of the bearing is observed. The five horizontal H arrows indicate five different horizontal directions in which five different elevation views of the bearing are seen. The H arrows are perpendicular to the V arrows. These observations lead to the conclusion:

Each of two adjacent views is observed in a direction that is perpendicular to the direction in which the other adjacent view is observed.

This basic principle should be understood and remembered, since it applies to each pair of adjacent views in every drawing. This principle is useful both when drawing views and when reading views. Two adjacent views may be two principal views, a principal view and an auxiliary view, an auxiliary view and an oblique view, or two oblique views.

A view is easily drawn in an incorrect, reversed position, unless care is taken to visualize the direction in which the view is seen. A useful way for the draftsman or reader of the drawing to think about adjacent views is to imagine that he moves toward the object in the direction in which an

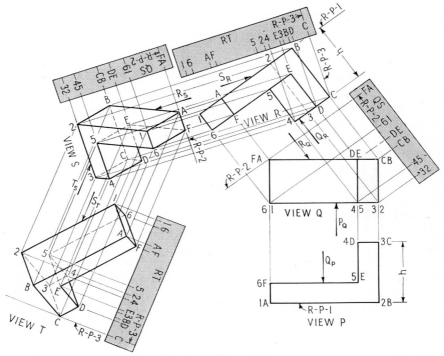

FIGURE 6. Corner brace.

adjacent view is seen: In Figure 5, as the observer moves in a vertical direction and downward toward the bearing, as shown in the front view, he comes first to the rounded cylindrical end of the bearing. And, when he moves in turn in a vertical direction toward each of the elevation views, he again comes first to the rounded cylindrical end of the bearing. Note that in each elevation view, including the front view, the top of the bearing is nearest the top view. These observations may be stated as a rule: The point that is nearest the observer in any view is nearest that view in every adjacent view. This rule is useful when checking and reading drawings.

These definite relations between adjacent views and the need for reference planes, as explained in Articles 8 and 9, should be understood by all who make or read orthographic drawings. The student should check his understanding of these relations by applying his knowledge to the views of Figure 6. Paper scales are shown in this figure as an aid in explaining how the same dimensions are measured from the same reference planes in two different views. It is much better to visualize the object and the reference plane in each view, and to understand why these definite measurements and spacings are equal, rather than to attempt to apply a rule. Paper scales are useful when it is necessary to transfer a considerable number of measurements from one view to another. Views should always be checked to determine if any view has been reversed.

10. Order in Which Views Are Drawn. The order in which the different views of an object are drawn depends upon the shape of the various parts of the object. No set order is possible. In general, any figure, such as a circle, hexagon, square, rectangle, should be drawn first in the view in which its true shape appears. It usually is poor practice to attempt to complete a single view of an object without first drawing parts of other views.

11. Problems.
   Group 7.   Auxiliary Elevations.

12. Frontal-auxiliary Views. Figure 7 is a photograph of a connecting rod, or link, surrounded by pointing arrows on a frontal ring. All these arrows are perpendicular to the direction in which the front view is observed. For studying this photograph the page should be held vertically. The four longer arrows indicate directions in which principal views—top, side, and bottom—are observed. The shorter inclined arrows on the ring, being perpendicular only to the direction in which the front view is seen, indicate typical directions in which one type of auxiliary view may be observed. The short inclined arrows are squarely in front of the observer of the front view, and all points of each arrow are equidistant from this observer. Arrows, lines, and planes having these directions are *frontal*. Auxiliary views observed in a frontal direction are *frontal-auxiliary views*. The observer of the front view sees the normal view and the true direction of every frontal arrow. Hence all frontal-auxiliary views must be drawn adjacent to the front view. The observer of a frontal-auxiliary view sees the *depth*, or front-to-back, dimensions of the object. Visualize this.

Frontal-auxiliary views may be observed by looking at the object in a downward- or upward-slanting frontal direction, from a position at the right or left of the object. A frontal viewing direction may be specified as making a definite angle above or below the horizontal.

Figure 8 shows the front and top views and four frontal-auxiliary views of the link. These are viewed in the directions definitely indicated by the four frontal arrows that point at the object in the front view. One of the frontal arrows is marked A_F in the front view. This is a normal view of this arrow. The top view of the same arrow is also shown, but this is not a normal view. The arrow A points downward. Visualizing this inclined direction in the top view is an aid in visualizing both the auxiliary view and the dimensions that are to be seen when the link is observed in the frontal direction A.

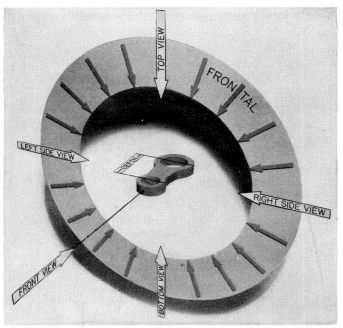

FIGURE 7. Viewing a connecting rod.

A frontal reference plane, from which depths may be measured, is first located through some point of the link in the top view. Since it will be necessary to plot points for the two circular ends of the link, judgment would indicate that two frontal reference planes would be useful, one through each center. The edge views of these frontal reference planes will be seen in the top view, and are lettered F-R-P 1 and F-R-P 2. The distance between them is c. The edge views of these frontal reference planes will be seen in every frontal-auxiliary view. And in each of these views reference plane 1 is in front of plane 2, and the distance between them is c. The front view is a normal view of the frontal planes.

Twelve or more equally spaced points are spotted on the circles in the top view, Figure 8. The front views of these points are then located on the edge views of the circles. Next, each point is located in the auxiliary view in line with its ray leading from the front view, and at its proper distance in front of or behind its reference plane.   The circles and straight lines of the frontal-auxiliary views are then drawn.   The lettering in each view squares with the rays and reference planes.   Methods of drawing

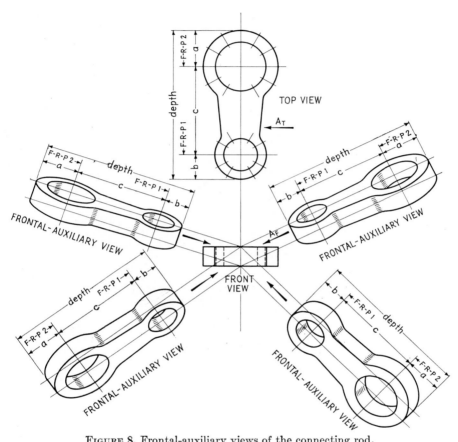

FIGURE 8. Frontal-auxiliary views of the connecting rod.

circles in different views are explained in detail in the chapter on Curved Lines.

Correct visualization of the direction in which a view is seen determines the dimensions of the object that will be seen in that view.   And correct visualization of the appearance of the object determines the orientation of the object in each view of the drawing, and prevents the reversal of views.

Note that R-P-1 and the smaller end of the link are nearest the front view in all five views that are adjacent to the front view.   Also, note that the four auxiliary views and the top view are observed in five different frontal directions, and that each of these five directions is perpendicular to the direction in which the front view is observed.

13. Problems.

Group 8.   Frontal-auxiliary Views.

14. Profile-auxiliary Views.
Typical directions in which profile-auxiliary views may be observed are indicated by the shorter arrows of

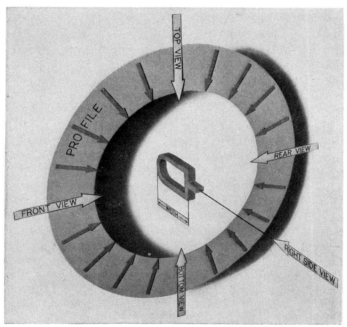

FIGURE 9. Viewing a finger clamp.

the photograph, Figure 9.   These profile arrows are perpendicular to the direction in which either side view is observed.   They are here shown in the same profile plane with the front-, top-, rear-, and bottom-view arrows. The observer who views the object in the direction of a profile arrow sees the *width*, or right and left, dimensions of the object.   The observer of a side view sees the normal view and the true direction of every profile arrow.   Hence, all profile-auxiliary views will be adjacent to a side view.

Profile-auxiliary views are viewed in a downward- or upward-slanting profile direction by an observer from a position forward or rearward of the object that he is viewing.

Figure 10 shows three principal views and four profile-auxiliary views of a finger clamp.   The profile arrow P_R in the side view indicates that the observer is looking in an upward-slanting direction from a position forward of the object. The same arrow is shown at P_F in the front view; but this is not a normal view of the arrow. It is pointing upward and away from the observer of the front view. Visualizing the direction of this arrow in the front view is an aid in determining the general appearance of the clamp and the width dimensions that will be seen when the clamp is viewed in the direction of the arrow P. The width dimensions may be

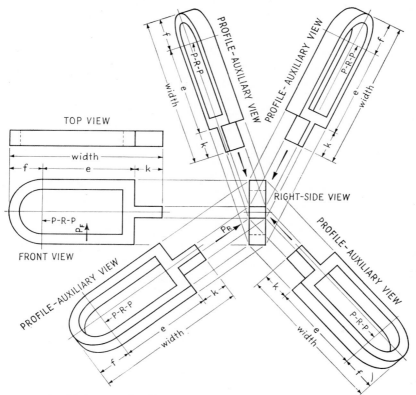

FIGURE 10. Profile-auxiliary views of the finger clamp.

measured from the profile reference plane P-R-P, of which the edge view is shown in the front view and in the four profile-auxiliary views. Four of the width dimensions are indicated in each of the six views in which they may be observed. The lettering in each auxiliary view is squared with the rays and reference planes.

15. Problems.

Group 9. Profile-auxiliary Views.

16. Reading Drawings. To one who is trained in the art of reading drawings, the different views should give a complete mental picture of the objects represented. The reader of a drawing should first glance quickly from one view to another in order to obtain a general idea of the appearance of the object.   He should then direct his attention to the view that best shows the characteristic shape of the object, but he must frequently refer to the other views for information not given in the most representative view.

The reader of a drawing should always imagine that he is looking at the object itself.   Each view should be visualized as a view of the object, never as a flat drawing on a sheet of paper.   The reader takes the place of the observer, and as the observer he must learn to imagine that he moves quickly from one position to another as often as is necessary while he is reading the different views.   When doing this he must not lose his sense of direction.   The final result of reading a drawing should be to leave in the mind of the reader a picture of the object, so clear that he imagines he is looking at the object itself and that he sees every detail.

17. Number of Views.   When a structure is to be described by means of a drawing, it is necessary to decide what views and how many views are to be drawn.   This is a matter of judgment.   The views that best represent the structure should be drawn.   If some necessary view is missing, then the structure is not fully described and it cannot be built from the drawings.   If unnecessary views are drawn, the time of the draftsman and of the reader of the drawing is wasted.   Any view that aids the draftsman in making the drawing will generally aid the workman in reading the drawing.   The draftsman must not neglect to show all details that he has in mind.

In many of the problems of this textbook extra views are called for in order to give the student experience in drawing and visualizing all types of views.   On working drawings, however, only a sufficient number of views should be shown.

18. Problems.

Group 10.   Multiple Auxiliary Views.

Chapter 4

OBLIQUE VIEWS

1. An oblique view is observed in a direction that is not parallel to any of the directions in which principal and auxiliary views are observed. The direction in which an oblique view is to be observed may be indicated by two principal views of an oblique pointing arrow. The exact direction in which the arrow points is determined by drawing normal and end views of the pointing arrow.

Principal views, auxiliary views, and oblique views include all the types of orthographic views that it is possible to draw. These three types of views require the use of all possible directions in which objects may be observed.

Oblique views are used to show objects in oblique positions, to solve problems related to the exact description of structures, and to obtain pictorial illustrations of objects. Some of the problems connected with the description of structures can be solved by drawing principal views, many can be solved only with the aid of auxiliary views, and others can be solved only by drawing oblique views.

Pictorial views that show a complete picture of the object in a single view are now extensively used in manufacturing plants. These pictorial drawings are called *production illustrations.* Their use has considerably increased production in many industries. Views in pictorial form are quite readily understood by everyone, while special training is required to understand front, top, and side views.

Pictorial views may be drawn either as oblique or as perspective views. Perspective views give a more nearly natural picture of the object, but they require considerably more time to draw than do oblique views. In oblique views, parallel lines of the object are drawn parallel, and dimensions are readily shown. Oblique and perspective views are derived from the principal and auxiliary views that the engineer draws when he designs structures. Methods of making perspective drawings are explained in Chapter 13. The method of drawing an oblique view in a chosen direction is explained in the following paragraphs.

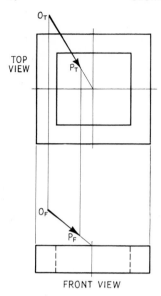

TOP VIEW

O_T

P_T

O_F

P_F

FRONT VIEW

FIGURE 1. Hollow square.

The proper choice of the direction in which an object may be viewed to best advantage requires visualizing and judgment if the oblique view is to provide a satisfactory picture of the object. The direction chosen for observing the oblique view is indicated in the front and top views by an oblique arrow.

2. Oblique Views Taken in a Chosen Direction. Figure 1 shows the front and top views of a hollow square, with an arrow, which is here shown pointing at the center of the upper square face. This affords a convenient check when the arrow is drawn in any additional views. When the name of an arrow is given, as O P for example, the arrowhead is on the last-named point. The view is to be taken in the direction from O toward P, and not in the reverse direction. The arrow naturally should point toward the object.

The front view shows that the arrow O P points downward and to the right. The top view indicates that the arrow points forward. Hence the viewing direction is downward, to the right,

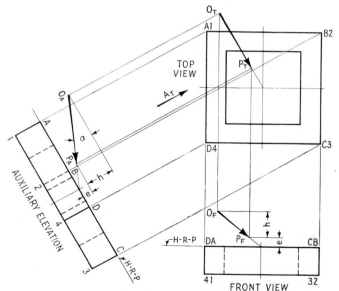

FIGURE 2. Auxiliary elevation of hollow square.

and forward. The approximate appearance of the oblique view is best visualized in the top view, since this view shows the characteristic shape of the hollow square. The observer imagines that he looks downward in a slanting direction along the arrow, from a position behind the hollow square.

The exact direction in which the arrow points must be determined by drawing a normal view of the arrow. Figure 2 shows an auxiliary view

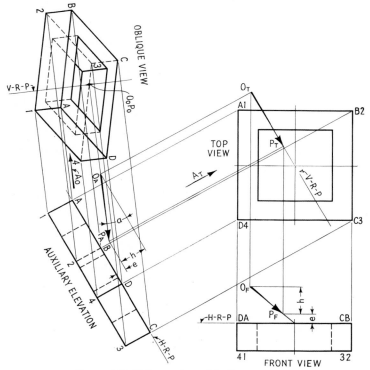

FIGURE 3. Oblique view of hollow square.

of the arrow O P and of the hollow square. This view is taken in the horizontal direction A_T perpendicular to the arrow O P. This auxiliary elevation shows the levels of the lower and upper faces of the object, and of the points O and P. These levels are obtained, of course, from the front view. The normal view O_A P_A indicates definitely the chosen direction in which the oblique view of the hollow square is to be observed.

Rays leading from all points of the auxiliary view are drawn parallel to the normal view of the arrow O P. Figure 3 shows the required oblique view. The end view of the arrow is seen at O_o P_o.

A vertical reference plane is located in the top and oblique views. This plane is best taken through the center of the hollow square. It is perpendicular to the arrow A_T in the top view, and to the same arrow A_O in the oblique view. The corners of the hollow square are located in the oblique view on the proper side of the reference plane, and at their correct near and far distances from the reference plane by obtaining these distances from the same reference plane in the top view.

The oblique view of Figure 3 is a form of pictorial view that clearly shows the general appearance of the hollow square and the relations between its parts. The oblique view is determined from three preceding views. Care must be used in drawing every view. Small errors in one view often are magnified in later views. A distorted view is unsatisfactory both to the maker and to the reader of the drawing.

When an oblique view of a complicated object is required, the work of drawing a complete auxiliary view of the object, and of transferring measurements, is avoided by using the method described in Chapter 13, Article 3.

3. Choice of Auxiliary Views. Figure 4 illustrates the possibility of saving time and work by choosing the easiest auxiliary view to draw, when

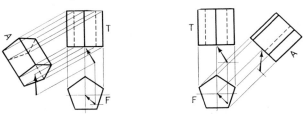

FIGURE 4. Choice of auxiliary view.

such a view is needed for the solution of a problem. Two groups of views of a pentagonal prism are shown. The front and top views of a pointing arrow indicate the direction in which an oblique view is to be observed. An auxiliary view that shows a normal view of the pointing arrow must be drawn. In the group of views at the left, an auxiliary elevation is drawn. In the group at the right, a frontal-auxiliary view is drawn. This requires fewer measurements and lines than does the auxiliary elevation of the group at the left. Time and work will be saved if good judgment is used whenever a choice of several views is possible.

In each auxiliary view of Figure 4, the normal view of the pointing arrow indicates the direction in which the oblique view is to be observed. The two oblique views will be alike.

4. Problems.

Group 11. Oblique Views Taken in Specified Directions.

5. Drawing Objects in Oblique Positions. In modern design an increasing number of structures and parts of structures are placed in oblique positions. The engineer must be able to visualize and to represent such structures.

The methods and the technique used when drawing an object in an oblique position are explained by showing the step-by-step solution of the following problem: The oblique line K L is the axis of a right hexagonal nut. The point C is one corner of the hexagonal base that is centered at K. A hole is drilled centrally through the prism. Draw the front, top, and right-side views, and the necessary auxiliary and oblique views of this hexagonal nut.

Figure 5 shows the front and top views of the given axis K L, but only the top view of the point C is given. Since the point C is a definite point in a plane that is perpendicular to K L, its front view can have but one definite location. This location must be determined later as a part of the solution of the problem. The complete solution of the problem is shown in Figure 11. When this drawing is begun, only

FIGURE 5.
Given data.

the statement of the problem and the data shown in Figure 5 are known.

The simplest views of the prism must be drawn first. These are an auxiliary view taken in a direction perpendicular to the axis, and an oblique view taken in the direction of the axis. The auxiliary view will show the normal view of the axis and the edge views of the hexagonal bases of the prism. The oblique view will show the end view of the axis and the true shape of the hexagons. The true shape of the hexagons must be drawn in the oblique view before the edge views can be completed in the auxiliary view. Visualize these requirements.

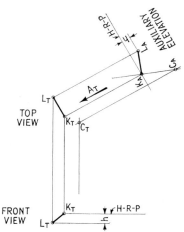

TOP VIEW

FRONT VIEW

FIGURE 6. Normal view of axis.

The hexagon centered at K will be considered first. Figure 6 shows one direction in which a normal view of the axis may be taken. This is indicated by the horizontal arrow A_T that is perpendicular to K L. The auxiliary elevation of K L is drawn, and a fine line is drawn through K and perpendicular to K L. This fine line represents the unfinished edge view of the hexagon that is centered at K. The corner C_A of the hexagon must be on this edge view, and on the ray coming from the top view of C. There are now two views of C. Its front view may now be located, since its level is known. If the given data had stated the location of the front view of C instead of its top view, the level of C would then have been known and C_A could then be located in the auxiliary elevation at its proper level.   Next, its unknown top view could be located.

Figure 7 shows the next step. $K_A L_A$ is a normal view of the axis.   A view taken in the direction of the arrow O_A will show the end view of the axis and the true shape of the hexagon.   The end view of the axis is $K_O L_O$. The corner C_O of the hexagon must be located in this view before the hexagon can be drawn.   This is accomplished by careful visualizing.   The observer who looks alternately in the directions A_T and A_O sees the auxiliary elevation.   The views seen in these two directions are identical.

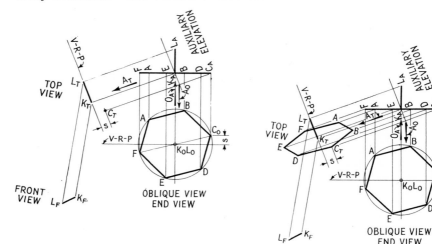

FIGURE 7. Normal and edge views of hexagon.

FIGURE 8. Top view of hexagon.

A vertical reference plane V-R-P is drawn through the top view of K L, perpendicular to the arrow A_T.   The same reference plane is drawn through K L in the oblique view, perpendicular to the arrow A_O.   The top view shows that the point C is the distance s nearer to the observer of the auxiliary elevation than is the reference plane.   The oblique view must also show that the point C is the same distance nearer to the observer of the auxiliary view than is the reference plane.   Figure 7 shows the point C in the top and oblique views at the same distance from, and on the near side of, the reference plane.

The hexagon is now drawn in the oblique view.   K is the center, and C is one corner.   The six corners are then lettered or numbered in regular order.   Opposite sides of the hexagon are drawn accurately parallel to the respective diagonals, by sliding one triangle on another.   A view is then taken in the direction A_O.   The edge view of the hexagon is drawn in the auxiliary elevation, and the corners are lettered.

Figure 8 shows the completed top view of the hexagon. In the oblique view, B is on the near side of the reference plane, E is on the far side, and these two points are equidistant from the reference plane. These same conditions must appear in the top view. The near and far distances must agree in the two views. One measurement suffices for locating two corners of the hexagon when the reference plane is taken as a plane of symmetry. The top views of the remaining points are now located in a similar manner, and the opposite sides are drawn parallel to the respective diagonals.

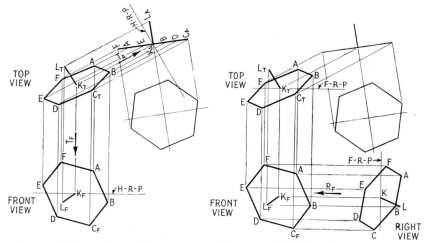

FIGURE 9. Front view of hexagon.　　　　FIGURE 10. Right-side view of hexagon.

Figure 9 shows the completed front view of the hexagon. The right and left spacings of the corners are determined by the rays extending from the top view. The levels are obtained from the auxiliary elevation. These latter are measured above and below the horizontal reference plane H-R-P taken through the point K in the auxiliary and front views.

Figure 10 shows the completed right-side view of the hexagon. Frontal reference planes F-R-P are located in the top and side views, and through the center K in each view. In the top view, point D is in front of the reference plane, and A is an equal distance behind it. In the side view, these points are located, respectively, in front of and behind the reference plane and at the distance measured in the top view.

The completed views of the hexagonal nut are shown in Figure 11. For the sake of clearness, some of the invisible lines have been omitted. All views of the second hexagonal base through L are determined in the same way that the corners of the first hexagon were located. The corners of the second hexagon are numbered in regular 1, 2, 3 order to agree with the

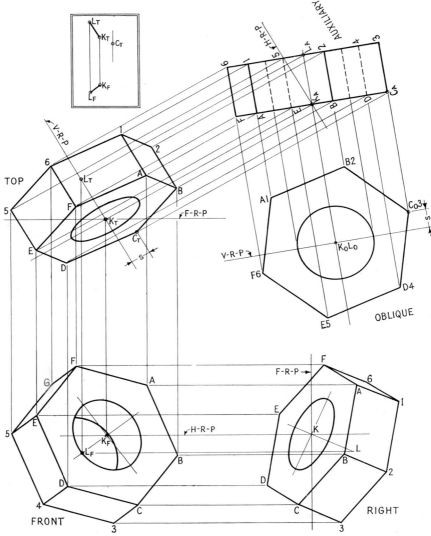

FIGURE 11. Prism in oblique position.

A, B, C lettering of the first hexagon. Systematic lettering is an aid in drawing the various views.

In every view of a hexagon, two of its parallel sides are parallel to one of the three diagonals. Each pair of sides should be drawn accurately parallel. Since the diagonal is longer than the sides, the short leg of the 30-60-degree triangle should be alined with the three points at the center and ends of one diagonal. A second triangle is now placed along the longer leg of the first triangle. The first triangle may now be slid parallel to itself, and the entire hexagon, with its diagonals if needed, may be drawn without moving the second triangle. This is the professional way of doing this job. It not only produces a better looking drawing, but also serves to check the accuracy of the locations of the corners of the hexagon. Points must be located accurately in every view, and parallel and perpendicular lines must be drawn accurately parallel and perpendicular, otherwise the views will be distorted and unsatisfactory.

The circular hole in Figure 11 is first drawn in the oblique view where its true shape is seen. Twelve or sixteen equally spaced points are located on the near circle. Two of these points should be located in the reference plane. Indiscriminate location of points requires more measurements in the views that follow. The points on the circle are then located in the other views in the same way that the corners of the hexagon are located. Figure 11 shows the complete solution of the problem. The original data, on which the solution is based, are shown in miniature in the upper left corner.

After the student has studied this article, he may readily check his understanding of the solution and fix it in his mind by drawing the views of the hexagonal nut without again referring to the explanation and figures. The following approximate data may be used: K225 L$1\frac{1}{2}$,$1\frac{1}{2}$,6; C$2\frac{3}{4}$,X,$4\frac{3}{4}$; diameter of hole $1\frac{1}{2}$ inches.

6. Series of Views. Figure 12 shows a series of views of an index bracket. This illustrates the possibility of drawing an unlimited number of views in any desired directions by using the methods explained in this textbook. A detailed study of this figure affords a review of all the principles that are involved in visualizing, drawing, and reading all types of views.

Starting with two simple views J and K that show all details of the object, one may take view L in any chosen direction that is perpendicular to the direction in which the adjacent view K is seen. View M is now taken in the direction of the arrow that points at the object as seen in the view L, and so on through the series of views. Other views may be drawn branching off from any view of the figure.

Each view is taken in a direction perpendicular to the direction in which its adjacent view is seen. Adjacent views L and M, for example, are taken in mutually perpendicular directions. Views L and N are taken in directions perpendicular to the direction in which the intermediate view M is seen. But views L and N are not here taken in mutually perpendicular directions.

Two views adjacent to any one view have certain dimensions in common. For example, the dimension c, and other dimensions parallel to it, may be measured in views L and N, both of which are adjacent to view M.

The reference planes from which these dimensions are measured are not here shown.

View P is here taken in a direction perpendicular to the arrow T shown in view O.   The arrow T is parallel to the axis of the hole and to several

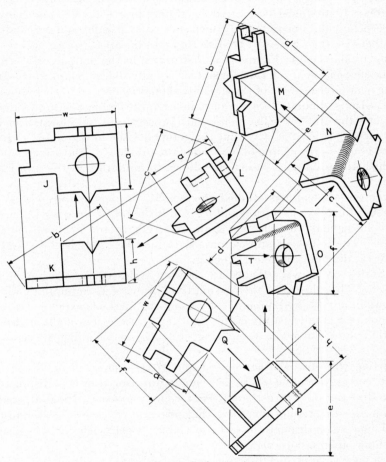

FIGURE 12. Series of views.

edges of the bracket.   After view P is completed, the dimension h in this view should agree with the same dimension in view K, since each of these views shows the true lengths of the same edges of the bracket.   If view Q is now taken in a direction parallel to these edges of the bracket, view Q should be the same as the original view J, since both are viewed in a direction parallel to the same edges of the bracket.   The dimensions a and w of the bracket should check as respectively equal in both of the views Q and J.

When drawing a series of views, one must use great care in drawing rays and in transferring measurements; otherwise the object is likely to become more and more distorted as the consecutive views are drawn.

7. Problems.

Group 12.   Objects in Oblique Positions.

Chapter 5

STRAIGHT LINES

1. Points, lines, and surfaces are the basic geometrical elements of structures. Points are basic elements of lines, and lines are basic elements of surfaces. Lines are generated by a moving point, and surfaces are generated by a moving line. The law that governs the motion of the generating point or line determines the nature of the generated line or surface.

2. Representation of Points. A point, or a view of a point, may be represented by a very small circle, a small dot, or cross lines, as shown at A, B, and C in Figure 1. Points are probably best indicated by a small open circle centered on the exact location of the point. The front and top views of a point D also are shown in this figure. Each view of a point must always be in line with its ray. The front and top views of the point E are incorrectly represented, since no view of a point is ever placed to one side of where it is seen. Subscripts are attached to the name of each point to indicate the view in which each point is seen.

oA •B +C

o D_T

o E_T

error→

o E_F

o D_F

FIGURE 1.
Points.

Figure 2 shows six different views of a group of four points. Since a group of points represents no object with which we are commonly familiar, three of the points have been joined by lines to form a triangle so that the drawing may be more easily read. The fourth point D is outside the triangle. In every view, each point is placed in line with its ray.

The relative elevations, or vertical height dimensions, between the points may be seen and measured in the front and side views, and in the auxiliary elevation. The relative width dimensions may be seen and measured in the front and top views. The relative depth dimensions may be seen and measured in the top and side views, and in the frontal-auxiliary view.

The horizontal and frontal reference planes, from which the dimensions of height or depth have been measured, are indicated in the views. In all views that are adjacent to the front view, the point C is nearest the front view. In the two views that are adjacent to the top view, the point B is nearest the top view. All these items agree with the principles that have been developed in the preceding chapters.

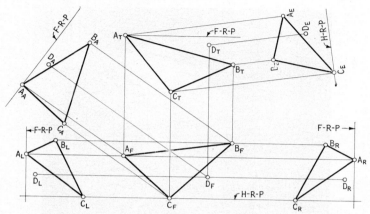

FIGURE 2. A group of points.

3. Straight Lines. A straight line is generated by a point that moves in one direction. A straight line appears straight from every point of view. Straight lines are drawn readily with the aid of a straightedge, such as a triangle or a T-square. Straight lines and circles are the only lines that may be drawn readily, and straight and circular objects are the easiest shapes to make. Accurate straightedges may be originated by removing the high spots on three approximately straight bars until each one of the bars accurately fits the other two. The location of a straight line may be definitely determined either by specifying the location of two points of the line or by specifying the location of one point of the line and, in addition, stating the direction of the line.

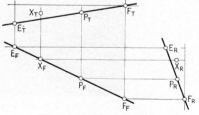

FIGURE 3. Straight line.

4. Representation of Straight Lines. If the front, top, and right-side views of a straight line are to be drawn, it is necessary first to locate the front, top, and right-side views of any two points of the line, for example, the points E and F in Figure 3. Next draw the three views of the line through the corresponding views of the points. In the figure the line is shown as extending beyond the points E and F. This indicates that the line is not limited in length. If the line had been shown as terminating at the points E and F, the line might then be considered as limited in length. If a point is on a line, then each view of the point must be on the corresponding view of the line. In Figure 3, the point P is on the line E F, while the point X is a short distance directly behind the line. The line

FIGURE 4. Transmission-line tower.   (*U. S. Bureau of Reclamation.*)

E F in space and each of its views are divided into the same proportional parts by the point P.

5. Directions of Lines. The transmission-line tower, shown in the accompanying photograph, Figure 4, is constructed of straight steel members having various directions and lengths. The tower is designed by drawing the necessary views, in which the direction of each member and its relations to the other members are definitely fixed.   Also, the size and length of each member must be determined.

The direction of a straight line may be stated as horizontal, vertical, frontal, oblique, etc.   Normal and end views of lines, and normal and edge views of planes, often are necessary when solving problems.   A normal view of a line shows its true length.   The end view of a line is not a point.   The end view represents all of the points in the line.

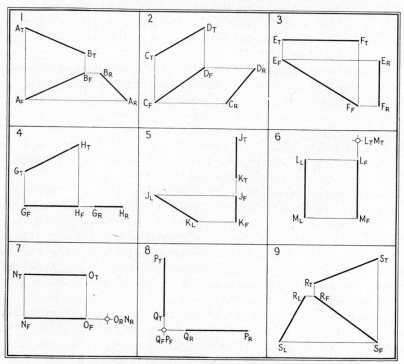

FIGURE 5. Lines to be visualized.

In any object, a number of lines may be horizontal, but they are not necessarily parallel or at the same level.   A frontal line is not necessarily located in the front face of an object.   In any single structure, vertical lines are assumed to be parallel.   Since the earth is a sphere, vertical lines determined by a plumb line are not parallel.

The definitions of various types of lines and planes are given in Chapter 2, Article 13.

6. Visualizing Straight Lines.   The front, top, and right-side views of an oblique line A B are shown in Figure 5.   The front view of this line shows that the line extends from the end A to the right and upward to the end B.   The top and right-side views give the additional information that the line extends forward from the end A to the end B. The reader of the drawing now should be able to picture the line as extending from A, to the right, upward, and forward. The reader should look at each view in turn, visualize the direction in which the view is taken, and visualize the line when seen in that direction.

For Figure 5 the student should make a numbered list, visualize the direction of each line in each view, and then state on the list the name and type of each line. Also, state the name of any view in which the true length of the line may be measured. Holding a pencil to indicate the direction of each line is an aid in visualizing the direction of the line in relation to each view.

7. Straight-line Problems. These involve drawing lines in specified directions, finding the true lengths of lines, drawing intersecting lines, drawing parallel lines, drawing perpendicular lines, finding the distance from a point to a line, and finding the angles between lines. These problems occur frequently in the design of structures.

8. Use of Subscripts. In a drawing of an actual object, each view occupies a certain position relative to the other views, so that usually it is not necessary to indicate the names of the views.

When solving problems, however, it is necessary to letter each point in every view, and to attach a subscript to each letter to indicate the name of the view. When there are many points in a view, subscripts may be left off, provided the name of each view is lettered on the drawing. The subscripts F, T, R, L, A, and O may be used, respectively, for front, top, right-side, left-side, auxiliary, and oblique views. X, Y, and Z, or numerals may be used when more than one auxiliary view is drawn. Care should be used in making subscripts so that they will be neither too large nor unreadable. The name of each point that is mentioned in the statement of a problem or that is used in solving the problem should always be lettered in every view in which the point is shown, so that the drawing will be easy to read. When a series of points is to be marked, it often is convenient to use numbers instead of letters for the names of the points.

9. Problems.

Group 13. Drawing Lines in Specified Directions.

10. True Lengths of Lines. One of the commonest problems in the design of a structure is to determine the actual or true lengths of the lines of the structure. A straight line appears in its true length in a normal view of the line. A normal view of a line is observed in a direction perpendicular to the line. In any view that is not a normal view of a line, the line appears shorter than it really is.

The top view of a horizontal line is a normal view of that line and shows its true length. The front view of a frontal line is a normal view and shows its true length. Either side view is a normal view of a profile line and shows its true length.   A view that shows the true shape of a triangle, a square, a circle, or other plane figure is a normal view of that figure. Such a view shows the true lengths of all lines of the plane figure, and also the true shape of the figure.

11. True Length of an Oblique Line.   This is found by drawing a normal view of the line.   An auxiliary view taken in a direction perpendicular to the oblique line will be the required normal view.   This auxiliary view may be taken in a horizontal, a frontal, or a profile direction.

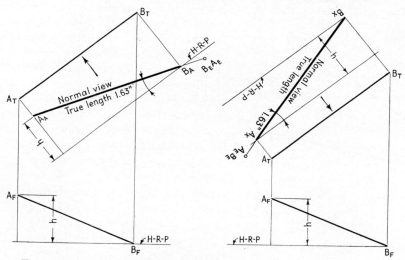

FIGURE 6. True length of a line.   FIGURE 7. True length of a line.

Figure 6 shows the front and top views of an oblique line A B.   The true length of the line is here found by taking a normal auxiliary elevation of the line A B in a direction perpendicular to the line as seen in the top view.   This direction is indicated by the pointing arrow.   Since the observer is here looking in a horizontal direction at the line, he will be able to see how far one end of the line is above the other end.   The front view shows that h is the distance that A is above B.   In the normal view, A is located the same distance above B.   In each case the distance h is measured from the horizontal reference plane H-R-P.   As soon as the points A_A and B_A are located in the normal view, they are connected by a straight line.   This line gives the true length of A B.   Since required data are to be drawn in broad lines, this normal view is drawn as a broad line, so that it will stand out from the lines used in solving the problem. On the normal view of a line, its true length should be stated in inches and decimals of an inch.   The solution of the problem is now completed. Incidentally, the slope of the line A B with the horizontal is indicated by the arc and arrowheads.

When determining the true length of an oblique line, it is poor practice to combine the auxiliary elevation with the top view by taking the horizontal reference plane coincident with the top view of the line A B. Adjacent views should always be separated a short distance, otherwise they are difficult to read.

When the normal view of the line is drawn as an auxiliary elevation, it may be taken from either side of the top view of the line. Figure 7 shows the normal view of the line A B taken from the rearward. This view may be read by imagining that the drawing is turned around so that the arrow points directly away from the reader. In this position the auxiliary elevation temporarily becomes a front view, in which the end A of the line is seen to be a distance h above the end B. This agrees with information to be obtained from the front view. An auxiliary elevation should never be drawn or lettered upside down, so that it reads in a direction contrary to the direction in which the observer is looking. Rays extend from the object to the observer, but never beyond the object. Figures 6 and 7 are both correct. In each of these two figures the end view of the line is shown. The end view is not needed, however, for determining the true length of the line. The end view is not a point.

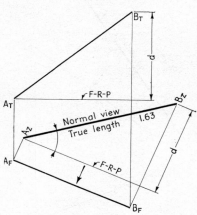

FIGURE 8. True length of a line.

The true length of the line A B can be determined as readily by drawing a normal frontal-auxiliary view, as is shown in Figure 8. This normal view is taken in a frontal direction perpendicular to the line as seen in the front view. When the observer looks at the line A B in the direction of the pointing arrow, he will be able to tell how far the point B is in front of or behind the point A. This distance d may be obtained from the top view and transferred to the frontal-auxiliary view. The frontal reference plane is used to determine the distance that B is behind A in the top view, and again is used to mark off the same distance in the auxiliary view. After the auxiliary views of the points A and B have been located, the solution of the problem is completed by drawing the true length of the line as required data. Note that the lettering is alined with the rays and reference plane, and that the length in inches is stated.

12. Problems.

Group 14. True Lengths of Oblique Lines.

Group 15. True Lengths of Lines—Miscellaneous Problems.

13. Calculating the Lengths of Lines. When it is necessary to obtain the length of a line, judgment must be used to decide whether or not the length can be determined with sufficient accuracy by graphical means. If proper tools and a proper drawing surface are used, and if the work is carefully done, drawings should not vary more than two or three hundredths of an inch from the correct measurements. Paper shrinks and stretches a considerable amount with change in humidity, and the lengths of lines drawn on the paper change correspondingly. This variation may easily be as much as $\frac{1}{8}$ inch per foot. For accurate work, drawings often are made on sheets of metal. If a structure is large, the error in the drawing will be multiplied in the structure as many times as the structure is larger than the drawing. In structures that must be very accurate, certain dimensions must always be calculated.

Experienced judgment is required to decide what degree of accuracy is necessary for each part of a structure. Close tolerances are expensive. Measuring to a thousandth of an inch or less is necessary at times; in many cases it has no justification.

As an example, suppose that the distance between centers of the rivet holes in a diagonal brace is about 12 feet and the drawing is made to a scale of $\frac{3}{4}$ inch = 1 foot. The drawing will be one-sixteenth of the size of the diagonal brace. An error of 0.01 inch in the drawing will produce an error of 0.16 inch in the center-to-center distance between rivet holes. The maximum allowable error would be less than this. In this case a small-scale drawing could not be used without calculating the distance between rivet holes.

The distance between two points whose coordinates are known may be calculated as follows: Subtract each coordinate of one of the points from the similar coordinate of the other point. These three differences represent the distances between the two points, measured in three mutually perpendicular directions. To calculate the true length of the line, find the square root of the sum of the squares of the above differences.

Take, for example, the points A137 and B625.

$$6 - 1 = 5 \qquad\qquad 2 - 3 = -1 \qquad\qquad 5 - 7 = -2$$
$$5^2 = 25 \qquad\qquad (-1)^2 = 1 \qquad\qquad -(2)^2 = 4$$
$$\sqrt{25 + 1 + 4} = 5.4772$$

Prove that the geometry of the above method of calculating the true length of an oblique line is similar to the geometry of finding the true length of an oblique line by means of a normal view.

14. Problems.

Group 16. Calculating the Lengths of Lines.

15. Intersecting Lines. Two lines intersect if they pass through a common point. In Figure 9 the lines C D and E F intersect at the point

O.   Here, the top view of O is on the top views of both lines, the front view of O is on the front views of both lines, and each view of O is in line with its ray leading from the adjacent view.   The lines C D and E F pass through the common point O; hence they intersect.

Two lines that do not intersect are shown in Figure 10.   In the front view the two lines appear to intersect at P_F.   But the apparent intersection in the top view is not in line with the ray leading from P_F, so that P_T cannot be located in line with its ray and also on the top views of both lines.   The lines J K and L M do not pass through a common point; hence they do not intersect.

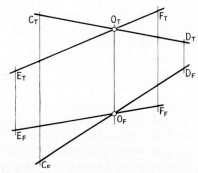

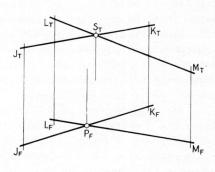

Figure 9. Intersecting lines.   Figure 10. Lines not intersecting.

16. Problems.

Group 17.   Intersecting Lines.

17. Parallel Lines.

Two lines are parallel if they extend in the same direction.   The distance between two parallel lines is constant.   Two lines are parallel if each is parallel to a third line.   Parallel lines and edges occur frequently in structures and objects.   It is therefore necessary to know how to draw parallel lines and how to recognize parallel lines in a drawing.

When considering parallel lines, it is necessary to distinguish between a requirement that specifies the direction of the line and a requirement that specifies the location of the line.   If a line is to be parallel to another line, its direction, but not its location, is determined.   If a line is to be drawn through a given point and parallel to a given line, both its direction and its location are determined.   If a line is to be parallel to a given plane, its direction is limited in part, but its location is not limited.

Parallel-line principles may be determined with the aid of Figure 11. In this figure any two horizontal-frontal lines A B and C D are drawn equal in length.   These two lines are parallel since they extend in the same direction from left to right only.   The lines A C and B D are drawn next.   Since the lines A B and C D are equal in length and parallel, the figure A B D C is a parallelogram.   Since the figure is a parallelogram, the opposite sides A C and B D also are parallel in space.   In the front view, the lines A B and C D appear parallel and equal in length; hence the front view of the parallelogram appears as a parallelogram.   Therefore, in the front view the parallel lines A C and B D appear parallel.   For similar reasons these parallel lines appear parallel in the top view and also in the auxiliary view.   The oblique lines A C and B D are parallel and will appear parallel in every view.

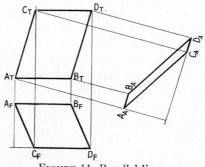

FIGURE 11. Parallel lines.

18. Parallel-line Principle.   From the above proofs the following general principle may be deduced:

Parallel lines appear parallel in every view.

Hence, lines that are known to be parallel must be drawn parallel in every view.

The inverse statement—important to the reader of the drawing— namely, *lines are parallel if they appear parallel*, is generally true.   The exception to be noted is that two lines, whether parallel or not, will always appear to be parallel in any view that is taken in a direction parallel to a plane that is parallel to the two lines.   For example, profile lines always appear parallel in both the front and the top views.   A side view is necessary to determine whether or not profile lines are parallel.   Also, it is impossible to tell from a single view whether or not lines are parallel.   Horizontal lines, for example, always appear parallel in the front and side views, and in auxiliary elevations, while the top view will determine if the lines are parallel or not.   To determine whether or not lines are parallel, it is necessary to refer to at least two views, and care must be taken to be sure that the exception stated above does not apply.

19. Problems.

Group 18.   Parallel Lines.

20. Force Polygons.   A force that acts on a point or on any part of an object may be represented by an arrow.   The line of the arrow represents the line in which the force acts.   A compression force, or force that pushes on the object, is represented by an arrow pointing at the object.   A tension force, or one that pulls on the object, is represented by an arrow pointing away from the object.   The length of the line of the arrow is proportioned to the strength of the force that the arrow represents.   That is, in the drawing the length of the arrow is scaled to some chosen number of pounds per inch of length.

A body that is stationary or moving at a uniform rate is said to be *free* when all the external forces acting on the body are represented by arrows pushing or pulling on the object. These forces form a balanced system. In any direction, they push just as hard as they pull on the object. The force arrows will form a closed space polygon, known as a *stress diagram*, if they are connected end to end in any order, with the arrows pointing in the same direction around the polygon. If the direction and the value of one force are not known, these are determined by the arrow that closes the space polygon.

21. Problems.
Group 19. Force Polygons.

22. Perpendicular Lines.
Two lines are mutually perpendicular if the direction of each line is at right angles to the direction of the other

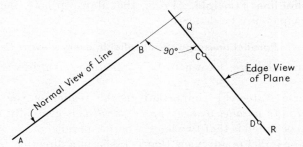

FIGURE 12. Perpendicular-line principle.

line. It is possible to have three straight lines, each of which is perpendicular to the other two. Lines may be perpendicular to each other whether they intersect or not. The requirement that lines be perpendicular is independent of the location of the individual lines. When only the direction of a line is stated, its location requires additional data. When one line is to be perpendicular to another, its direction is limited only in part. When one line is to be perpendicular to two nonparallel lines or to a plane, its direction is definitely determined.

Since the lines of a structure are so frequently perpendicular to each other, it is important to know how to draw one line perpendicular to another, and also how to determine whether two lines that are represented in a drawing are perpendicular or not.

23. Perpendicular-line Principle.
Figure 12 shows a single view of the line A B. This may be a principal, auxiliary, or oblique view. It is here specified as a normal view of the line A B, although no adjacent view is shown. In the same figure is shown the edge view of a plane Q R drawn perpendicular to the normal view of the line A B. The plane Q R

is now perpendicular to the given line.   And, the line A B is perpendicular to every line of the plane Q R.

Take the points C and D in the plane Q R.   These points may be at different or at equal distances from the observer.   C D may then be either a view of an oblique line C D, or a normal view of the line C D. For every position of C D in the plane Q R, the lines C D and A B will be perpendicular, and their views will be perpendicular.

If A B is now taken as a view of an oblique line A B, then the line A B will be not perpendicular to the plane Q R.   If A B and C D are views of two oblique lines, then these lines are not perpendicular, even though the views are perpendicular.   If, however, A B is an oblique line and C D is a normal view, the lines are perpendicular, since C D and A B may be interchanged in the proof of the preceding paragraph.   From these proofs a general principle may be derived:

Two perpendicular lines appear perpendicular only in a view that is a normal view of one or both of the lines.

This principle is useful when perpendicular lines are to be drawn.   It indicates that these lines must first be drawn perpendicular in some view that is a normal view of at least one of the lines.   A normal view of both lines is not necessary.   As an aid in visualizing the above reasoning, turn Figure 12 so that plane Q R and the line C D are horizontal.   The line A B will then be vertical.

Frequently, one of the principal views will be a normal view of one (or both) of the lines.   If one (or both) of two perpendicular lines is horizontal, the lines will appear perpendicular in the top view; if frontal, they will appear perpendicular in the front view; if profile, they will appear perpendicular in a side view.   Oblique lines that are perpendicular will not appear perpendicular in any principal view.

The following inverse statement is useful to the reader of drawings:

If two lines appear perpendicular in any view, the lines are perpendicular only if the view is a normal view of one or both of the lines.

24. Applying the Principle.   Figure 13 shows the top and front views of 10 different lines.   The student should consider in turn each pair of these lines and determine by inspection whether the two lines are perpendicular or not.   The perpendicular-line principle and its inverse statement determine this.

A list should be made as follows: In the first line of the list, state A B $\perp$: --, --, --, by filling in the names of the lines that are perpendicular to A B.   In the next line, make the same statements regarding C D and the lines to the right of C D.   And, so on until all possible pairs of the 10 lines have been considered in turn.   This should be done without drawing any additional views of these lines.   The angular relations between a pair of profile and oblique lines shown in the figure need not here be considered, since additional views would be required. The unit dimensions indicated on the profile lines will enable the reader to visualize the slopes of these lines so that the question of their perpendicularity may be decided by inspection.

To draw one line perpendicular to another, slide the hypotenuse of a draftsman's triangle along one edge of another triangle. The two legs of the sliding triangle are perpendicular to each other, and may be used for drawing or checking perpendicular lines.

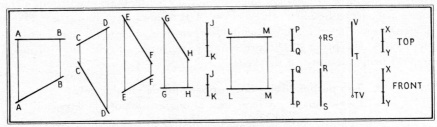

FIGURE 13. Are the lines perpendicular?

25. Problems.

Group 20.   Are the Given Lines Perpendicular?

Group 21.   Horizontal, Frontal, and Profile Lines Perpendicular to Oblique Lines.

26. Perpendicular Oblique Lines.   *Problem:* Draw the line R B perpendicular to the given line R C. Since it is possible to draw an infinite number of lines through the point R and perpendicular to the given line R C, the solution of the problem can be limited to a single line by stating some limiting condition; for example, one view of the required line may be given. In the problem just stated it is assumed that the front and the top views of the line R C are given, but that only the top view of R B is given and that its front view is to be found.

The solution of the problem is carried out in Figure 14. After the given data have been located, the various points and lines leading to the solution of the problem are located and drawn in the consecutive order indicated by the numbers in the illustration. These numbers enable the reader readily to review the solution.

Perpendicular-line principles apply. To draw one line perpendicular to another, it is necessary to have a normal view of one of the lines. In Figure 14, draw a normal auxiliary elevation of the given line R C taken in the direction indicated by the arrow. The lines R C and R B will appear perpendicular in this view. After the normal view $R_A C_A$ is found, draw the line 8 through R_A and perpendicular to $R_A C_A$. This is a view of the line R B. B_A will be on ray 5. In the auxiliary view, B is found to be located a distance *b* below the point R. In the front view, B is now located the same distance *b* below the point R, at the level 9 and on the ray 10. The front view of R B is next drawn. All views of the line R B are drawn heavy, and the solution of the problem is completed. It should be noted that these perpendicular oblique lines do not appear perpendicular in either the front or the top view.

It must be definitely understood that the auxiliary view in Figure 14 is a normal view of the line R C, but not of the line R B. The top view indicates that, when a view is taken in the direction of the arrow, the

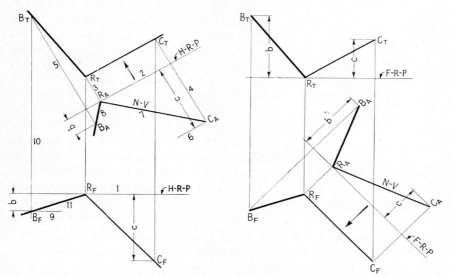

FIGURE 14. Perpendicular oblique lines.   FIGURE 15. Perpendicular oblique lines.

points R and C will be equidistant from the observer, while the point B is a greater distance from the observer. Misinterpretation of a view causes much trouble.

If the problem as stated above were now changed, so that the front view of R B is given and the top view is to be found, the same lines would be drawn as in Figure 14, but some of the lines would be drawn in a different order.

Figure 15 shows that a normal frontal-auxiliary view of the line R C, taken in a direction perpendicular to the line as shown in the front view, serves as readily to solve the problem as does the normal auxiliary elevation.

The student should not limit himself to some set method of solving problems. When drawing perpendicular lines, the general perpendicular-line principles always apply and a normal view is necessary; but this need not be a normal view of the given line.   Figure 16 illustrates this.   The top view, but not the front view, of R B is known.   An auxiliary elevation

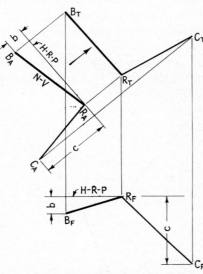

is here taken in the direction of the pointing arrow perpendicular to the top view of R B.   R C is first located in the auxiliary elevation, but this is not a normal view.   R B is then drawn perpendicular to R C. R_A B_A must be a normal view, since the lines R C and R B are specified as perpendicular.   The level of the point B is now known. The front view of B may now be located, and the front view of R B is then drawn.   Judgment should be used when deciding the question as to which normal auxiliary view it is best to draw in order to keep views from overlapping and to make a drawing that is easily read.

FIGURE 16. Perpendicular oblique lines.

27. Test for Perpendicular Lines.

If two oblique lines are given and it is required to determine whether or not they are perpendicular, proceed as follows: In Figure 17, the intersecting lines V C and V A are given.   To determine whether or not the angle at V is a right angle, draw a view that is a normal view of either one of the lines.   A normal auxiliary elevation of V A is here chosen.   In the normal view take one point on each line, as A and C, and on the line A C as a diameter draw a circle.   If V falls on the circle, then the angle C V A is a right angle.   If the vertex V falls inside or outside the circle, then the angle at V is not a right angle, and the lines V C and V A are not perpendicular. The true size of the angle at V is not here shown, since this is a normal view of V A, but not of V C. Perpendicularity of lines may also be checked by using two triangles, as previously explained.

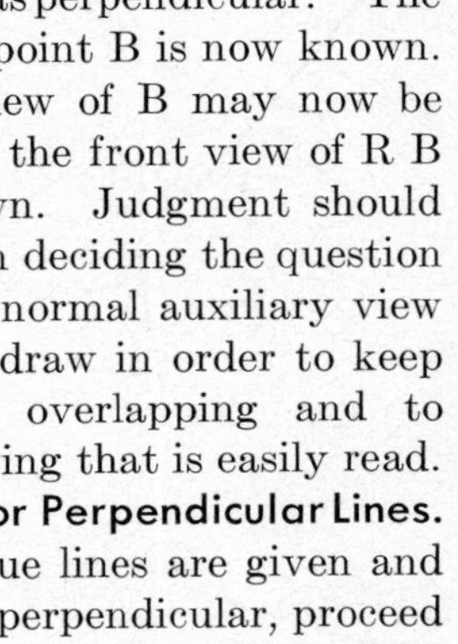

28. Problems.

Group 22.   Perpendicular Oblique Lines.
Group 23.   Right-angled Figures.

FIGURE 17. Test for perpendicular lines.

29. Distance from a Point to a Line.   Through

the given point draw a line that is perpendicular to and intersects the given line.   Locate the point of intersection.   The true length of the straight line connecting the point of intersection with the given point is the required distance.

The solution of this problem is illustrated in Figure 18. O is the given point and K L is the given line. After the front and top views are located, draw a normal view of the line K L. This is here shown as an auxiliary elevation taken in the direction of the pointing arrow. In this view locate the point O, and then draw the line $O_A P_A$ perpendicular to the normal view of K L, and intersecting it at P_A. This is one view of the

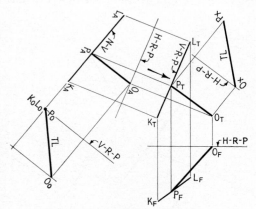

FIGURE 18. Distance from a point to a line.

required distance; but it is not a normal view of this distance. This auxiliary elevation is a normal view of the line K L, but not of O P. The front and top views of P may now be located, and the front and top views of O P drawn. To find the distance from O to P, it is necessary to obtain a normal view of O P. It may be drawn adjacent to any one of the three views previously found. It is here shown as an auxiliary elevation, $O_x P_x$. This is the true length of the required distance from the point O to the line K L. The true length of O P may also be found by drawing an oblique view taken in the direction of the line K L, as shown in the drawing.

30. Problems.

Group 24. Distance from a Point to a Line.

31. To Draw a Line Perpendicular to Two Lines. The problem may be stated definitely as follows: Determine the line A D that is perpendicular to the given lines A B and A C. The location of the required line A D is definitely limited by the requirement that it must pass through the fixed point A, and its direction is determined by the requirement that it must be perpendicular to the two given lines. The point D is used to give a name to the required line A D and may be located at any point on this line.   The given lines A B and A C must not be parallel, but they may or may not be perpendicular.

To solve this problem it is necessary to draw a normal view of each of the given lines.   In each of these two normal views, the required line is drawn perpendicular to one of the given lines.   The point D must be located on each view of the required line so that the different views of D will agree as to its location.

The front and top views of the given lines are drawn in Figure 19.   The given data are also shown in miniature in the insert.   The order in which

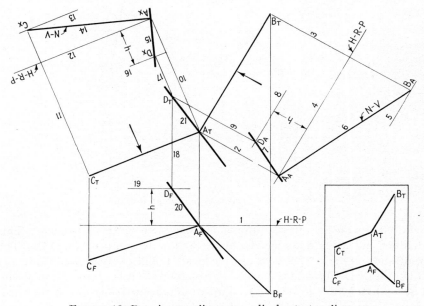

FIGURE 19. Drawing one line perpendicular to two lines.

the remaining lines are drawn and the points are located is indicated by the consecutive numbers in the figure.

After the normal view $A_A B_A$ is obtained, the line 7 is drawn perpendicular to $A_A B_A$.   This is one view of the required line A D. D_A is then located at any convenient level h above or below A.   The top view of D is somewhere on ray 9.

A normal view of the line A C is now drawn, and in this view the line 15 is drawn perpendicular to $A_X C_X$.   Line 15 is another view of the required line A D.   The point D is now located on 15 at D_X, which must be the same distance h above the level of A_X as D_A is above A_A; otherwise the two views would not agree as to the location of D.   The top view of D is somewhere on the ray 17.

Since the top view of D is on the ray 17 and also on the ray 9, D_T is located at the intersection of these rays. The front view of D should now be located on the ray 18 and at the same level h above A_F as the point D is above A in both normal views. The point D is now above A in three views of this drawing, and the difference in level of the points is h. The three views must agree. The distance h is measured in a vertical, never in a slanting, direction. As soon as all views of D are located, the required line A D may be drawn in all views. As usual, required data should be heavy. In order to make a drawing readable, all auxiliary views should be located so that views do not overlap.

Note, in Figure 19, that the point A is common to the three lines, and that the point A appears in every view. Hence the reference plane is taken through A. It would be a mistake to take a reference plane through some other point. This problem could be solved as readily by drawing frontal-auxiliary views of the two given lines. Note, however, that the problem could not be solved by drawing an auxiliary elevation of one of the lines and a frontal-auxiliary of the other line, since there would then be no way of locating either the top or the front view of the point D. Usually it is convenient to take the dimension h as some definite length in inches.

32. Problems.

Group 25.   Drawing One Line Perpendicular to Two Lines.

Group 26.   Rectangular Objects.

33. Common Perpendicular to Two Nonintersecting Lines.

The solution of this problem is useful, whenever it is necessary or desirable to connect two nonintersecting and nonparallel straight-line parts by means of another straight-line part, in order to meet either or both of the requirements that the connecting part is to have the shortest possible length or is to be perpendicular to each of the first two parts. Examples of such cases are connecting two pipes by means of a third pipe, when using right-angled pipe fittings; determining the least diameter of skew gears to drive one shaft from another; locating the shortest tunnel to connect two tunnels; determining that sufficient clearance exists between two cables or ties, as in an airplane.

The following problem may be taken as a specific example: Find O P, the common perpendicular to the two given lines A B and E F. The required line O P is to be perpendicular to both of the given lines and will intersect them, respectively, at O and P.

Perpendicular-line principles apply in the solution. To solve the problem, it will be necessary to draw a normal view of one of the given lines and then to draw a view that is a normal view of the other given line or of the required line.

The plan for solving the problem, as carried out in detail in Figure 20, is as follows: Draw first a normal auxiliary elevation of the line A B, and locate the line E F in the same view. Next, draw an oblique view taken in the direction of the line A B and showing both given lines. Since the required line O P is perpendicular to A B and since the oblique view shows the end view of A B, the oblique view will be a normal view of the line O P. The required line O P also is to be perpendicular to the line E F,

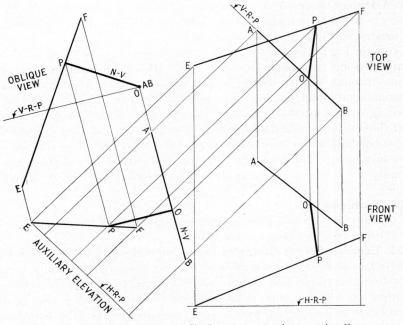

FIGURE 20. Common perpendicular to two nonintersecting lines.

and it may now be drawn perpendicular to E F in the oblique view, because this view is a normal view of O P. Visualize these conditions.

The point P is next located on E F in the auxiliary elevation. Since O P is perpendicular to A B and since the auxiliary elevation is a normal view of the line A B, the line P O may now be drawn perpendicular to A B in the auxiliary elevation. The top and front views of the points O and P are now located and the views of the line are drawn. If the shortest distance between the lines A B and E F is required, it may be measured from O to P in the oblique view which is a normal view of the line O P.

The horizontal and vertical reference planes used in the solution are indicated in the figure. Since some rather sharp intersections occur between rays and lines, the following measurements should be checked: the distance of P from the vertical reference plane in the oblique and top views, and the distances of O and P from the horizontal reference plane in the auxiliary elevation and front view.

34. Problems.

Group 27. Common Perpendicular to Two Nonintersecting Lines.

35. Angle between Two Lines. Two methods for finding the angle between two lines are here described: the normal-view method and the revolution method.

To find the angle between two lines by the normal-view method, obtain a view that is a normal view of both lines. In this view the true angle will be seen.

To find the true size of the angle B A C in Figure 21, proceed as follows: Draw a horizontal line B E. The point E is taken on the line A C, and the line A E now replaces the line A C in the consideration of the problem. The problem is to find the angle A of the triangle B A E. Draw an auxiliary elevation taken in the direction of the horizontal side E B. This elevation shows an edge view of the triangle. Now take a normal view of the triangle in a direction perpendicular to the edge view, as indicated by the pointing arrow. In this oblique view the true size of the angle a is seen. The points B and E are the same respective distances from the vertical reference plane in the oblique view as they are in the top view. B is the far point, and E is the near point. This problem may be solved as readily by taking a frontal-auxiliary view in the direction of a frontal line that intersects the two given lines.

Determining the angle between two lines by the revolution method consists in revolving the given lines about an axis, without changing the angle between the lines, until both lines are horizontal or frontal. The true angle will then be seen in the top or front view. The method is illustrated in Figure 22.

The given lines are A B and A C. Draw a horizontal line B E that intersects the line A C at E. The line A E is the same line as A C and now replaces A C in the consideration of the problem. In the triangle B A E, the angle at A is required. The horizontal side B E of the triangle is used as an axis of revolution, and the triangle is revolved about this axis until all sides of the triangle are horizontal. An auxiliary elevation of the triangle is taken in the direction of the axis E B. In this elevation A_A is now revolved to A_1 about the axis E B. The three corners of the triangle are now at the same level. In the top view the edge view of the circle of revolution is seen perpendicular to the axis. The point A revolves from A_T to A_1 where it is in line with its ray leading from the auxiliary elevation. The point A has no motion parallel to the axis. Since the points B and E are on the axis, they do not move. The true shape of the triangle is shown in the top view as B_T A_1 E_T, and the true size of the required angle a is seen.

The revolution method requires one line and two measurements less than does the normal-view method, but in a complicated drawing it would not be desirable to use this method, since it adds more lines to the top view. The normal-view method keeps the lines in their normal position and leaves the top view clearer. Both methods are useful.

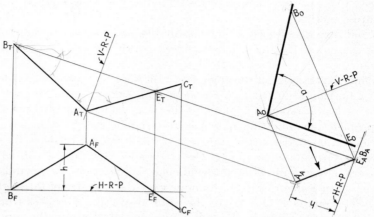

FIGURE 21. Angle between lines—normal-view method.

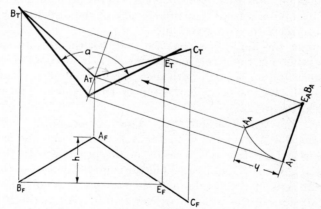

FIGURE 22. Angle between lines—revolution method.

36. Summary. Objects are represented and problems are solved by drawing principal, auxiliary, and oblique views. Each view must be properly placed in relation to its adjacent view. No view should ever be reversed. Each view shows certain dimensions of the object. All views adjacent to the same view have certain dimensions in common. The direction in which a view must be taken depends upon the analysis of the problem that is to be solved. Normal views and end views of lines often are useful. The true length of a line is seen in a normal view of the line.

Parallel lines appear parallel in every view.   Perpendicular lines appear perpendicular only in a view that is a normal view of one or both of the lines.

37. Problems.

Group 28.   Angle between Two Lines.
Group 29.   Straight-line Questions.

Chapter 6

CURVED LINES

1. Points, lines, and surfaces are basic elements of structures. A line may be either straight or curved. The engineer draws straight and curved lines to represent the edges, the contours, and the surfaces of the structures that he designs. Straight lines and circles are the only lines that can be drawn readily.

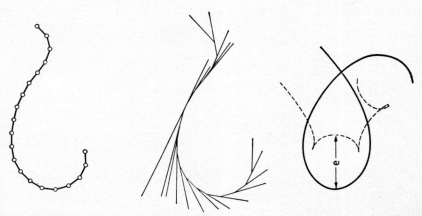

FIGURE 1. Curved line generated by a moving point.

FIGURE 2. Curved line generated by a moving line.

FIGURE 3. Parallel curved lines.

2. **Curved Lines.** A curved line is generated by a point that moves in a constantly changing direction. The exact nature of each curved line is determined by the motion of its generating point.

Curved lines may be imagined as consisting of short, straight-line elements, infinitesimal in length. The generating point is conceived as moving an infinitesimal distance in one direction, and then changing its direction and again moving an infinitesimal distance. No two consecutive elements of a curved line lie in the same direction. Curved lines having

72

definite geometrical properties may be definitely defined by stating the law that governs the motion of the generating point. There are two general classes of curved lines: single-curved and double-curved.

3. Single-curved Lines. All elements of a single-curved line lie in the same plane. Single-curved lines also are called *plane curves*. Figure 1 shows consecutive positions of the generating point of a single-curved line. Short, straight-line elements of the curve join consecutive positions of the generating point.

Figure 2 illustrates the possibility of generating a curved line by means of a moving straight line. Two consecutive positions of the straight-line generatrix intersect. The generated curved line is called the *envelope* of the straight lines.

The solid line and the broken line of Figure 3 represent two parallel curved lines. The constant normal distance between these two lines is *e*. Parallel curved lines are useful when designing certain mechanisms.

Among the commonly used single-curved lines that may be definitely defined are the circle, ellipse, parabola, hyperbola, involute, sinusoid, and several kinds of spirals and cycloids. An infinite variety of single-curved lines having no special names frequently are used to represent structures. Among these are the contour lines of topographical maps, lines of ships and aircraft, and lines and contours of the curved surfaces of a great variety of structures. Curved structures are definitely represented in drawings by means of single-curved lines.

4. Tangents to Curved Lines. A tangent to a curved line has the same direction as the element of the curve at the point of tangency. Tangents have considerable use in various construction problems. For curves of known geometrical properties it usually is possible to draw tangents accurately.

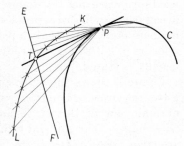

FIGURE 4. Tangent to a curve.

Tangents to curves of unknown geometrical properties may be closely approximated by the following method. Figure 4 shows a single-curved line. A tangent is to be drawn at P. Through P draw a number of chords and extend these outside the curve. Draw any straight line E F approximately perpendicular to the unknown tangent. On each chord, lay off the length of the chord from the line E F. Chords to one side of P are measured to one side of E F, and those on the other side of P are measured on the opposite side of E F. Through the points thus determined draw a smoothly curved line K L. The lines K L and E F intersect at T. The required tangent is P T. The curve K L is called a *curve of error*.

Figure 5 illustrates a method for determining the point of tangency when a curve and a tangent are known. Draw a number of chords parallel to the given tangent. From both ends of each chord, and perpendicular to the chord, lay off the length of the chord. Through the points thus found draw a smooth curve. This curve will intersect the given tangent at the point of tangency. P is the required point. K L is a curve of error. Such curves give nearly correct results if carefully drawn.

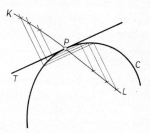

FIGURE 5. Point of tangency.

5. Circles. A circle is a single-curved line generated by a point which moves so that its distance from a fixed point, called a *center*, is constant. The constant distance is the radius. The word *circle* is also used to designate the plane area within the circle. The tangent to a circle is perpendicular to the radius at the point of tangency. The straight line that passes through the center of a circle and is perpendicular to the plane of the circle is called the *axis* of the circle. The axis is the center line of the shaft on which the circle would rotate when running true on its shaft.

A circle is definitely specified by stating its diameter or radius, the location of its center, and its axis or plane. The size of a circle generally is specified by stating its diameter. In structures, the centers of circular parts are not normally available as a point from which to measure, and calipers are used for measuring the diameters of cylindrical parts, cylindrical holes, shafts, drills, reamers, etc. When only a part of a circle appears in a drawing, the radius of the arc usually is stated.

Figure 6 shows three principal views of a frontal circle. The front view is here a normal view of this circle and shows its true shape. The top and right-side views are edge views of the circle. These edge views should never be visualized as a

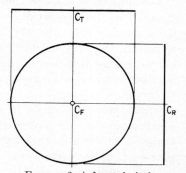

FIGURE 6. A frontal circle.

straight line, nor is it correct to say that the circle appears as a straight line in the edge view. Although the circle is a very familiar figure, there is danger that it will not be correctly visualized when its edge view is seen.

6. Inclined Circle. A circle having an inclined axis A B is shown in Figure 7. The circle is first drawn in the auxiliary view on the center C_A. This auxiliary view is taken in the direction of the axis A B and shows the end view of the axis and the normal view of the circle. The front view is next drawn. This is an edge view of the circle.

Before attempting to draw the top view, a number of points, not less than 12, should be located on the circle in the auxiliary view. These points should be evenly spaced around the circle. First, draw the horizontal and frontal diameters 4 12 and 0 8. The points are consecutively numbered and then transferred, by means of rays, to the front view.

Next, draw the rays leading to the top view. Locate each point in line with its ray, and at the proper distance in front of or behind the axis. This distance is determined from the auxiliary view. The distances may be transferred from the auxiliary view to the top view by means of the dividers or compass. As an aid in transferring points, it should be noted that the points 10 and 14 are the same distance behind the axis that the points 2 and 6 are in front of the axis. Four settings of the compass will transfer all 16 points. The points in the top view must be carefully located if the resulting ellipse is to have the proper shape. If greater accuracy is desired, the circle should be divided into 24 equal parts. After the points in the top view are located,

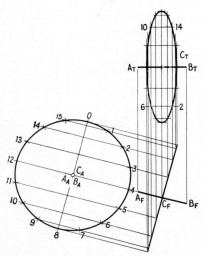

FIGURE 7. An inclined circle.

the curve may be drawn through the points. This should be done with care, by using the method that is explained in the last paragraph of Article 9.

Before starting to divide the normal view of a circle into a number of equal parts, care should be taken to start the divisions on the diameter of the circle that will require the least number of settings of the compass in order to transfer dimensions from the normal view to the view in which the circle appears as an ellipse. The proper choice of a reference plane will not only save time but will also produce a better drawing.

7. Circle in Oblique Position. Figure 8 shows four views of a circle in an oblique position. The point C is the center of the circle, and A C is the axis of the circle. Given the front and top views of the axis, a normal view of the axis is next drawn. This is here taken as a normal auxiliary elevation of the axis. The oblique or end view of the axis $A_O C_O$ is then located. In this view the true shape of the circle will be seen, and here the circle of the desired diameter is drawn. The horizontal diameter 9 3 and the diameter 0 6 perpendicular to it are drawn. Twelve or more points equally spaced are then located on the circle and numbered, and these points are transferred by means of rays to the auxiliary elevation of the circle. The last-named view is an edge view of the circle. In it the circle appears perpendicular to the axis A C. This is an application of perpendicular-line principles. The auxiliary elevation is a normal view of the axis. Since all diameters of the circle are perpendicular to the axis, they are drawn perpendicular to the axis in this normal auxiliary view.

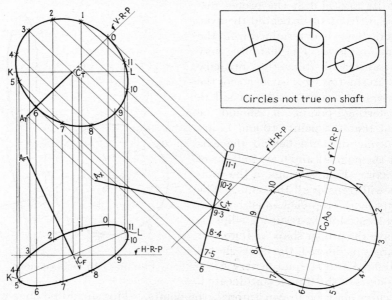

FIGURE 8. A circle in an oblique position.

The rays leading from the auxiliary elevation to the top view are now drawn; and the top view of each point is located in line with its ray, at the correct distance from, and on the proper side of, the vertical reference plane V-R-P. When the circle is divided into equal parts about the diameter 0 6 in the reference plane, only three settings of the compass are necessary to transfer the locations of 12 points from the normal view to the top view. Care must be taken that the points located on the near side of the reference plane in the oblique view are not placed on the far side in the top view. Although such a mistake will not change the appearance of the circle in the top view, the points are incorrectly located; and when the front view is drawn, the elliptical front view will be in an entirely wrong position.

The rays leading from the top view to the front view are now drawn, and each point in the front view is located at its proper level, above or below the horizontal reference plane H-R-P, as determined from the auxiliary elevation. Each view of every point should be lettered as soon as it is located. The front and top elliptical views of the circle are now drawn, and the solution of the problem is finished.

The knowledge of the correct relation that should be maintained between a circle and its axis is particularly useful to the engineer or illustrator when he is drawing or sketching pictorial views. The insert of Figure 8 shows a small circle that is not mounted true on its shaft or axis, and two incorrectly drawn right circular cylinders. Errors of this kind appear frequently in illustrations of technical articles and in textbooks. They should be avoided. The correct relation is explained in the following paragraphs.

In every view where a circle is represented by an ellipse, the perpendicular-line principle is useful for determining the correct relation between the axis of the circle and the major axis of the ellipse. Every diameter of the circle is perpendicular to the axis of the circle. But in every view that is an oblique view of the axis, only one diameter of the circle will show as a normal view perpendicular to the axis. This diameter must be the major axis of the ellipse. Hence the major axis of the ellipse will always appear perpendicular to the axis of the circle.

In Figure 8 the diameter 3 9 is a horizontal diameter. Its top view is a normal view. Hence in the top view 3 9 is the major axis of the ellipse, and it is perpendicular to the top view of A C. The frontal diameter K L is the major axis of the ellipse in the front view, and it is perpendicular to the front view of the axis A C.

8. Problems.

Group 30. Circles.

9. Ellipses.

An ellipse is a single-curved line generated by a point which moves so that the sum of its distances from two fixed points, called *foci*, is constant.

Elliptical-shaped structures are not very common, but the ellipse often appears in drawings as a view of a circle, or as a section of a cylinder or cone. An ellipse is shown in Figure 9. The longest diameter A B is the major axis, and the shortest diameter C D is the minor axis. Each axis is a perpendicular bisector of the other axis. If the ellipse is horizontal, the top view will be a normal view of the ellipse and will show its true shape, and the front and side views will be edge views of the ellipse as is shown in the figure.

One focus of the ellipse is located at F_1 and the other at F_2. The point P is taken as any point on the ellipse. The definition of the ellipse requires that, as P moves around the curve, the sum $P F_1 + P F_2$ shall remain constant. This constant can be represented by a straight line of fixed length. Since the point B is on the curve, the sum $B F_1 + B F_2$

must be constant; and since B F$_2$ = A F$_1$, this constant is equal to A B, the major axis of the ellipse. Also, since C is a point on the curve, C F$_1$ = C F$_2$ = one-half of the major axis. Knowing this, it is possible to locate the foci with the aid of a compass, if the major and minor axes are known.

Given the definition of the ellipse, and the major and minor axes—or either axis and the distance between the foci—to draw the ellipse, proceed as follows: Locate the foci. Next, on the major axis, as shown in Figure 9, locate a number of points, as 1, 2, 3, 4, and 5. Set one compass to the length B 1, and another compass to the remaining length of the major axis A 1. The sum of these lengths is equal to the length of the major axis. Next, center one compass on one focus and center the other compass on the other focus. Swing the leads of the compasses near each other, and with each compass mark a short arc where the two circles cross. Locate a second crossing point on the other side of the major axis. Now center each

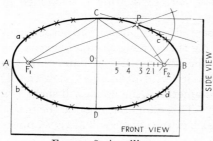

FIGURE 9. An ellipse.

compass on the other focus, and locate two more crossing points. Four points as shown at a, b, c, and d are thus found. Locate as many points on the ellipse as are needed, by setting the compasses to the other divisions 2, 3, 4, etc., marked on the major axis. Points may be located on the ellipse by using one compass instead of two, but this is much slower. To produce accurate work, the leads of the compasses must be kept very sharp. The compasses must be accurately set, particularly when points near the ends of the major axis, where the circular arcs intersect at sharp angles, are located.

After a sufficient number of points are found, draw the curve of the ellipse. Curves should first be sketched in freehand in a rather fine line. Sketch the curve around the ends of the axes, not up to the ends. The ends of an ellipse are not pointed. The french curve may then be used to finish the penciling. The tangent to the ellipse at the point P bisects the exterior angle between the focal radii, as is shown in Figure 9.

10. Pin-and-string Ellipse. A rough ellipse may be drawn by setting a pin or stake at each focus, and a third pin or stake at some point of the curve. Around these three pins or stakes is stretched an inelastic cord. The third pin or stake will trace an ellipse if it is now moved within the loop of the cord, provided the cord is kept taut. An ellipse so drawn is called the *gardener's ellipse*. A fairly accurate large ellipse may be drawn by this method if care is used in carrying out the details. It is not a practical plan for accurate work.

11. Ellipse by Trammel Method. When the major and minor axes of an ellipse are known, the draftsman often uses a strip of paper called a *trammel* for locating points on the curve. As shown in Figure 10, a mark or notch is made on the straight edge of the trammel at a point x, and two other marks, a and b, are made at distances equal, respectively, to one-half the minor axis and one-half the major axis from the point x. The trammel is then placed so that the point a is on the major axis and the point b is on the minor axis of the ellipse. In this position the point x will indicate the location of a point on the ellipse. This point should be marked on the drawing. The trammel is moved to new positions and the process repeated until a sufficient number of points are found. The points should be marked lightly and not indented into the paper with the lead pencil. Enough points should be located so that each point will check the location of the adjacent points. The points on the curve should be located closer together as the curve becomes sharper.

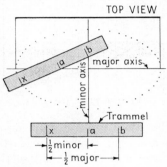

FIGURE 10. Ellipse by trammel method.

The trammel method of locating points on an ellipse is the quickest method, and it is accurate if the work is carefully done. The axes should be clean-cut lines drawn with a sharp pencil, the edge of the trammel should be straight, and the marks on the trammel should be sharp and should extend to the edge of the trammel. A small notch in the edge of the trammel at x aids in locating points accurately.

The ellipsograph is an instrument used for drawing ellipses and for cutting elliptical shapes in glass and metal. The design of the ellipsograph is usually based on the trammel principle explained above. Elliptical shapes may be turned on the lathe or cut in the milling machine by using a chuck based on the same principle. Methods of drawing approximate ellipses are described in engineering drawing textbooks.

12. Problems.

Group 31. Ellipses.

13. Parabolas. A parabola is a single-curved line generated by a point which moves so that its distance from a fixed point, or *focus*, is constantly equal to its distance from a fixed straight line, or *directrix*.

Figure 11 shows a parabola. F is the focus and C D is the directrix. The definition of the parabola requires that the point P on the curve shall move so that P F = P X; that is, the focal radii are equal. P X is perpendicular to the directrix.

To draw the parabola: Locate the focus and the directrix. Draw a number of straight lines, 1, 2, 3, etc., parallel to the directrix. Set the compass to the distance that one of these lines is from the directrix. Then, using the focus as a center, describe two short arcs across this line.

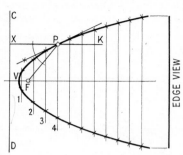

FIGURE 11. A parabola.

The two points thus located are points on the curve. In a similar manner, locate two points on each of the lines that is parallel to the directrix. The vertex V of the curve is halfway between the focus and the directrix. Locate a sufficient number of points, and then pencil the curve according to the plan given for penciling the ellipse. The tangent to the curve at the point P is the bisector of the angle F P X.

The parabola appears in structures of the beam type that are designed to carry the required load and at the same time to use the least amount of material possible in the beam. Some arches and road sections also are parabolic in shape. Since, in Figure 11, P F and P K make equal angles with the tangent, a reflector that is parabolic in shape and has a light located at F will throw a pencil of light, because it will reflect all rays of light parallel to the axis. The parabola also appears frequently in the development of the theory of engineering problems.

14. Problems.

Group 32. Parabolas.

15. Hyperbolas.

A hyperbola is a single-curved line generated by a point which moves so that the difference of its distances from two fixed points, called *foci*, remains constant. This definition should be compared with that of the ellipse.

A hyperbola is shown in Figure 12. F_1 and F_2 are the foci. The point P, on the curve, moves so that the difference of the distances P F_1 and P F_2 remains constant. This known constant may

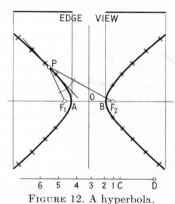

FIGURE 12. A hyperbola.

be expressed as a line of a certain length.

To draw the hyperbola, take a straight measuring line, as shown in the lower part of Figure 12, and mark off the common difference C D. Locate several points, numbered 1 to 6, on this line. Set one compass to the distance D 3, for example, and set another compass to the distance C 3.   The difference in these distances is C D.   Now center one compass at F_1 and the other at F_2, and draw short arcs that cross at two points.   These points are on the curve.   Interchange the compasses on the foci and locate two more points.   Reset the compasses to a new numbered point on the measuring line and repeat the above operation.   When a sufficient number of points are found, draw the hyperbola.   A hyperbola has two separate branches.   The tangent to the curve, at any point P, is the bisector of the angle between the focal radii P F_1 and P F_2.   The distance between the vertices A and B is equal to the constant difference C D.

The hyperbola is the curve that represents the relation between the volume and the pressure of a perfect gas.   The hyperbola appears in only a few structures, some of which are described in the chapter on Warped Surfaces.

The ellipse, parabola, and hyperbola are the *conic sections*.   Other intersections of a plane with a cone are a point, two straight lines, and a circle.   These are limiting forms of the three conic sections.

16. Problems.

Group 33.   Hyperbolas.

17. Spirals.

Of the various spirals, the spiral of Archimedes is most frequently used.   The spiral of Archimedes is a single-curved line generated by a point that revolves at a uniform rate about a fixed point, called the *pole*, and at the same time moves at a uniform rate toward or away from the pole.   In other types of spirals the generating point moves at a variable rate.

The Archimedean spiral is used in the threads of scroll chucks and similar devices.   Here the thread is cut into a plane disk and travels uniformly away from the center as it travels around the center.   The outlines of cams, designed to convert uniform rotary motion into uniform reciprocating motion, are Archimedean spirals.

In Figure 13 is shown an Archimedean spiral.   The pole is at P.   The distance that the generating point travels away from the pole in one turn is the lead or pitch of the spiral.   In the figure a right-hand spiral is shown.

To draw the Archimedean spiral, it is first necessary to locate the pole and to determine the lead and hand of the spiral.   A paper scale S, as shown in Figure 13, provides a convenient means of locating various positions of the generating point.   The lead of the spiral is marked on the scale and is divided into any convenient number of equal parts.   Not less than 12 or 16 divisions should be made.   If more than one turn of the spiral is to be drawn, other points, as A and B, should be marked on the scale at the distance indicated, but these distances need not be divided into smaller divisions.   The space around the pole is divided into equal sectors. The number of sectors is the same as the number of equal parts into which the lead was divided on the paper scale. The radii should be extended as far as is necessary.

Points on the spiral are located by first assuming that the generating point is at the pole and that it is beginning to move away from the pole on some chosen radius, P 0, for example. The generating point now moves one-twelfth of a revolution around the pole and one-twelfth of the lead away from the pole. The scale should be placed with the first one-twelfth division at the pole, and the zero point 0 and the points A and B on the radius P 1. The locations of one or more of the points are marked on

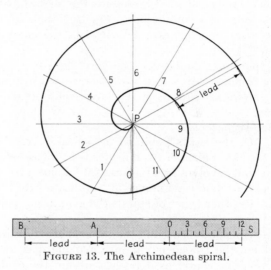

FIGURE 13. The Archimedean spiral.

the radius to indicate points of the spiral. The scale is next moved to the radius P 2; the second one-twelfth division point on the scale is set at the pole; and one or more points of the spiral are marked on this radius. This process is continued around the circle until points have been located on each radius. The curve may now be drawn. Instead of a paper scale, a draftsman's scale may be used, provided it carries a division equal to the lead of the spiral. Approximate methods of drawing spirals are based on the plan described in Article 19.

18. Problems.

Group 34. Archimedean Spirals.

19. Involutes. The involute is a single-curved line generated by a fixed point in a straight line which rolls on a circle. The straight line is tangent to the circle and must roll without slipping. An involute may be generated by fixing a marking point in an inelastic cord that is wound around a cylinder, and keeping the cord taut as it unwinds from the cylinder. This method should not be used for accurate work.

The involute is used as the curve to which gear teeth are shaped. Teeth so shaped will maintain a constant gear ratio for all positions of contact of the gear teeth. A few other curves are used for this purpose, but the involute system of gearing offers certain advantages. The involute is also used for the outline of cams.

An involute is shown in Figure 14. Before the involute is drawn, the size of the director circle and the hand, right or left, of the involute must be determined. The circle is divided into 12 or more equal parts, and a tangent extending in one direction is drawn at each of these points. The circumference of the director circle is calculated. A scale S is made by marking the length of this circumference on a straight line, and then dividing this length into the same number of equal parts as the number into which the circle is divided.

The generating point starts at some point 0 on the circle. The tangent rolls until it is tangent at the point 1. The generating point is now on the tangent, and one-twelfth of the circumference from the tangent point 1. This is the distance that the tangent has unrolled from the circle. This distance is measured with the scale, and the location of the generating point is marked on the tangent. The tangent now rolls

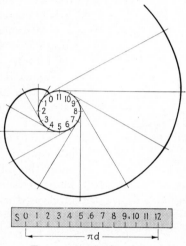

FIGURE 14. An involute.

to 2, and by means of the scale a point on the curve is marked two-twelfths of the circumference from 2. This process is carried on for as many turns of the involute as are needed. Attempting to locate a point on the tangent 10, for example, by stepping off the chord ten times on the tangent is likely to produce incorrect results, since any error is multiplied by 10. Calculating the circumference and dividing it into equal parts will avoid multiplication of an error.

It should be noted that the curve of the involute is perpendicular to the tangent, because the generating point is rotating around the point of tangency as an instantaneous center. This information aids the draftsman when he draws the curve. The mistake should not be made of extending the tangents in the wrong direction from the point of tangency.

Involutes of plane figures such as a line, a triangle a square, and a pentagon also may be drawn and are often used to represent a spiral in a drawing. Involutes of plane figures, with straight sides, are made up of circular arcs and may be drawn with the compass. Figure 15 illustrates this.

20. Problems.

Group 35. Involutes.

21. Trochoids and Cycloids.

These belong to a class of single-curved lines that are generated by a fixed point on the radius, or on the radius extended, of a circle that rolls on another circle, or on a straight line which may be regarded as a circle of infinite radius. These curves are also called *roulettes*, or *roll-traced curves*. The cycloid, epicycloid, and hypocycloid belong to the class of trochoids. The involute may be considered as a trochoid generated by a circle of infinite radius rolling on a circle of finite radius.

Figure 16 shows three curves that are generated by three points fixed to a circle that rolls on a straight line. The circle centered at 0 rolls on the line E F. The generating points are A, B, and C.

The line E F is made equal to the calculated length of the circumference of the rolling circle. The line and the circle are here divided into 16 equal parts, as is the line K L along which the center of the circle travels. As the equal parts of the circle in turn come into contact with the equal parts

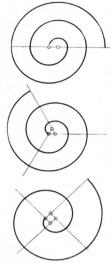

FIGURE 15. Involutes of a line, a triangle, and a square.

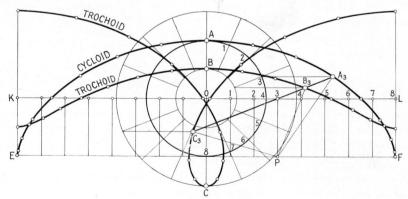

FIGURE 16. Trochoids.

of the line E F, the center of the circle is located in turn at the consecutively numbered points on the line K L. When the center of the rolling circle is at 3, for example, the vertical line of the circle on which the points A, B, and C are located will have turned through three of the equal angles and will now be parallel to the radius 0 3 of the original circle. The points A_3, B_3, and C_3 are now located on this straight line, each on a circular arc centered at 3 and having a radius equal to the fixed distance that the respective generating point is from the center of the rolling circle.

As checks on the accuracy of the drawing, it should be noted that A_3 is at the same level as is point 3 on the rolling circle; B_3 and C_3 should check similarly, as is indicated by the horizontal check lines through these points. Also, it should be observed that when the rolling circle is centered at 3, the three generating points are then rotating about the point P as an instantaneous center. Hence, each generated curve should be perpendicular to its instantaneous radius centered at P. The curve at B_3, for example, is perpendicular to the radius P B_3. And a tangent to the curve at this point will be perpendicular to this radius. Also, at any instant, the lowest point of the rolling circle is stationary and the top point of the circle moves at twice the speed that the center is moving. This property is useful in a variety of mechanisms. When a wheel rolls on a track, various points of the wheel trace the curves shown in the illustration.

22. Problems.

Group 36. Trochoids and Cycloids.

23. Epicycloids. The epicycloid is a single-curved line generated by a fixed point on a circle that rolls on the outside of another circle. This curve is used in mechanisms and for the outline of gear teeth.

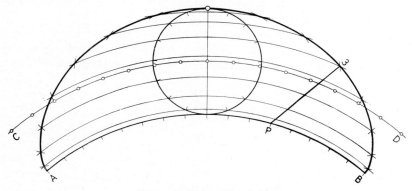

FIGURE 17. An epicycloid.

Before starting to draw the epicycloid of Figure 17, determine the diameters of the fixed director circle and of the rolling circle. The circumference of the rolling circle is then calculated, and this distance is marked off from A to B on the arc of the director circle. This distance may be measured by stepping off the distance around the arc, or by calculating the angle between the radii of the fixed circle. The method to be used depends upon the accuracy desired. The arc of the director circle and the circumference of the rolling circle should now be divided into the same number of equal parts. Since it is always possible to bisect an arc, this number should be 16 or 32. Eight divisions usually are not sufficient. The greater the number of divisions, the more nearly accurate is the work likely to be.

As the generating circle rolls on the director circle, each division point on the generating circle will in turn come into contact with the corresponding division point on the fixed arc, and the center of the generating circle will move along the arc C D. The locations of the center when the division points are in contact should be determined by marking the points where each radius through the division points on the arc A B meets the arc C D. The top point of the rolling circle in its central position is taken as the generating or marking point. As the circle rolls and the different division points come into contact, the generating point will be located successively on the arcs that have been drawn concentric with the arc A B, and at a distance from the successive centers equal to the radius of the rolling circle. After these points are located, the curve may be drawn. For any position of the generating circle, its contact point with the director circle is an instantaneous center about which the generating point is rotating. Hence, the epicycloidal curve will be perpendicular to the instantaneous radius. For example, P is an instantaneous center, and P 3 is an instantaneous radius. At the point 3, the curve is perpendicular to this radius. At the points A and B, the generated curve is perpendicular to the director circle.

24. Hypocycloids. The hypocycloid is a single-curved line generated by a fixed point on a circle that rolls on the inside of another circle. This curve also is used in mechanisms and for the outline of gear teeth.

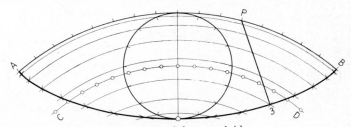

Figure 18. A hypocycloid.

The hypocycloid is shown in Figure 18. The method of drawing this curve is similar to the method of drawing the epicycloid.

25. Problems.

Group 37. Epicycloids and Hypocycloids.

26. Sinusoids. The sinusoid, or sine curve, is a single-curved line generated by a point which moves so that its distance from one of two perpendicular straight-line axes is equal to the arc of a circle, and its distance from the other axis is equal to the sine of the angle of the arc.   The sinusoid may be visualized more readily by considering a circle rolling on a horizontal straight line.   The point that generates the sinusoid moves so that it is at the same level as a fixed point on the rolling circle, and on the vertical diameter of that circle.

The sine curve expresses the law of harmonic motion, of vibration of perfectly elastic bodies, of sound and water waves, of the variation of current and voltage in an alternating electric current.

The sine curve is shown in Figure 19.   The length of the line A B is equal to the circumference of the circle, and both are divided into the same

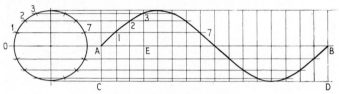

FIGURE 19. The sinusoid.

number of equal parts.   The circle is first centered at A and then rolls along the line C D.   When the center of the circle is at E, the point 3 of the curve is on the vertical diameter of the circle, and at the same level as the position 3 of the fixed point 0 on the rolling circle.   In practice, the sine curve is often made sharper or flatter by scaling the vertical or the horizontal dimension to some arbitrary scale.

27. Problems.

Group 38.   Sinusoids.

28. Double-curved Lines.   In a double-curved line no three consecutive elements lie in the same plane.   Lines of this type are also called *space curves*.   A double-curved line cannot be completely represented in a single view.   At least two views must be drawn.   A double-curved line will appear curved from every point of view.   It is impossible to obtain a normal view of such a line.   The most commonly used double-curved lines having names are the cylindrical helix and the conical or tapering helix.   Double-curved lines of infinite variety may be drawn on the surfaces of curved structures.   In the views of drawings, double-curved lines frequently are used to represent the line of intersection between two curved surfaces.

29. Helices.   The helix is a double-curved line generated by a point that revolves around an axis at a uniform rate and at the same time moves parallel to the axis at a uniform rate.   A helix may be right-hand or left-hand; that is, it may be generated by a point which may revolve in either direction around the axis or which may move in either direction parallel to the axis.   The distance that the generating point travels parallel to the axis in one turn or revolution is called the *lead* of the helix.   It is possible to have a helix of variable lead.

The curve of the helix is very generally used in structures: for screw threads, springs, "spiral" stairways, and conveyers.   Its use in connection with the structures just named is explained in the chapter on Warped Surfaces.   The helix should not be confused with the spiral.   Methods of

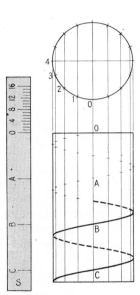

FIGURE 20. A right-hand
cylindrical helix.

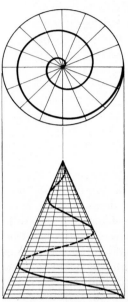

FIGURE 21. A left-hand
conical helix.

developing the helix and of determining its radius of curvature are described in Chapter 9, Article 53.

Before drawing the helix, determine the diameter, hand, and lead of the helix.   In Figure 20 the cylinder of the helix is first drawn.   As the generating point travels around this cylinder, it also travels along the cylinder. The circular end view of the cylinder is divided into any number of equal parts, not less than 12 or 16.   The rays extending from these division points to the front view are then drawn.

In the end view the generating point appears to move around the cylinder as many times as there are turns in the helix.   When the generating point makes one turn in the end view, it travels parallel to the axis in the front view a distance equal to the lead.   When the generating point makes one-sixteenth of a turn in the end view, it travels parallel to the axis in the front view a distance equal to one-sixteenth of the lead.

To locate points on the helix, a scale, as shown at S, may be made.   On this scale, the lead is marked off as many times as there are turns in the helix, and the lead at one end of the scale is divided into as many equal divisions as were found for the circle.   One end of the cylinder may be used as a base line for measuring—the top end, for example.   Starting with any point 0 on the cylinder, the scale is placed with its zero point at 0 on the base line and with its edge parallel to the axis in the front view, and each lead point, 0, A, B, and C, is marked on the ray.   The scale is now moved to the next ray, and then parallel to that ray until the next division (1) of the scale is on the base line.   The lead points are then marked on this ray.   As the scale is moved from one ray to the next, the scale also is moved one-sixteenth of the lead parallel to the axis.   This operation is continued from one ray to the next, until an entire revolution has been completed.   Locating points on a cylindrical helix by using a scale takes less time than ruling the cylinder with parallel circles as is done on the cone of Figure 21.

The turns of the helix may now be drawn, but care must be taken to indicate as invisible the parts of the curve that are at the rear of the cylinder.   This will depend upon whether the helix is right-hand or left-hand. The helix may be considered simply as a curved line, independent of a cylinder, in which case there will be no hidden part.   The end view of the helix is drawn as if it were a circle, but it is visualized as a helix.   As an aid in drawing the helix accurately, it should be noted in the front view that the curve representing the helix is reversed in the middle and that it cannot come to a sharp point at the sides.

30. Conical Helix.   The conical helix is a double-curved line generated by a point that revolves around an axis at a uniform rate and also moves at a uniform rate along a line that intersects the axis.   It is a helix on a cone.

To draw a conical helix, it is first necessary to determine the lead and hand of the helix, and the taper of the cone.   The lead should be measured parallel to the axis of the cone.   The method of locating points on the conical helix is similar to the method used for the cylindrical helix, except that here a scale does not save time.   Instead, it is probably better to rule equally spaced elements of the cone, and divisions of the lead across the front view of the cone, as in Figure 21.   In the top or end view the conical helix appears as a spiral of Archimedes.

31. Problems.

Group 39.   Double-curved Lines.

Group 40.   Helices.

Chapter 7

PLANES

1. The geometrical elements of structures are points, lines, and surfaces. Surfaces are conceived as being generated by a moving line called a *generatrix*, and are classified as ruled and double-curved. Ruled surfaces have a straight-line generatrix. The three classes of ruled surfaces are plane, single-curved, and warped.

A plane is a ruled surface having two intersecting straight-line directrices. This means that a plane is generated by a straight line which moves so as always to touch two intersecting straight lines.

A plane face of an object is never a true plane. The allowable variation from a true plane depends upon the use that is to be made of the plane surface. The flat faces of master gages and surface plates are made with a variation from a true plane of less than one one-hundred-thousandth of an inch. With greater care, the variation from a true plane may be reduced to less than one-millionth of an inch. Such surfaces are made by grinding and lapping, and their accuracy is tested by optical methods.

Cast-iron surface plates, strongly ribbed on the back, may be generated by machining three of these castings approximately flat, wiping each plate on the other two to determine the high spots, and scraping away the high spots of each until all three are as nearly true planes as is desired.

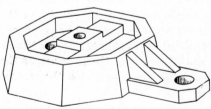

FIGURE 1. An object bounded by planes.

2. **Plane Surfaces of Structures.** A structure is limited by the surfaces that bound it. In turn, each surface of a structure is limited by the lines that bound the surface. The molded base of Figure 1 is an example of a structure or object bounded by plane and cylindrical surfaces. Each plane surface of this base is bounded by straight lines or circles. The plane faces vary in shape. They are triangular, rectangular, trapezoidal, approximately

octagonal, etc.   A plane area may be bounded by any possible combination of straight lines and/or single-curved lines.

3. Directions of Planes.   Plane faces of structures may take various directions as is illustrated in Figure 1.   Because of the generally rectangular nature of structures, planes in certain directions are used frequently and are given special names as follows: horizontal, frontal, profile, oblique, vertical.   These are defined in Chapter 2, Article 13.

4. Representation of Planes.   The location of a plane may be specified definitely by stating the location of three points that lie in the plane. These three points, however, must not lie in the same straight line.   Also, two intersecting lines, two parallel lines, a point and a line, a triangle, a circle, may serve to locate a plane.   Certain planes may be specified by locating one or two points in the plane, and, in addition, stating the direction of the plane as vertical, frontal, horizontal, or as making a given angle with the horizontal.   A plane has the same name as the points or lines that specify its location.   The extent of a plane is, in theory, not limited. When solving problems the lines of a plane may be extended as far as is necessary.

5. Visualizing Planes.   In Figure 2 eight different planes are represented.   Each should be studied in detail and visualized as to its shape and direction in each view.   Each student should do this for himself. Training in visualizing these planes will make easier the work that follows. The sense of direction should not be lost when visualizing a view.   The edge view of a plane is not a straight line and should never be visualized or considered as such.   If necessary, the shapes of the planes can be cut from a piece of cardboard and held in the positions indicated; but it is better to learn to visualize without models.

The oblique plane Q R S in Figure 2 is shown as a triangle.   To visualize the position of this plane, it is necessary to read the views of the drawing so as to determine the relative locations of the points Q, R, and S. Reading one view is insufficient.   To picture the plane as seen from the front, it is necessary to observe in the top or side view that R is a short distance in front of Q and that S is several times this distance in front of Q.   One is now prepared when looking at the front view of the plane to realize that Q is the rear point of the plane, that R is nearer, and that S is the nearest point.   These relative distances should be visualized in the front view.   When the plane is observed from above, the relative elevations of the various points and the slope of the plane should be pictured. Similar observations should be noted when looking at the side view of this plane.   Each view of each plane of Figure 2 should be visualized.

6. Plane Problems.   To design a structure, it is necessary to know how to represent plane surfaces of every possible shape, in every possible position, and in every possible geometrical relation to the other geometrical elements of the structure. In this chapter are explained the methods of solving problems involving a point and a plane, a line and a plane, and two or more planes. The solutions are based on the principles and methods developed in the preceding chapters.

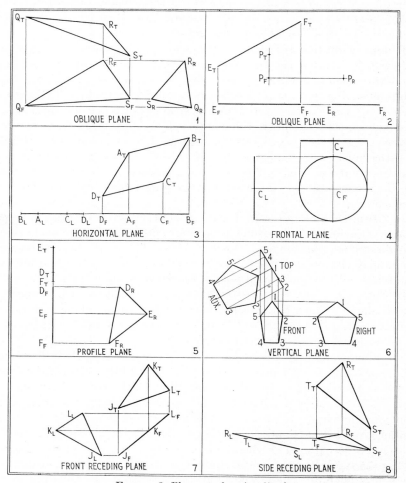

FIGURE 2. Planes to be visualized.

Many of the planes in the problems of this textbook are specified as triangles, rather than polygons of four or more sides, to save time in locating and drawing the given data. Careful visualizing of the plane will expedite the solution of the problem.

7. Points and Lines in a Plane. Figure 3 shows a plane area represented by the front and top views of a parallelogram Q R S T. This area is a plane since it is possible to pass a plane through two parallel lines. The four corners and edges, and also the diagonals of the parallelogram, lie in the plane. Every point on these six lines is in the plane. The point C on the diagonal Q S, and the point D on the diagonal R T, are in the plane. The line C D must also be in the given plane. The line C D may readily be checked by locating the intersections E and F in both views and then by checking to be sure that the ray through the top view of each point passes through its front view. The point P on the line B C, although outside the given area, is in the same plane with the parallelogram. Points as close together as B and C are not dependable for accurately determining the

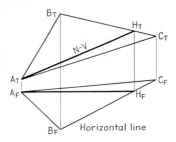

Horizontal line

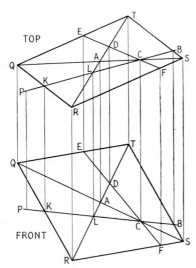

FIGURE 3. Points and lines in a plane.

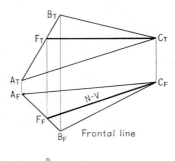

Frontal line

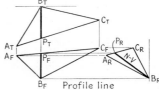

Profile line

FIGURE 4. Horizontal, frontal, and profile lines in a plane.

views of a line. K and L are used as checking points. The correctness of the location of all points in a plane may readily be checked, and this should be done when solving problems. It is possible to locate any number of points and lines in a plane.

8. Horizontal, Frontal, and Profile Lines of a Plane. Figure 4 shows a horizontal line, a frontal line, and a profile line of the plane A B C. Such lines frequently are needed when solving problems. The horizontal line is drawn first in the front view; the front and top views of the point H are located; and then the top view is drawn. The front view of the line A H shows that this line is horizontal. The top view of A H is a normal view. Many horizontal lines may be drawn in a plane, and all horizontal lines of a plane are parallel. The plane A B C is quite easily visualized by observing the direction of the horizontal line and by noting that the point B is behind and below this horizontal line.

The frontal line C F of the plane A B C is first drawn in the top view, and then in the front view. The normal view of this line is seen in the front view. The profile line B P is drawn in the front and top views, and then its side view is drawn. The side view shows a normal view of the profile line.

9. Problems.

Group 41. Points and Lines in Planes.

10. Edge View of a Plane.

In the principal views of a structure the plane faces of the structure frequently appear as edge or normal views of the plane. The edge view of a plane is seen in any view that is taken in a direction parallel to any line of the plane. The edge view of a plane should never be visualized as a line. It always should be visualized as a plane in which points are located at varying distances from the observer. Edge views often are useful in solving problems involving lines and planes. When the edge view of a plane is seen in any view, that plane may be called a *receding plane* in that view, since the plane extends directly away from the observer of the edge view.

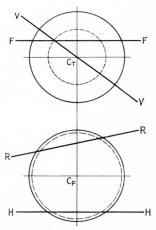

FIGURE 5. Horizontal, vertical, and receding planes.

In Figure 5 are shown the edge views of four different planes, and the front and top views of a sphere centered at C. In the top view, F F is the edge view of a frontal plane. The front view of this plane is not indicated, except when certain points, lines, or plane figures are located in this plane. The front view is a normal view of a frontal plane. Also, in the top view, is shown the edge view of a vertical plane that is marked V V. This plane is here taken through the center of the sphere. In the front view of Figure 5 are shown the edge view of a horizontal plane H H, and the edge view of the receding plane R R. The lighter circles show the intersections of two of these planes with the sphere. Edge views of planes find frequent use as reference planes from which distances are measured, and they often are needed as an aid in solving problems.

11. Edge View of an Oblique Plane.

A view taken in the direction of any line of a plane will show the edge view of that plane. An edge view of an oblique plane usually is obtained by drawing an auxiliary view taken in a direction parallel to a horizontal, a frontal, or a profile line of the plane.

To obtain one edge view of the oblique plane J K L of Figure 6, draw first the horizontal line J H of this plane. An auxiliary elevation taken in the direction of this line will show the end view of the line and the edge view of the given plane. The level of each point is measured from the horizontal reference plane in the front and auxiliary views. If the three points J, K, and L are correctly located in the auxiliary elevation, it will be possible to draw the straight, edge view of the plane through the three

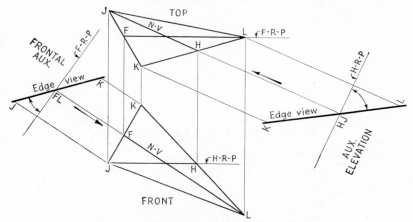

FIGURE 6. Edge views of an oblique plane.

points. This is a check on the accuracy of the drawing. The angle of dip, or slope, of the plane J K L is indicated. The angle of dip is always measured below the horizontal.

Figure 6 also shows an edge view taken in the direction of the frontal line F L of the given plane. A frontal reference plane is taken through the point L in the top view and in the frontal-auxiliary view. The respective distance of each point in front of or behind this reference plane must be equal in the top and frontal-auxiliary views. The angle that the given plane makes with the frontal reference plane is indicated.

12. Normal View of a Plane. The normal view of a plane is taken in a direction perpendicular to the plane. In a normal view of a plane all points of the plane are equidistant from the observer, and any figure in the plane is seen in its true shape and size. All lines in this normal view are seen in their true length, and all angles in their true size. The top view of a horizontal plane, the front view of a frontal plane, and the side view of a profile plane are normal views of those planes.

To draw the normal view of an oblique plane, it first is necessary to

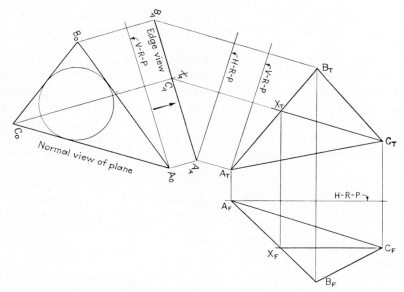

FIGURE 7. Normal view of an oblique plane.

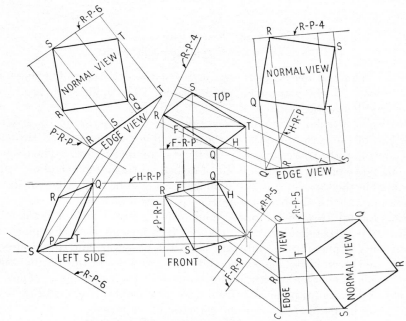

FIGURE 8. Edge and normal views of a square.

obtain an auxiliary view that shows the edge view of the plane. This edge view gives definite information as to the direction of the plane. The normal view is then taken in a direction perpendicular to the edge view of the plane. This is illustrated in Figure 7. A horizontal line C X of the plane is first drawn. The edge view of the plane is then drawn in the auxiliary elevation taken in the direction of the line X C. The normal view of the plane is now taken in a direction perpendicular to the edge view. This direction is indicated by the pointing arrow. The vertical reference plane V-R-P, through the point A, is used in the top and oblique views as a base from which to measure the distances to the points B and C. Care must be taken not to reverse the oblique view.

In the normal view the true shape of the triangle A B C is shown. Any figure that lies in this plane may now be drawn in its true shape in the normal view and then transferred through the auxiliary view to the top and front views. For example, to draw the circle that is inscribed in the triangle A B C, it is first necessary to inscribe the circle in the normal view of the triangle. A number of equally spaced points are then marked on the circle, and these points are transferred through the auxiliary elevation back to the top and front views, as is explained in the chapter on Curved Lines.

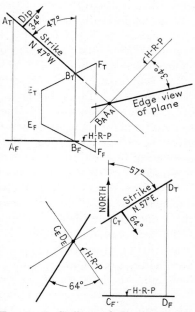

FIGURE 9. Strike and dip of planes.

Figure 8 shows three principal views, three edge views, and three normal views of a square. The three edge views are observed respectively in the direction of a horizontal, a frontal, and a profile line of the given plane Q R S T. And each normal view is observed in a direction perpendicular to the corresponding edge view. The three normal views will be exactly alike in shape and size, provided that each view is taken in the proper direction, that all rays are correctly drawn, that every point is correctly located, and that each line is drawn exactly through the points of the line.

13. Strike and Dip of Planes. Another method that frequently is used for representing planes is shown in Figure 9. The horizontal line A B gives the location of one line of the plane A E F, and this line indicates the direction of all horizontal lines of the plane. This line A B indicates the direction of the *strike* of the plane. The *bearing* of the strike is N 47° W. These terms are defined and their uses are explained in Chapter 12.

The top view of any horizontal line shows the strike of the plane, and the front view shows the level at which that strike is located. The arrow, marked 34 degrees, indicates that the plane slopes, or dips, downward at the indicated angle, in a northeasterly direction. The angle of dip is always measured from, and below, the horizontal. The auxiliary elevation taken in the direction of the strike shows the edge view of this plane and its angle of dip below the horizontal. Another plane having strike C D that bears N 57° E and a dip of 64 degrees southeasterly is shown. Visualize these planes. Veins of ore usually are indicated by showing their strikes and dips.

14. Problems.

    Group 42. Plane Figures.

15. Parallel Relations of Lines and Planes. To draw a line parallel to a given plane, it is necessary only to draw it parallel to any line of the given plane. Unless some other condition limits the required line, the number of possible solutions is infinite.

To pass a plane through a point and parallel to a given line, it is necessary to draw through the given point a line parallel to the given line. The line last drawn is a line of the required plane. If no other condition limits the plane, the number of solutions is infinite.

To pass a plane through a given point and parallel to a given plane, draw through the given point two lines that are parallel to any two nonparallel lines of the given plane. The two lines last drawn will definitely determine the location of the required plane.

The edge views of parallel planes are parallel. Lines parallel to a given plane are parallel to the edge view of the given plane.

16. Line Perpendicular to a Plane. If a line is perpendicular to a given plane, it is perpendicular to every line of the plane. The direction of the required line is completely determined by making it perpendicular to any two nonparallel lines of the given plane. Some other condition is necessary to determine the location of this perpendicular line.

In Figure 10, the point A and the plane C D E F are assumed to be given data. The line A B is to be drawn perpendicular to the given plane. Perpendicular-line principles apply. It is necessary to locate normal views of two lines of the given plane. The required line will be perpendicular to both of these lines.

Draw a horizontal line D L of the given plane. The top view is a normal view of this line. In the top view, draw A B perpendicular to D L. This definitely determines that the line A B in space is perpendicular to the line D L, without any need for considering the direction of the front view of A B. Next, draw the frontal line C K. In the front view, C K is a normal view. Here, draw the front view of A B perpendicular to C K. The line A B in space is now perpendicular to the line C K. Since the line A B, as represented by its front and top views, is now perpendicular to two lines of the given plane, it is perpendicular to the plane, and the problem is solved.

It should here be well understood that no intersection of A B with lines of the plane is involved in the solution of this problem. Point B should be located in some open space on the views of required line A B. It is misleading, and frequently leads to mistakes, to locate B in the top view at the apparent intersection of A B and D L, or in the front view where A B apparently intersects C K. These are false intersections.

The top view of point L and the front view of K are determined in Figure 10 by rather sharply intersecting lines. If these are not accurately located, the direction of A B will not be correct.

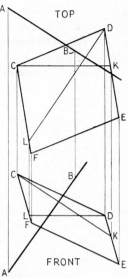

FIGURE 10. Line perpendicular to a plane.

Point L divides line C F into the same proportions in both views. The top view of L may be located accurately by determining the proportional division from the front view. And the front view of K may be similarly located.

A line that is perpendicular to a plane will appear perpendicular to that plane in an edge view of the plane. The perpendicular-lines principle applies here.

17. Plane Perpendicular to a Line. *Problem:* To pass the plane R S T through a given point R and perpendicular to a given line K P. The problem is solved by drawing through the point R two lines that are perpendicular to the given line K P. These two intersecting lines will represent the required plane.

Figure 11 Through R, and perpendicular to the line K P, draw the horizontal line R S and the frontal line R T. These two lines are perpendicular to the given line and represent the required plane R S T. The line S T may be drawn to form a triangle, but this is not necessary. The required

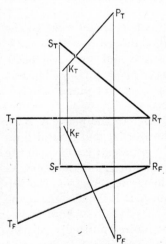

FIGURE 11. Plane perpendicular to a line.

plane R S T will not be changed if K P is in some other location, provided the direction of K P is not changed.

18. Plane Perpendicular to a Plane.   Two planes are perpendicular if either plane is perpendicular to any line of the other plane.

Problem: To pass the plane A B C through the given line A B and perpendicular to the given plane D E F.   Through any point of the given line, A, for example, draw a line A C perpendicular to the given plane, by using the method of drawing a line perpendicular to a plane.   The lines A B and A C will determine the required plane.

19. Problems.

    Group 43.   Parallel Planes.

    Group 44.   Perpendicular Lines and Planes.

20. Three Mutually Perpendicular Lines and Planes.   It is a common occurrence in rectangular structures that three mutually perpendicular plane faces of the structure intersect at a point which is a corner of the structure.   The plan here described offers a simple method of drawing three mutually perpendicular plane faces of a rectangular structure in an oblique position, when the plane of one face of the structure and one edge in that plane are given.   At the same time the solution determines the three mutually perpendicular, intersecting edges of the structure.

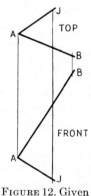

FIGURE 12. Given data of problem.

The given data are shown in Figure 12.   The point A is a corner of the rectangular structure or object.   A B is one edge, and one face lies in the plane A B J.   From these simple data the solution of the problem shown in Figure 13 is derived.

A second edge may be drawn perpendicular to the plane A B J by using the method described in Article 16. With the aid of the horizontal and frontal lines A K and A L of the plane A B J, the line A N is drawn perpendicular to the plane A B J.   The line A N is a second edge of the rectangular structure, and the plane A B N is the plane of the second face of the structure.

The third edge A F is now drawn perpendicular to the plane A B N. Its direction is determined by means of the horizontal and frontal lines O N and A P of the plane A B N.   The edge A F necessarily will lie in the original plane A B J, and its intersection with the line B J is the point X. If the front view of the point X is in line with the ray leading from the top view of X, the drawing is accurate.   The plane A B F is the same plane as the original plane A B J.

The planes A B F, A B N, and A N F are the required mutually perpendicular planes.   They intersect at the corner A.   The lines A B, A N, and A F are three mutually perpendicular edges of the structure.   After the directions of these three edges have been found, it is possible to proceed with the front and top views of the structure.

The three lines A B, A N, and A F, determined in Figure 13, have been transferred to Figure 14. If these lines coincide with the edges of a cube

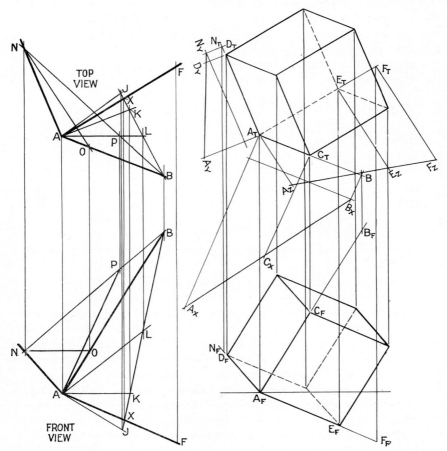

FIGURE 13. Three mutually per-   FIGURE 14. A cube.
pendicular planes and lines.

of a given size, the cube may now be drawn by finding the true length of each line, laying off the length of the edge of the cube on each true length, and transferring the points so found to the top and front views. Three edges of the cube are thus found, and the remaining edges may be drawn by applying parallel-line principles.

21. Problems.

Group 45. Three Perpendicular Lines and Planes.

22. Intersection of a Line and a Plane. A line intersects a plane at a point that is on the line and in the plane. Two methods of finding this intersection are explained in Articles 23 and 25. One method is useful when the intersection of one or two lines of a plane is to be found, and the other when the intersections of several lines and a plane are to be determined. Both methods are based on the simple fact that the intersection of a line and a plane is immediately visible in a view that shows the line and the edge view of a plane.

Figure 15 shows a line A B and a vertical plane V. The top view shows the edge view of the vertical plane, and in this view the line A B is seen to

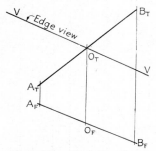

FIGURE 15. Intersection of a line and a vertical plane.

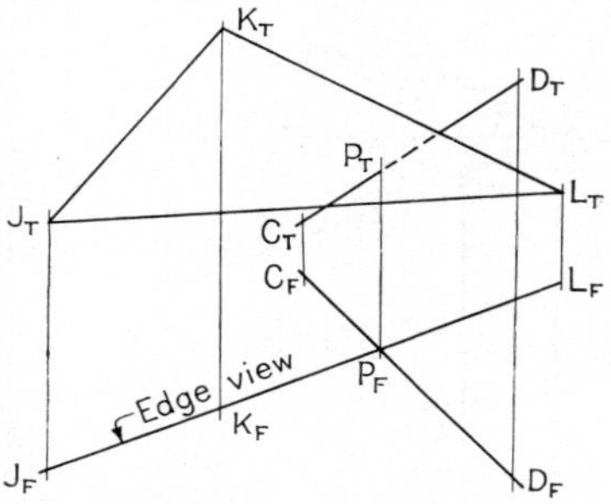

FIGURE 16. Intersection of a line and a receding plane.

intersect or pierce this plane at O_T. The front view of O is next located on the front view of the line A B, and the problem is solved.

Figure 16 shows a line C D and a plane J K L that is receding in the front view. Since the front view shows the edge view of the plane, the line C D is seen to intersect the plane at P_F. The top view of P is then located on the top view of C D, and the problem is solved. The top view of the plane J K L is ignored when solving this problem.

23. Intersection of a Line and an Oblique Plane. The solution of this problem is used frequently as an aid in solving other problems. Although based on simple ideas, the method here explained requires careful attention so as to avoid mistakes when solving problems.

The general plan for finding the intersection of a line E F with an oblique plane Q R S is illustrated in pictorial form in Figure 17. A vertical plane is passed through the given line E F. A top view, taken in the direction of the vertical pointing arrows, shows the edge view of this vertical plane. The line Q R is seen to intersect the vertical plane at the point 1, and the line R S intersects it at the point 2. These points (1 and 2) are in the vertical plane and also in the plane Q R S; hence the line 1 2 is in both of these planes. Since lines E F and 1 2 lie in the vertical plane they intersect at the point marked P. The point P is on the given line E F and in the given plane Q R S. Hence, P is the required point of intersection.

The solution of this problem is shown in Figure 18. A vertical plane V is passed through the given line E F. The line Q R of the given oblique

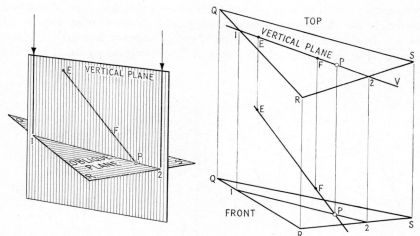

FIGURE 17. Pictorial view of a line intersecting a plane.

FIGURE 18. Intersection of a line and an oblique plane.

plane intersects the vertical plane at the point 1 which is located first in the top view and then in the front view. The point 1 is on Q R, but not on E F. Likewise, the line R S intersects the plane V at the point 2 which is on the line R S in both views. The line 1 2 is in both of the planes. The lines E F and 1 2 intersect at the point P. First, the front view of P must be located at the intersection of E F and 1 2. Then, the top view of P is located on its ray and on the top views of the lines E F and 1 2. The point P is on the line E F and in the plane Q R S. P is the required point of intersection.

This problem may be solved as readily by passing a receding plane through the given line in the front view. This is illustrated in Figure 19. The line E F

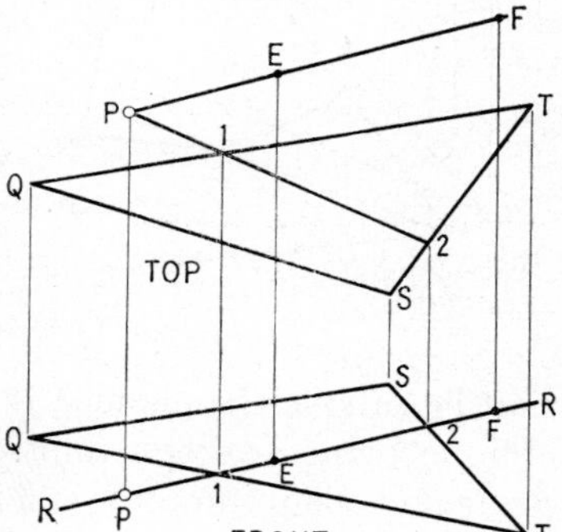

FIGURE 19. Intersection of a line and an oblique plane.

intersects the plane Q S T at the point P. The area of the given plane is not necessarily limited to the triangle shown. Intersections often are found outside this area.

The method of finding the intersection of a line and a plane should be fully understood, since it repeatedly is used in the solution of many problems.

24. Problems.

Group 46.   Intersection of a Line and a Plane.

25. Intersections of Several Lines and a Plane.

When it is necessary to find the intersections of several lines and an oblique plane, it is generally advisable to draw an auxiliary view that shows an edge view of the plane. In this view the intersection of each and every line with the plane is seen. For example, show the part of the triangular pyramid V A B C

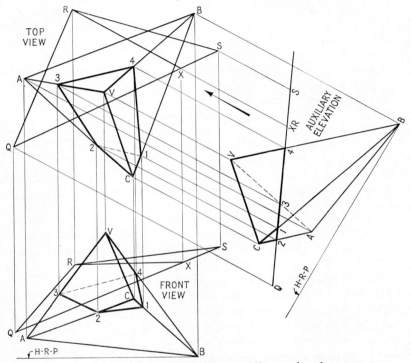

FIGURE 20. Intersections of several lines and a plane.

that lies above the plane Q R S, Figure 20. A horizontal line R X of the oblique plane is drawn first. Next, draw an auxiliary elevation of the plane and the pyramid taken in the direction of the pointing arrow, which is parallel to the line R X. The level of each point in the auxiliary elevation is measured from the horizontal reference plane H-R-P, to agree with its level above the same reference plane in the front view.

In the auxiliary elevation four lines of the pyramid are seen to intersect the oblique plane. The four points of intersection should be numbered consecutively and in the proper order around the quadrilateral that the plane cuts from the pyramid. The order in which the points come is best determined by visualization.

The rays extending from the auxiliary view to the top view are now drawn, and each point is located on its proper line. Similarly, the front views of the points are located. It is advisable to check the elevations of the numbered points in the front view with their elevations in the auxiliary elevation. Unless the work has been done carefully, these views will not agree. This is a check on the quality of the workmanship. The part of the pyramid that is above the oblique plane may now be drawn in heavier lines as required data in each view.

It should be recognized that the edge views of planes are often seen in drawings and that the intersections of lines with these planes are readily found. The end view of a hexagonal prism, for example, shows edge views of six planes. Also, the end view of a cylinder may be considered as the edge view of a plane that has been curved. In the end view of the cylinder the intersections of a line with the curved surface are seen.

26. Problems.

Group 47. Intersections of Several Lines and a Plane.

27. Distance from a Point to a Plane.
There are a number of ways in which this problem could be solved. The plan that requires the fewest lines is to locate the view of the point in a view that also shows the edge view of the plane. In this view, the required perpendicular distance may readily be drawn and measured.

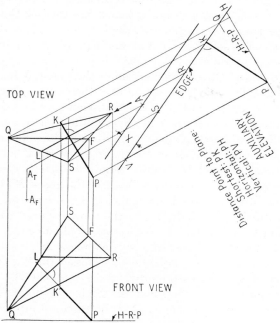

FIGURE 21. Distance from a point to a plane.

In Figure 21, P is the given point, and Q R S is the given plane. An auxiliary elevation is taken in the direction of the horizontal line R L of the given plane. This view shows the point P and the edge view of the plane Q R S. The line P K is then drawn perpendicular to the edge view of the plane. This is the normal view of the line P K, and its length is the measure of the shortest distance from the point P to the plane. The front and top views of the line may be drawn if required. The top view of P K is drawn perpendicular to the top view of the horizontal line R L, and the front view is drawn perpendicular to the front view of the frontal line Q F.

The shortest horizontal distance from P to the plane is seen at P H in the auxiliary elevation. And the vertical distance from P to the plane is P V. In case it should be desired to draw another plane parallel to the given plane and at a distance of x from it, this readily may be done as is shown in the auxiliary elevation. Any point A taken in this second plane may be chosen, and its top and front views may then be located. Or, if the point A is given, x may be determined.

28. Problems.

Group 48. Distance from a Point to a Plane.

29. Intersection of Planes.
The intersection of two planes is a straight line. It may be found by locating two points that lie in both planes and then drawing the required straight-line intersection through these points. To locate one point that lies in both planes, find the point of intersection of a line of either plane with the other plane. In a similar manner locate a second point. The solution is based on the problem of finding the intersection of a line and a plane, Article 23.

Problem: To find C D, the intersection of the planes J K L and Q R S, Figure 22. First, find the intersection C of the line K L, for example, of one plane with the other plane. In the front view assume a receding plane through the line K L. Locate 1 in this receding plane and on the line Q R, in both the front and top views. Locate 2 in the same receding plane and on the line R S in both views. In the top view the line 1 2 crosses the line K L at C; and in the front view C is in line with its ray, on 1 2, and on K L. The point C is common to both of the given planes.

Choose some other line of either plane, Q S, for example, and find its intersection with the plane J K L. In the top view pass a vertical plane through the line Q S. Locate 3 in this vertical plane and on the line J K in both views. Locate 4 in the same vertical plane and on the line K L in both views. In the front view the line 3 4 crosses the line Q S at D; and in the top view D is in line with its ray, on 3 4, and on Q S. The point D is common to both of the given planes. Since the points C and D are common to both planes, the line C D is the required intersection. It is now drawn through both of these points.

The accuracy of the solution should be checked. In the top view locate the point A where the line C D intersects the line J K. Do the same in the front view. If, now, the rays from the front and top views of the point A are in line, then the point A is on the lines C D and J K, and the point A is in the plane J K L. A similar check is needed to determine if the point B is on the lines C D and R S, and in the plane Q R S. If

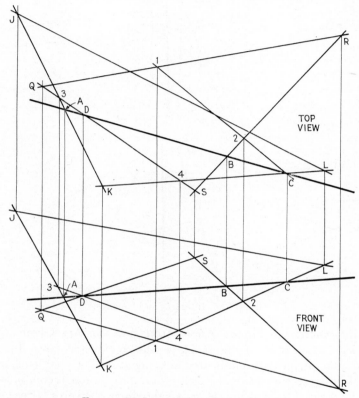

FIGURE 22. Intersection of two planes.

these checks show that the points A and C are in one of the given planes, that B and D are in the other given plane, and that these four points are on the same straight line, the solution is correct. The solution will not check accurately unless the drawing has been carefully done.

At times the given data are such that it is difficult or impossible to find the intersection of the two planes by means of the method just explained. The following plan may then be used. To find the intersection of the planes A B C and D E F, Figure 23: Choose any vertical plane, as indicated by V V in the top view. This plane intersects the plane A B C in the line 1 2, and the plane D E F in the line 3 4. The lines 1 2 and 3 4 intersect at the point O. This point is in both of the given planes, and hence is a point on the intersection of the two planes. Take another receding plane T T, and in a similar manner locate the point P. The required intersection is the straight line O P.

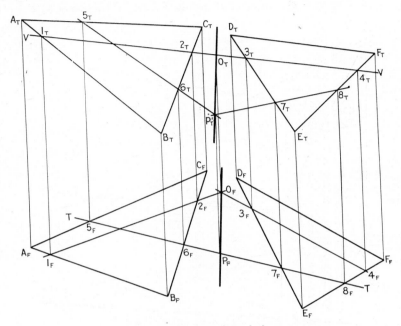

FIGURE 23. Intersection of planes.

30. Intersection of Planes When Strike and Dip Are Given.

In the upper left-hand corner of Figure 24 are shown the strike and dip of two planes. The strike A B is indicated as being at the 200-foot level, and the strike J K is at the 300-foot level. The locations of veins of ore are usually indicated by showing the strike and dip of the veins. See Chapter 12. The intersection of the two planes of the veins is important, since enrichment of ore may be expected along the line where the veins meet. In the figure, ascending levels are shown. In mine drawings, descending levels starting from the surface often are used.

In Figure 24 the original data are redrawn to an enlarged scale. The intersection of the two planes is found as follows: At the right is drawn an edge view of the plane through J K, and the strike L M at the 200-foot level is determined. To the left is drawn an edge view of the plane through A B; and the strike C D at the 300-foot level is determined. Since the strikes A B and L M are both at the 200-foot level, they will intersect. The point of intersection O is located first in the top view and then in the front view. Likewise, the intersection P of the strikes J K and C D at the 300-foot level is located. The required intersection is the line O P.

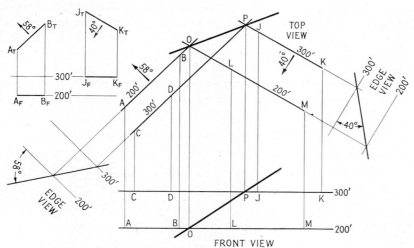

FIGURE 24. Intersection of strike and dip planes.

31. Problems.

Group 49. Intersection of Planes.

32. Angle between a Line and a Horizontal, Frontal, or Profile Plane.

Figure 25: To determine the angle that the given line C D makes with all

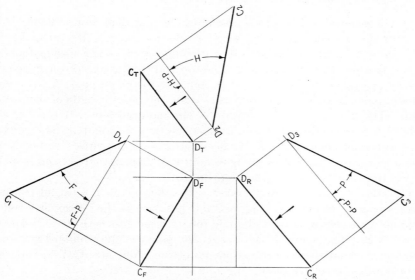

FIGURE 25. Angle between a line and horizontal, frontal, and profile planes.

horizontal planes, draw a normal auxiliary view of this line taken in a horizontal direction. This view will show a normal view of the line C D, the edge of a horizontal plane, and the angle that C D makes with this plane. H is the required angle. The angle that the line C D makes with all frontal planes is shown at F in the view that is a normal auxiliary view of this line taken in a frontal direction. The angle that the line C D makes with all profile planes is shown at P in the view that is a normal auxiliary view of the line taken in a profile direction.

33. Line Making Specified Angles with Horizontal and Frontal Planes. If a line A B is to pass through a given point A and is to make an angle H

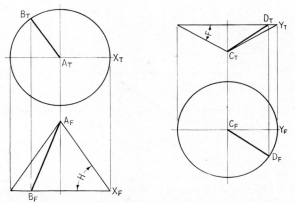

FIGURE 26. Lines making a given angle with a horizontal or a frontal plane.

with a horizontal plane, all possible lines meeting these requirements will be straight-line elements of a right circular cone having its vertex at A, its base a horizontal circle, and its base angle equal to the specified angle H. Visualize these conditions. The top and front views of the cone are shown in Figure 26. Any line that connects the given point A with any chosen point B on the base circle will satisfy the requirements of the problem. The line A B is one position of the required line. If there is no other limiting condition, the number of solutions is infinite. The length of A B remains constant for any position of B on the circle. Since X is one possible position for B, the true length may be measured from A to X in the front view. This is the slant height of the cone.

Likewise, a line C D that makes a specified angle F with all frontal planes may be found. In Figure 26, C is taken as the vertex of a right circular cone having a frontal circle for its base, and with its base angle equal to F. The point D is chosen as any point on the circular base, and the line C D satisfies the requirements of the problem. C Y in the top view is the true length of this line.

The problem of finding a line that passes through a given point and makes specified angles with both a horizontal and a frontal plane may be solved by combining two cones similar to those shown in Figure 26.

Problem: Find the line V K that passes through the point V, makes an angle of H degrees with all horizontal planes, and an angle of F degrees with all frontal planes. If desired, the length of the line V K also may be specified. The problem is solved in Figure 27. The given point V is taken as the vertex of two right circular cones. In one cone, the base is a horizontal circle, the base angle is made equal to the given angle H, and the slant height V_F G_F is made equal to the required or chosen length of the line that is to be found. In the other cone, the base is a frontal circle, the base angle is made equal to the given angle F, and the slant height V_T E_T of the cone is made equal to the slant height of the first cone. Since the slant heights of the two cones are equal, all points on the two circles are equidistant from the point V. Hence the two circles will intersect. The top view is the normal view of the horizontal circle and the edge view of the frontal circle. The circles are seen to intersect at K and L. Similarly, these

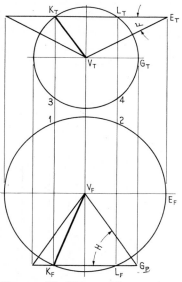

FIGURE 27. Line making a given angle with horizontal and frontal planes.

circles intersect at K and L in the front view. If the drawing is accurate, the front views of K and L will be in line with the rays leading from their top views. These points will not check unless the drawing is carefully made.

The required line may now be drawn as V K. This line has one end at the given point V, and the other end at K on both circles. V K is a line of both cones, and hence it makes the specified angles H and F with all horizontal and frontal planes. The line V L also meets the requirements of the problem. The required line may be drawn in eight different positions, or in four different directions. The top view of the line may extend from V to K, L, 3, or 4; and the front view from V to K, L, 1, or 2.

It is understood that the angle between a line and a plane is measured by the smaller of the two angles that it makes with the plane. The sum of the specified angles H and F must then be less than 90 degrees. Determine why this is so.

34. Angle between a Line and an Oblique Plane.   In Figure 28, A B is the given line, and the parallelogram Q R S T is the given plane.   To find the angle between the line A B and the given plane, draw the line A C perpendicular to the plane.   The angle B A C is the complement of the required angle.

Frontal and horizontal lines of the given plane are drawn, and these determine the direction of the line A C.   To determine the angle B A C, draw first the horizontal line C H.   An auxiliary elevation taken in the

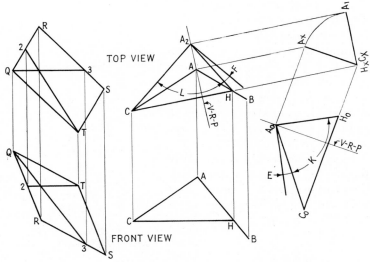

FIGURE 28. Angle between a line and an oblique plane.

direction of the line H C shows the edge view of the plane of the lines. The angle H A C, which is equal to the angle B A C, may now be found by taking a normal view of the plane of the lines, or by revolving the angle into a horizontal plane, as explained in Chapter 5, Article 35.   Both solutions are shown in Figure 28.   The angle K is found by the normal-view method, and the angle L by the revolution method.   The two angles are equal.   The required angle is the complement of these.   It is shown at E and F.

35. Angle between a Line and a Plane. *Second Method.*   Consider A B as the given line and J K L as the given plane.   Draw a plane A B C perpendicular to the given plane.   A normal view of the plane A B C will show the edge view of the given plane J K L, and a normal view of the given line A B.   And in this normal view the true angle between the given line and plane may be seen and measured.

The solution is carried out in Figure 29.   A B is the given line, and

J K L is the given plane. The line A C is drawn perpendicular to the given plane, and this determines the plane A B C perpendicular to plane J K L. Next, an auxiliary elevation is taken in the direction of the horizontal line C D of the plane A B C. This auxiliary view shows an edge view of the plane A B C, and a non-normal view of the plane J K L. A view is next taken in a direction perpendicular to the edge view of the plane A B C. This view shows normal views of the plane A B C and of the line A B, and it also shows the edge view of the given plane J K L, since the two planes are perpendicular to each other. And, since this view shows

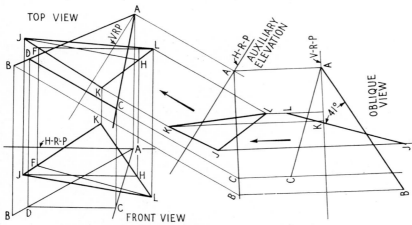

FIGURE 29. Angle between a line and an oblique plane.

an edge view of the plane J K L and a normal view of the line A B, the required angle between these two may here be seen and measured. The answer is 41 degrees. The method here explained requires more lines than does the method presented in the preceding article.

36. Problems.

Group 50. Angles between Lines and Planes.

37. Angles between Planes.

The angle between two planes is called a *dihedral angle*. The planes are the faces of the dihedral angle, and the straight-line intersection of the faces is the edge of the dihedral angle. The true size of the dihedral angle may be seen in a view that shows the edge views of both plane faces of the angle. Such a view is taken in a direction parallel to the straight-line edge of the dihedral angle. Other methods of finding the angle between two planes also are used.

A polyhedral angle is determined by three or more planes that meet at a point called a *vertex*. The planes form the faces of the polyhedral angle, and the straight-line intersections of the planes are the edges of the angle.

A trihedral angle is bounded by three planes, and a tetrahedral angle by four planes.

38. Angles between an Oblique Plane and Horizontal, Frontal, and Profile Planes. To determine the angle that the square J K L M of Figure 30 makes with all horizontal planes, take a view in the direction of a horizontal line, H L, of the square. This auxiliary elevation shows the edge views of the plane of the square and of a horizontal reference plane. The true size of the angle between the planes is shown at H.

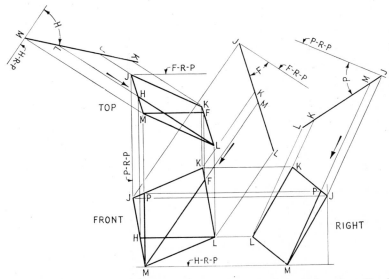

FIGURE 30. Angle between an oblique plane and horizontal, frontal, and profile planes.

The true size of the angle that the given square makes with all frontal planes is seen at F in a frontal-auxiliary view taken in the direction of the frontal line F M of the square. The angle that the given square makes with all profile planes is seen at P in a profile-auxiliary view that is taken in the direction of the profile line P M.

39. Angle between Two Oblique Planes. The angle between two planes usually is determined in actual designs by taking a view in the direction of the intersection of the two planes. This will show the edge views of both planes and the true size of the angle between them.

Figure 31 shows two plane faces of a structure represented by parallelograms. The intersection A B of the given planes is one edge of the structure. A normal auxiliary elevation of the line A B, in which all lines of the planes are shown, is drawn first. Next, an oblique view is taken in the direction of the line B A. This view shows the edge views of both planes. The true size of the angle between them is indicated by the arc and arrowheads. Either the angle indicated or its supplement may be taken as a measure of the angle between the two given planes. If the given data do not show the intersection of the two given planes, it is necessary to find this intersection and then to proceed as explained above.

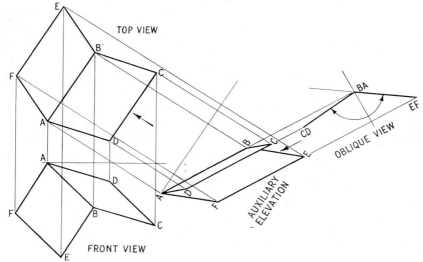

FIGURE 31. Angle between two planes by edge-view method.

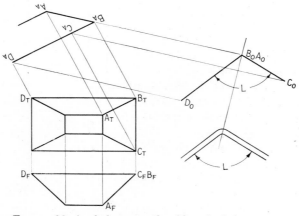

FIGURE 32. Angle between the sides of a hopper.

Figure 32 is an example of the application to a simple structure of this method of determining the actual angle between two plane faces of the structure. The front and top views of a hopper are shown. The inclined edge A B is the intersection of the plane trapezoidal faces that are lettered A B C and A B D. An auxiliary elevation is taken in a direction perpendicular to the edge A B. The complete hopper is not shown in this view. Next, an oblique view is taken in the direction of the line B A. This oblique view shows the edge view of the two plane faces and the end

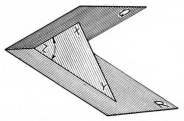

view of their intersection. The required angle between the faces is shown at L. The steel sides of this hopper are then bent to this angle as indicated in the drawing, or they are held at this angle and welded.

At times, a different method for finding the angle between two given planes is useful: Choose any point P. Through P draw two lines perpendicular, respectively, to the two planes.

FIGURE 33. Pictorial view of a plane making a given angle with a given plane.

The angle between these two lines is a measure of the angle between the given planes. The intersection of the two planes need not be found when this method is used. Judgment should determine which of the two methods it is better to apply in any given case.

40. Plane Making Specified Angles with Horizontal and Frontal Planes.

The general plan, upon which the solution of this problem is based, is illustrated in Figure 33. A right-angled triangle X Y Z is taken in a plane perpendicular to the intersection of a given plane R and a required plane Q. The angle Z is then a measure of the angle between the planes Q and R. The line X Y is perpendicular to the required plane Q and makes the angle Y with the given plane R. The angle Y is the complement of the angle Z. To draw a required plane that makes a given angle with a given plane: First draw a line that makes with the given plane an angle equal to the complement of the given angle, then pass the required plane perpendicular to this line.

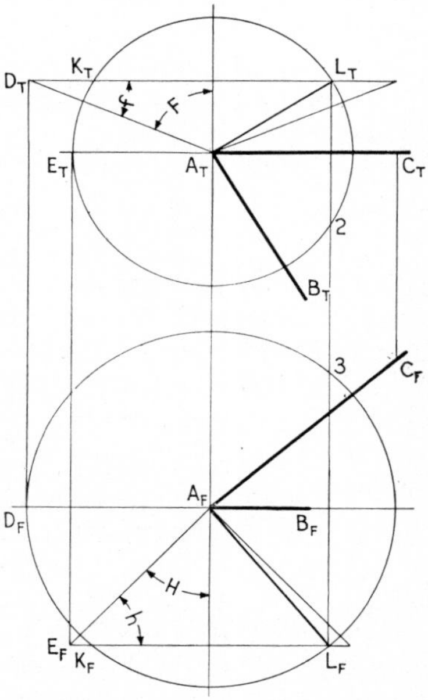

The specific problem is to determine

FIGURE 34. Plane making a given angle with horizontal and frontal planes.

an oblique plane that passes through a given point A, makes an angle H with all horizontal planes, and an angle F with all frontal planes. The problem is solved by first locating a line A L that makes angles equal to the complements of the given angles H and F, respectively, with all horizontal and frontal planes. The required plane is perpendicular to the line A L.

The solution of the problem is shown in Figure 34. The line A L is determined by the methods explained in Article 33. The angles h and f are the complements of the given angles H and F and are determined graphically as shown in the figure. Once the line A L is determined, the required oblique plane is drawn perpendicular to A L, by drawing the horizontal line A B and the frontal line A C perpendicular to the line A L. A B C is the required plane.

Since it is possible to draw the line A L in four different directions, it also is possible to locate four planes that satisfy the requirements of the problem. In specifying the angle between two planes, it is here understood that the smaller of the two angles between the planes is the one intended. The larger angle is the supplement of the smaller. The specified angle is always taken as an acute angle. The sum of the acute angles that an oblique plane makes with a horizontal and a frontal plane must be between 90 and 180 degrees. Determine the reason for this.

41. Problems.

Group 51.   Angles between Planes.

42. Timbered Structures.

When a wooden framework is to be built, the framer usually cuts the timbers to fit the structure, before lifting them into place. In Figure 35 a hip roof is shown as an illustration of a framed structure.

In the front and top views, showing the assembled roof frame, the names of the different types of rafters are indicated. The rise and run of the roof are also indicated. The slope of the roof is equal to the rise divided by the run. This is equal to the tangent of the angle that the plane of the roof makes with the horizontal. The term *pitch* as applied to roofs is equal to the rise of the roof divided by the total width of the roof. The slope of all parts of the hip roof is generally made uniform, so that the common rafters can all be made alike and the jack rafters can be made in pairs, right-hand and left-hand.

In the lower part of Figure 35 are shown, to a larger scale, the details of the common and hip rafters, and one method of forming the joints at the peak of the roof. The center lines of the ridge, two hip rafters, and three common rafters meet at P. The ridge may be left rectangular as shown at L; or it may be beveled as shown at M, in case a better finished job is desired.

The common rafter is cut as shown at D. The angle to which the rafter is cut is measured by the framer by means of a steel square, as indicated at S in the upper right-hand corner of the figure. The 12-inch mark on the body of the square, corresponding to the run, and the mark on the tongue of the square, indicating the corresponding rise, are placed on one edge of the timber, and a mark is scribed along the tongue of the square. The timber is cut to this mark. The length of the rafter is determined from tables of figures given on the face of the square, or by measuring diagonally with the square.

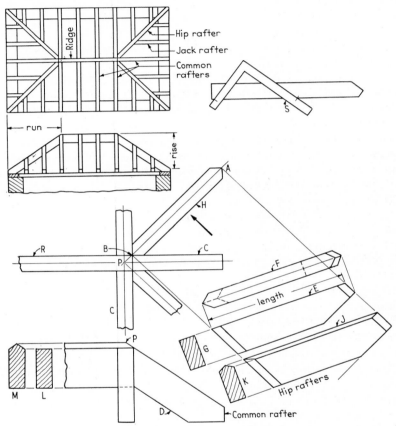

FIGURE 35. Framing of a hip roof.

The face view of the hip rafter is shown at E, the edge view at F, and the end view at G. The upper edge of this rafter may be beveled to fit exactly the theoretical shape of the roof, as shown in the face view at J and in the end view at K. The views E and J are auxiliary elevations; G and K are end or oblique views; the edge view F is an oblique view. The angles to which the hip rafter must be cut are marked on the timber, and the length of the rafter is determined by the framer with the aid of his steel square and the tables thereon. In the drawing, the angles and length to which the hip rafter is cut are determined, as usual, by maintaining the same relative elevations of points in the front view and in the auxiliary elevation.

A short jack rafter is shown in Figure 36. The top view is at 1. At 2 is the front view that is also a face view of the rafter. In this view the slope of the rafter is the same as the slope of the roof. The edge view of the jack rafter is shown at 3, and the end view and the size of the timber at

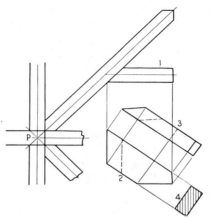

FIGURE 36. Jack rafter.

4. The angles of the cuts, as shown in the face and edge views, are determined by the framer with the aid of his steel square.

In Figures 35 and 36 the rafters are represented in the drawings by means of points and lines; the angles between the lines have been determined by obtaining normal views of the planes of the lines; the angles between pairs of planes have been determined by obtaining views taken in the directions of the intersections of the planes. The theory of the geometry of engineering drawing thus finds continual applications in practice.

43. Problems.

Group 52.　Timber Framing.
Group 53.　Miscellaneous Problems.

Chapter 8
INTERSECTION AND DEVELOPMENT
OF SURFACES

1. Progress in every field of engineering accelerates at a rapid rate. New materials having new properties, and new and improved tools, machines, methods, and processes continually are being made available. Each advance makes possible radical changes and improvements in design. These require of the engineer an ever-expanding fund of knowledge and an increasing ability to visualize his designs thoroughly and to represent them accurately in drawings.

FIGURE 1. Stratojet. (*Boeing Aircraft Company.*)

The continuous plate-rolling mill reduces the cost of producing steel plate. The gas-cutting torch and the electric arc offer means for readily cutting intricate shapes from light and heavy metal plates at much lower cost than formerly was possible. Electric and gas welding provide means for readily joining one part to another. Welded objects replace castings. Many products are molded from plastics, and plastic cements are used

120

FIGURE 2. Welded bow section of a tanker. (*United States Steel Corporation and The Welding Engineer.*)

for joining materials.   All of these require new techniques and open up new possibilities in intricate design.

These advances require of the engineer definite knowledge of the methods of finding the intersections between the various parts of a structure, and of accurately determining the development or pattern for parts that are to be made from thin or thick sheet materials.   These methods are explained in this and the following chapters.

2. Typical Engineering Designs.   Examples of these are shown in Figures 1 to 3.   The photograph of the airplane shows the intersections between adjacent sheets. Each sheet is accurately cut and formed to secure a smooth streamlined structure without aerodynamic dead spots. The joints, or lines of intersections, between sheets must be indicated on the drawings, and an accurate development, or pattern, must be drawn to show the shape to which each sheet must be cut. The intersections between the fuselage and the wings and between the nacelles and the wings also are shown. The intersections between these larger adjoining units must be determined in advance, so that each will slip exactly into its place.

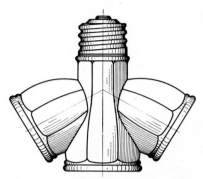

FIGURE 3. A molded light socket.

Full-scale drawings of airplanes and ships are made on a lofting floor, and the exact shapes of many of the parts are there determined. A photograph of a lofting floor is shown in Chapter 11, Figure 19. It is a large drawing board.

Figure 2 shows the double-curved bow section of a ship. This is an example of fine workmanship, involving the design of curved surfaces, making the patterns for each plate and the templates for checking its curvature, cutting the plates to shape, forming the heavy metal plates to exact shape, and joining the plates by welding. The curved edge of the hull section must match the edge of the bow section as the two parts are brought together to be welded. Errors in designing structures of this size are costly.

Figure 3 shows the design of a small object to be molded in plastics. Since molds are expensive, the design requires careful consideration so that the molded object will be satisfactory in appearance. This multiple light socket is designed by first drawing a satisfactory contour outline of the three parts. Next, the intersection of each cylindrical face with its adjacent face is determined. Finally, the intersections of each angle socket with the middle socket are determined. In every design, most of the lines drawn are lines of intersection.

INTERSECTIONS

3. A structure is limited by the surfaces that bound it. Each surface of the structure is, in turn, limited by the straight or curved lines in which it intersects the adjacent surfaces. These lines of intersection determine the edges and joints of the structure and are shown in drawings to describe the structure. If any of the lines are not shown, the structure is not completely described, and the drawing has an unfinished appearance. In addition to the lines of intersection, the outlines, or contours, of curved surfaces of structures also are shown in drawings.

The intersections between the adjoining surfaces of a structure must be accurately located and shown, both to give a finished appearance to the drawing and for use in making developments. Approximate intersections give an unnatural appearance to a view and result in inaccurate developments that multiply difficulties and aggravations in the shop and increase costs.

Adjoining surfaces of a structure intersect in one or more lines. The line of intersection may be straight, single-curved, or double-curved, or it may be some combination of these. If the line of intersection is known to be straight, it is necessary to find only two points of the line in order to determine the line. If the line of intersection is curved, it usually is necessary to locate a series of closely spaced points of the line to determine the line accurately.

Four methods of finding intersections are commonly used. A general description and an example of each method are given below. Other methods that are used in special cases are described in the chapters where they are applied. When an intersection is to be found, judgment, dictated by experience, will determine which method is best to use. Often it is expedient to use several methods in solving a single problem. The reader should visualize each method here described so that he will be able to choose and to apply the method best suited for use in solving each individual problem.

4. First Method. To find the intersection of two surfaces: Pass a cutting plane through the two surfaces. This cutting plane will cut from each surface a straight or curved line. These lines will intersect at one or more points that are common to both surfaces and hence are points on the required intersection. Repeat the above operation until enough points are found to determine the line of intersection accurately. Then draw the line of intersection. The method of passing cutting planes is generally used when both of the given surfaces are curved, but it also is useful when one or both surfaces are planes.

5. Second Method. To find the intersection of two surfaces when one of the surfaces is a plane: Obtain a view that shows an edge view of the given plane. In this view, the points where the lines of the other surface intersect the plane are at once seen. These points are then transferred to the other views, and the line of intersection is drawn.

The second method is particularly useful when several lines intersect a plane, or when one or both of the given surfaces are prisms or cylinders. A prism may be considered as a folded plane, and a cylinder as a plane that has been curved.   An end view of the prism or cylinder will immediately show the location of all points of intersection with the lines of the other given surface.

6. Third Method.   To find the intersection of two surfaces when both surfaces are plane-faced: Find the intersection of each straight line of each surface with the plane faces of the other surface.   This is done by finding the intersection of a line and a plane as explained in Chapter 7, Article 23.

This method is useful when finding the intersection of one or two lines and a plane; for example, when finding the intersection of two pyramids, two prisms, or a pyramid and a prism.

7. Fourth Method.   To find the intersection of surfaces of revolution when their axes intersect: Pass cutting spheres that are centered at the point where the axes intersect.   Each cutting sphere will cut one or two circles from each surface of revolution.   These circles will intersect at two or more points that are on the line of intersection of the surfaces of revolution.   This method is explained in Chapter 11, Article 10.

8. Example of First Method.   The intersection of the sphere and cylinder of Figure 4 is best found by passing cutting planes.   This example is discussed at considerable length to show the need for giving consideration to many details.   Preliminary thinking and planning expedite the solution of the problem.

Judgment must be used in choosing the direction in which cutting planes should be passed through the two intersecting surfaces.   Since only straight lines or circles may be readily drawn, it is practically necessary to pass cutting planes so that they cut from a given surface either straight lines or circles.   If circles are cut from a surface, the cutting plane should usually be frontal, horizontal, or profile, in order that the circle will not appear as an ellipse in any of the principal views.   Also, whenever it is possible to pass cutting planes in several directions, time is saved by choosing the direction that will give the greatest number of points for each plane that is used.

For Figure 4 determine first the best direction for the cutting planes. Consider the sphere: Any cutting plane will cut a circle from the sphere; hence, as far as the sphere is concerned, the cutting planes may be passed in any direction.   The cutting plane should, however, be frontal, horizontal, or profile; otherwise the circle cut from the sphere would appear as an ellipse and would be difficult to draw.   Consider the cylinder: A plane perpendicular to the axis will cut a circle from the cylinder, while a plane parallel to the axis will cut two straight lines from the cylinder.   Any oblique plane would cut an ellipse, and this would not be desirable.   As far as the cylinder is concerned, the cutting plane should be frontal, horizontal, or profile.

Consider both surfaces: If horizontal cutting planes are used, each plane will cut a circle from the sphere and a circle from the cylinder, and these two circles will intersect at two points. If frontal or profile cutting planes are used, each plane will cut a circle from the sphere and two straight lines from the cylinder, and the two straight lines will cross the circle at four points. This latter plan is better, since each cutting plane will determine four points on the required intersection, and the work will proceed

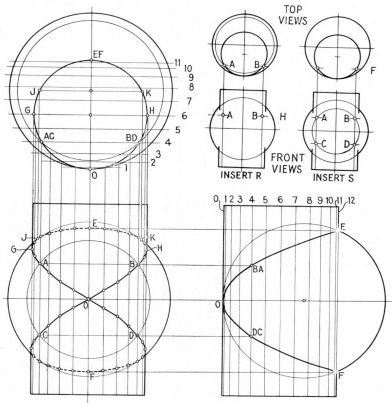

FIGURE 4. Intersecting cylinder and sphere.

twice as fast as it would if horizontal cutting planes were used. These two plans are illustrated in inserts R and S in Figure 4.

A frontal cutting plane is shown in the top and side views at 4. In the front view are shown the circle that is cut from the sphere, and the two straight lines that are cut from the cylinder by plane 4. The straight lines and the circle intersect at the points A, B, C, and D. These are points on the required intersection. Points of intersection are probably best indicated by a small circle. The top and side views of the points are then located, each in line with its ray and on the top and side views of the straight lines and circle. The operation is repeated by taking other frontal cutting planes, as shown in the figure. Enough cutting planes should be used to determine accurately the line of intersection. Cutting planes should usually be more closely spaced as the curve of intersection becomes sharper.

In the problem just explained, for each frontal cutting plane that is passed in front of the axis of the cylinder, another plane should be passed an equal distance behind the axis. This will make it necessary to draw only one-half as many straight lines in the front view.

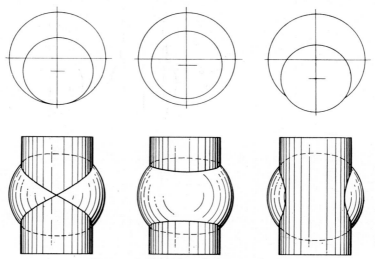

FIGURE 5. Variations in intersections.

Several points may be found by inspection. The point O is directly in front of the center of the sphere. The points E and F on the rear line of the cylinder and on the profile great circle of the sphere are located first in the side view and then in the front view. It should be noted that the frontal cutting plane 6, which passes through the axis of the cylinder, determines the four points where the intersection passes around the contour of the cylinder from the front to the back of the cylinder. Two of these points are shown at G and H. At these points the intersection changes from visible to invisible. Also, a frontal cutting plane that passes through the center of the sphere determines the four points where the intersection meets the contour circle of the sphere in the front view. Two of these are shown at J and K. The location of these special points is important in order to give a satisfactory appearance to the line of intersection.

After sufficient points are found, the curve of intersection should be penciled. Care should be taken to indicate by broken lines the parts of the curve that are invisible, and to draw very fine, or erase, the lines that disappear when the two surfaces are considered as one structure.

In Figure 4 the intersection of the sphere and cylinder might be found by passing horizontal cutting planes. Assume that a horizontal plane has been passed at the level of the points A and B in the front view, as is shown in insert R. This plane will cut a circle from the sphere and

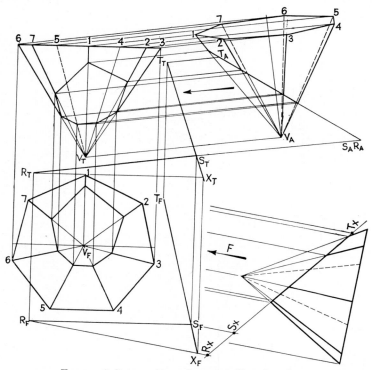

FIGURE 6. Intersection of a pyramid and a plane.

another circle from the cylinder. The circles are shown in the top view. They intersect at the points A and B. The front views of these points are next located on the edge views of both circles.

For solving this problem, the disadvantage that horizontal cutting planes have as compared with frontal cutting planes is partly overcome by the fact that the circle cut from the cylinder needs to be drawn but once. But the disadvantages of using horizontal cutting planes are that the method is slower; that the intersections of some of the circles cannot be located accurately, since they cross at such sharp angles; and that the intersections must be transferred from the top view, where they are not needed, to the front view. At times it is convenient to pass cutting planes in more than one direction. Experience will aid in choosing the best plan. Figure 5 shows that a slight change in the relation of the sphere to the cylinder will result in a considerable change in the appearance of the intersection.

9. Examples of Second Method. Find the intersection of the heptagonal pyramid and the plane of Figure 6 by means of an edge view of the plane. The edge view, taken in a direction parallel to the horizontal

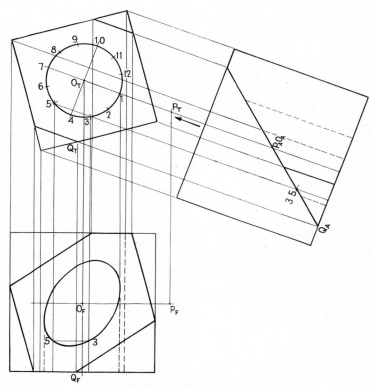

FIGURE 7. Intersection of a prism and a plane.

line R S of the plane, shows immediately which of the 14 edges of the pyramid pass through the plane. The seven points of intersection thus found are transferred from the auxiliary elevation to the top view, and from the top view to the front view. Check to be sure that each point in the front view has the same relative elevation that it has in the auxiliary elevation. The intersection on the line V 1 must be located by this method. The straight-line intersections connecting the points are then drawn, and the solution of the problem is complete.

Since the base of the given pyramid of Figure 6 is frontal, this problem may be solved with less work by drawing a frontal-auxiliary view in which the edge views of both the plane and the heptagonal base are seen. The frontal arrow F, parallel to the frontal line R X of the given plane, indicates the direction in which the frontal-auxiliary view is taken. The advantages of drawing a frontal-auxiliary view, rather than an auxiliary

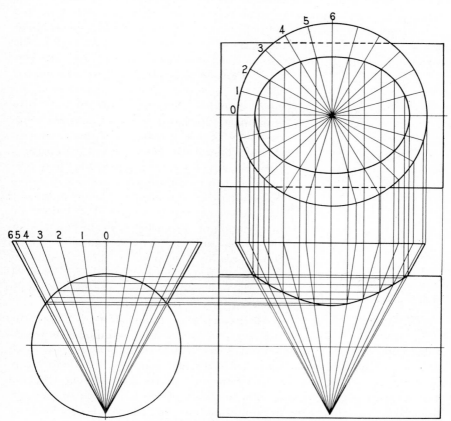

FIGURE 8. Intersection of a cylinder and a cone.

elevation, are clearly apparent. Visualizing in advance the best method for solving a problem expedites the solution.

In another example shown in Figure 7, the edges of the hollow prism are horizontal and vertical. An auxiliary view is taken in the direction of the horizontal line O P of the plane O P Q. The elevations of points in the front view must be determined from the auxiliary view. The end view of the cylindrical hole is divided into 12 equal parts. Two lines of the cylinder, for example, intersect the plane at 3 and 5 in the auxiliary view, and the level of the front views of these points is determined from the auxiliary view.

The edge-view method may be used for determining the intersection of the cylinder and the cone of Figure 8. The side view is here an edge view of the curved surface of the cylinder. In this view the point of intersection of each straight-line element of the cone with the surface of the cylinder is at once apparent. The points of intersection are next located in the front view, each in line with its ray and on its straight-line element of the cone. The top views of these points are then located from the front views, but the depth dimensions should be checked with the side view. The intersection is a double-curved line. To save work, the circular base of the cone should be symmetrically divided into equal parts, so that in the front and side views each line of the drawing will represent two straight lines of the cone. Since the intersection is symmetrical, only one-fourth of the lines need to be numbered.

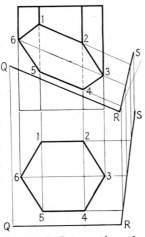

FIGURE 9. Intersection of a prism and a plane.

To illustrate the need for using judgment when choosing the best method of finding the intersection of two surfaces, the intersection of the prism and the plane in Figure 9 may be found readily by passing three horizontal cutting planes. Obtaining an edge view of the plane would in this case require more work.

10. Example of Third Method. Find the intersection of the two pyramids shown in Figure 10. Each of the eight edges of either pyramid may intersect one or two of the five plane faces of the other pyramid. To solve this problem, it is theoretically necessary to find the intersection of a line and a plane eighty times. The amount of work may be materially reduced by visualizing the pyramids and deciding which lines are likely to intersect which planes. In any case, the solution requires careful attention to details. The solution is based on finding the intersection of a line and a plane by the method explained in Chapter 7, Article 23.

To find whether or not the line 0 3 of one pyramid intersects the plane face V D C of the other pyramid, proceed as follows: In the front view locate the point K on the line V C and directly in front of, or behind, the line 0 3. Now locate the top view of K on the top view of the line V C. Next, in the front view locate the point L on the line V D and directly in front of, or behind, the line 0 3. Then locate the top view of L on the top view of the line V D. Draw the views of the line K L. In the top view the line K L will intersect the line 0 3 at the point P.   In the front view, P is on the lines 0 3 and K L.   The point P is on the line 0 3 and in the plane V D C and, hence, is a required point of intersection.   This process is repeated with as many lines and planes as are necessary fully to determine the intersection of the two pyramids.

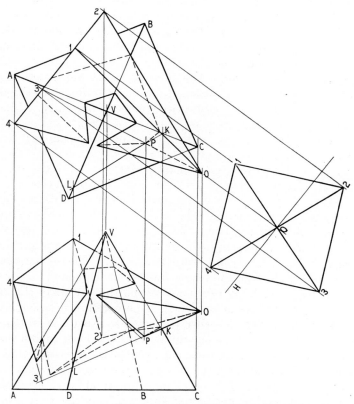

FIGURE 10. Intersection of two pyramids.

11. Problems.

Group 54.   Miscellaneous Intersections.

DEVELOPMENTS

12. Flat sheets of metal or other materials may be cut to any necessary shape and then folded, curved, or stretched to form articles of manufacture having a great variety of shapes.   The metal sheet may be thin as is used to form light articles like ordinary household and similar equipment. It may be heavier plate as is used for heavy pipes, tanks, and boilers, or

for thick armor plate of battleships. Other frequently used materials are veneers, plywood, paper, fiber, and plastic sheets.

13. Nature of Developments. An article that is to be made from sheet material is first designed by drawing the needed views. Then it is necessary to draw the developments that are to be used as patterns for marking the shapes to which the flat sheet must be cut before it is folded or curved to form the individual parts of the article of manufacture. The flat development is also called a *stretchout*, a *pattern*, or a *blank*. Developments must be carefully drawn so that the parts will fit accurately when they are assembled in the shop.

14. Master Development. The original development may first be drawn on paper. But paper is not a desirable medium, since the size of a paper pattern changes appreciably with change in humidity. Blueprints particularly are not suitable for use as patterns. For accurate work, the master development is drawn with a pencil or scriber directly on a flat sheet of painted or surfaced metal.

The outline of the development must be transferred to the sheets that are to be cut to shape in the shop. The metal master development may be trimmed to shape and its outline scribed on the metal sheets. Even slight scratches are not permissible on thin metal sheets that are to be used in structures subject to vibration, as in aircraft. In some industries where large patterns are required, as in shipbuilding, the patterns are made from sheets of heavy waterproofed paper. The outline may then be prick-punched through the paper onto the metal plate.

Photography is much used for transferring the outline of the development. The metal master development is photographed on a glass plate. The design on this negative is then projected to exact size on light-sensitized metal sheets by using an enlarging camera. The exposed sheets are developed and are then ready to be cut to shape in the shop. The photographic method ensures exact duplicates of the original drawing and has several other advantages. Another useful method is to scribe the lines into the metal plate of the master development, and then to transfer these lines onto other metal plates by means of a direct-contact electrolytic process.

15. Cutting the Blank to Shape. After the outline of the pattern has been transferred to the sheets or plates, these are cut to shape by shearing, sawing, or nibbling; by using a routing cutter in a profiling machine; or by means of a cutting torch. Blanking dies shaped to the desired outline are used when the number of pieces to be cut is large enough to justify the cost of the dies. Before the advent of the cutting torch, heavy plates were cut to shape by drilling a line of holes just outside the desired outline. Visualize the ragged edge that this would leave. Thinner sheets may be cut in multiple with a torch by clamping or welding the sheets together in stacks.   The original development must be accurate.   Too much or too little material anywhere along the edge multiplies troubles and expense when the parts are assembled in the shop.

16. Forming the Blank.   The blank is cut to the proper shape from the specified sheet material and is then folded, curved, or stretched until it assumes the desired form.   The blank may be folded in a machine called a *brake*, curved by means of rolls, stretched by means of dies or hammering, or formed by spinning.   Dies may be used for all three operations.

After the blank is formed to shape, the edges that meet are joined by seaming, welding, soldering, cementing, or riveting.   The net development usually is indicated by solid lines, and the allowance for seams is indicated by broken lines outside the boundary of the development.   The seam should generally be on the shortest line.   When possible, the development should be symmetrical.   Sharp bends or folds should not be made in sheets that are more than $\frac{1}{32}$ inch in thickness.   Allowances must be made for bends.   See Chapter 9, Article 3.

17. Surfaces That Can Be Developed.   Sheet metal bends or folds along a straight line; hence only ruled surfaces may be developed.   Of the ruled surfaces, plane-faced and single-curved surfaces may be developed; but warped surfaces cannot be developed, since the consecutive straight-line elements of warped surfaces do not intersect.   An article that is to be made simply by folding or curving sheet metal, therefore, must be designed so that its surfaces are either plane-faced or single-curved.   That is, the article must be composed of pyramids, prisms, wedges, polyhedrons, cones, cylinders, or convolutes.   Other surfaces can be approximately developed.

18. Surfaces That Cannot Be Developed.   Warped surfaces and double-curved surfaces cannot be developed.   These surfaces cannot be formed from sheet metals except by stretching the metal by means of dies.   Since dies are expensive, these surfaces should not ordinarily be used in the design of large articles that are to be made from sheet metal, or for small sheet-metal articles that are to be made in small quantities without dies.   Double-curved surfaces of revolution may be made at relatively low cost by spinning.   Warped surfaces may be approximated in sheet-metal work by dividing the surface into triangles.   Doubled-curved surfaces may be approximated in shape by designing them so that they may be constructed from cones, cylinders, or convolutes.

19. Modelmaking.   Much may be gained by making models of the objects specified in the problems.   Modelmaking helps to fix the ideas of the practical use of developments and of the methods of obtaining them. The maker of a model that fits well at the joints and that has a well-finished appearance derives a considerable amount of satisfaction from the experience.   After a model is made, its relation to the drawing should be

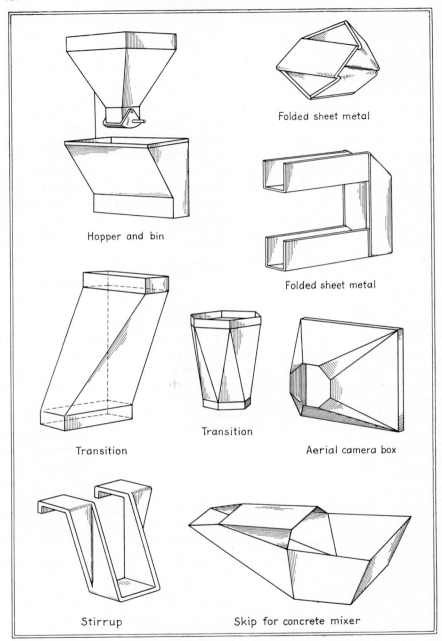

Folded sheet metal

Hopper and bin

Folded sheet metal

Transition

Transition

Aerial camera box

Stirrup

Skip for concrete mixer

FIGURE 11. Plane-faced structures.

studied and checked.   A model is an aid in visualizing the object; but the object must be visualized before the model can be made.   Models may be made to any multiple of the size shown in the drawing by multiplying the length of each line in the development by a chosen factor.   Small models should be made from stiff paper; large ones should be made from stiffer paper or sheet metal.   An allowance for the seam or lap should be added to the development, and the lap may be glued to the part that it meets.   Attractive models may be made from nitrate or acetate cellulose sheets.   Acetone may be used as a cement for this material.   Accurate mockups of newly designed aircraft and automobiles are made with plaster and other materials and are used for checking the general appearance and accuracy of the drawings and for determining the locations and shapes of the parts.

20. Typical Folded Metal Objects.   Figure 11 shows a number of plane-faced objects formed by folding sheet metal.   The smaller articles are made from quite thin metal sheet, while the larger objects are made from heavy metal plate.   The stirrup is made by folding a length of flat bar iron.   Each piece is designed by drawing its views, and from these the pattern is made.

The methods of developing pyramids, prisms, polyhedrons, and other plane-faced objects are explained in this chapter.   The methods of developing curved surfaces are explained in the next chapter.   The reason why a given surface may or may not be developed is stated in the articles dealing with that surface.

RIGHT PRISMS AND PYRAMIDS

21.   Figures 12 and 13 illustrate several kinds of right and oblique prisms and pyramids.   The bases of these plane-faced objects are polygons. The axis and the parallel sides of a right prism are perpendicular to the base of the prism.   The faces of right prisms are rectangles, while the faces of oblique prisms are parallelograms.   The axis of a right pyramid is perpendicular to its base at the center of the base.   The faces of pyramids are triangles.   A wedge may be considered as a right or oblique triangular prism, or as a truncated prism.

22. Development of Right Prism.   In Figure 14 is shown a truncated right prism that is tipped to the left.   The top view is here of no use for determining the development.   The front view is a normal view of the parallel edges, and the end view is a right section that shows the true lengths of the sides of the base.   The development of the entire prism is the rectangle A B C D.   The length A B is equal to the perimeter of the square base.   The folding lines divide the development into four equal rectangles.   The development is here placed on a slant, in line with the front view, to aid the draftsman in transferring the true lengths from the front view to the development. The development of the frustum is shown in heavy lines. The pattern is cut for the shortest seam, but it cannot be made symmetrical. Were the upper face of the prism to be considered as a part of the development, it would be necessary to obtain a normal view of this quadrilateral and to attach it to the development.

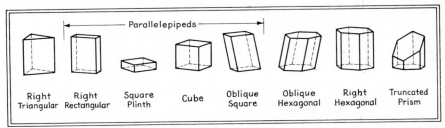

FIGURE 12. Prisms.

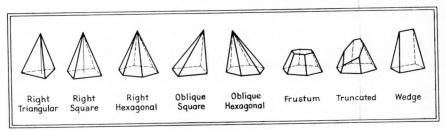

FIGURE 13. Pyramids.

23. Practical Details. It should be noted that, if the development of the truncated prism of Figure 14 were now cut from sheet metal or stiff paper, it would be possible to fold it so that either one side or the other of the development would be inside the prism. Folding the development one way would make what might be called a right-hand object, and folding it the other way would make it left-hand. The two would not be alike. The drawing specifies a definite shape. Developments should be drawn so that the side nearest the draftsman is the inner side, and the development should always be folded so that the required object will be produced.

Making an accurate development requires patience and careful workmanship. One of the common mistakes is to leave off one section of the development; for example, one face of a pyramid or one section of a cone. A hexagonal pyramid has six edges that pass through the vertex, but on the development there are seven. Two of these join at the seam to form one edge. The joining lines should be checked to make sure that they are of equal length.

If possible, the development should be symmetrical, and the seam or cut should be on the shortest line. When an article is made from several developments, care is usually taken to see that the patterns are cut so that two or more seams do not come together at one point.

24. Development of Right Pyramid. The surface of the hexagonal right pyramid of Figure 15 consists of six equal isosceles triangles. The true length of the base of each triangle may be seen in the top view at 1 2, and the true length of the equal sides of the triangles may be seen in the front view at V 1. The fan-shaped development or pattern is made by

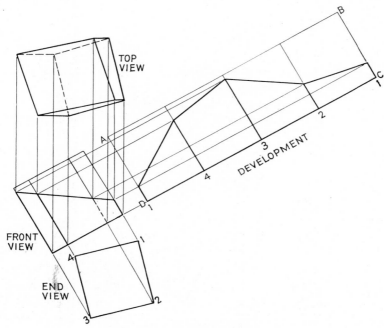

FIGURE 14. Development of a right prism.

drawing these triangles side by side. If the bottom of the sheet-metal pyramid is to be closed, the hexagonal base should be shown in the development. Since it is difficult to fold this development to a sharp point at the vertex, it is best to discard a part of the development, as indicated in the drawing, and to insert in its place a short pointed pyramid formed from solid metal in case a sharp-pointed tip is needed.

25. Development of Truncated Pyramid. In the auxiliary elevation of Figure 15 the top of the pyramid has been cut off by an inclined plane. To develop the part of the pyramid that is below the cutting plane, proceed as follows: First, obtain the fan-shaped development as explained in the preceding paragraph. Next, determine the point of intersection of each edge of the pyramid with the inclined plane, and locate each point in the development.   As an example take the edge V 5.   In the auxiliary elevation, V 5 is seen to intersect the inclined plane at the point E.

Obtain the true length of the line V E by revolving the element V 5 about the axis of the pyramid to the position V K in the top and auxiliary views.   The point E revolves with its element to E_1.   In the auxiliary view, V K is a normal view.   It shows the true length of the element V 5, and V E_1 is the true length of V E.   This distance V E_1 is laid off on the development at V E_2 on the line V 5.   Other points on the development

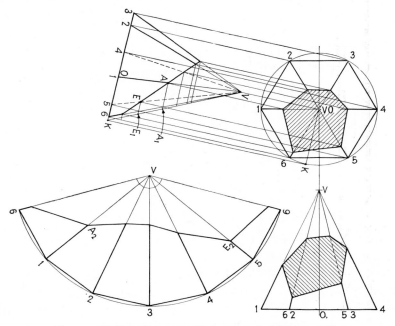

FIGURE 15.   Development of a truncated right pyramid.

are similarly found, and the development is completed by drawing the straight lines connecting the two points in each face.   The development of the truncated pyramid is shown by the heavy outline.   The folding lines are also indicated.   The development is cut to provide the shortest seam.

26. Problems.

Group 55.   Right Prisms and Pyramids.

OBLIQUE PRISMS AND PYRAMIDS

27. Development of Oblique Prism.   Given the front and top views of the oblique prism of Figure 16, draw an auxiliary view that is a normal

view of the axis and of the six parallel edges of the prism. Since the
hexagonal bases are horizontal, the auxiliary view should be taken in a
horizontal direction.   In the auxiliary elevation pass a plane X perpendicular to the axis.   The plane X is passed best through the middle point
of the axis.   The plane X will cut from the prism the six-sided right section centered at A_o B_o.   This is not a regular hexagon.   Its sides are of
three different lengths.

The oblique prism may now be developed as if it were two truncated
right prisms having a common base in the plane X.   In the development,

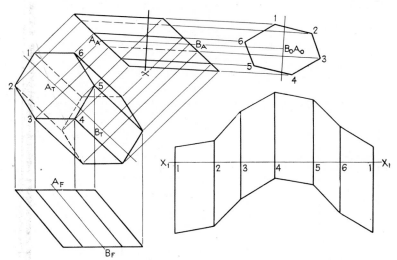

FIGURE 16. Development of an oblique prism.

the six sides of the right section will be unfolded into a straight line, as
shown from X_1 to X_1.   The folding lines of the development will be perpendicular to the sides of the right section.   The distance that each folding line extends on either side of the right section is determined from the
auxiliary elevation.   The pattern is then completed by drawing the upper
and lower edges.   Since the plane X is taken through the middle point of
A B, the folding lines 2 and 5 will extend equal distances on opposite sides
of the line X_1.   A similar statement applies to lines 3 and 6 and to 4 and 1.

The development is drawn, as usual, so that the near side forms the
inside of the prism.   Right-hand and left-hand prisms will be formed if
the pattern is folded first in one direction and then oppositely folded.
When the sheet of paper is large enough, the development may be drawn
to advantage in line with the auxiliary view.   The development should be
checked to be sure that the 12 upper and lower edges are equal in length,
since they are to form two equilateral hexagons when the development is
folded.

A different method of developing an oblique prism is now explained. This method is generally used by mechanics in the shop, since they normally have to work from the front and the top views of the object. For work on the drafting board, the method explained in the preceding paragraphs is likely to produce a development more nearly correct. Both methods should be understood.

Figure 17: The bases of the oblique prism are horizontal triangles, and the true lengths of their sides are shown in the top view. The inclined faces of the prism are parallelograms. To reproduce the true shapes of the parallelograms in the development, it is necessary to determine not

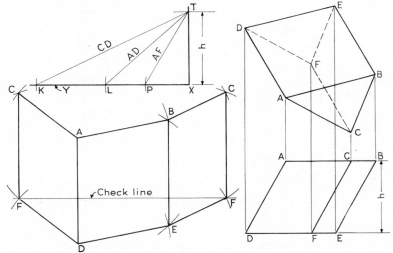

FIGURE 17. Development of an oblique prism.

only the true lengths of the sides but also the true lengths of the diagonals of each parallelogram. This has been done in part in the construction diagram shown in Figure 17. A right angle T X Y is drawn. The constant difference in the levels of the two bases is measured from X to T. The distance P X is made equal to the distance from A to F in the top view. The true length of A F is equal to T P. Determine why this is so. The lengths of A D, C D, and of the remaining diagonals are found in a similar way.

The development is started with any line. Let this be A D. Its length is taken from the diagram above the development. One compass is now set to the true length of A C and is centered at A in the development, and a second compass is set to the true length of C D and is centered at D in the development. The two arcs drawn by these compasses intersect at C. The corner F is similarly located, and the drawing is checked to make sure that the figure A D F C is a parallelogram. The two remaining parallelo-

grams are drawn in a similar manner.   When the development is completed, the check line F F should be drawn.   If this check line is not perpendicular to the folding lines of the development, then the development
will not close properly when it is folded along the lines A D and B E.

28. Oblique Pyramid Development.   The oblique pyramid shown in
Figure 18 is symmetrically divided by a vertical plane passing through the
vertex and the corners 1 and 4 of the hexagonal base.   The surface is
formed of three pairs of similar triangles.   The development or pattern

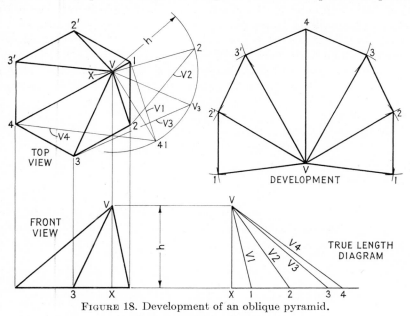

FIGURE 18. Development of an oblique pyramid.

should be symmetrical, and the cut should be on the shortest line V 1.
The development should be started by finding the length of the longest
line V 4 and using it as the middle line of the development.

The true lengths of oblique lines may be found by drawing normal
views of the lines.   In certain problems, however, less work is required
by adopting one of the methods here described.   These methods are useful when the width, or depth, or height dimension between the ends of
several oblique lines is a constant distance.   In Figure 18, the distance h
is constant.   To find the true length of the line V 3, for example: V X is a
vertical line equal in length to h.   X 3 is a horizontal line.   The oblique
line V 3 is the hypotenuse of a right triangle of which V X and X 3 are the
two sides.   Two methods of drawing this right triangle are shown.

In the top view a horizontal circle centered at X and having a radius
equal to h is drawn.   The point V, when revolved about the horizontal

line X 3, falls at V_3 on the circle just drawn.   The required right triangle is X 3 V_3, and the required true length of V 3 may be measured from 3 to V_3.   Similarly the length of V 2 may be measured from 2 to 2 in the top view.   After the true lengths of all lines are found, the development is drawn.   One compass should be set to the length of the sides of the hexagon, and another compass should be used for transferring the true lengths of the slanting lines to the development.   The crossing points of the arcs are indicated in the development.

A second method for finding the true lengths of the slanting lines of the oblique pyramid is illustrated in the true-length diagram of Figure 18.   V X, equal to h, is one leg of several right triangles.   The other leg, X 3 for example, is equal to the length of X 3 in the top view, and the hypotenuse is equal to the true length of the slant line V 3.   Both of the methods just described should be understood.   As to the amount of work required, there is little to choose between them.

29. Problems.

    Group 56.   Oblique Prisms and Pyramids.
    Group 57.   Hoppers and Transitions.

REGULAR POLYHEDRONS

30. Figure 19 shows the five regular polyhedrons that it is possible to construct.   Each polyhedron is equilateral, and its plane faces are similar and equal.   Views of these polyhedrons may be drawn by starting with

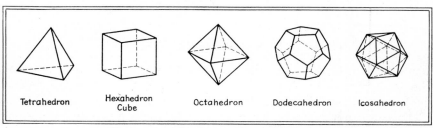

Tetrahedron   Hexahedron Cube   Octahedron   Dodecahedron   Icosahedron

FIGURE 19. The five regular polyhedrons.

the development and then folding it to form the object.   This is illustrated in Figure 20.

The development of the upper part of a dodecahedron is shown centered at T and is here considered to be horizontal.   Two of the pentagons are revolved downward about the folding lines or axes K and L until their edges E B and E C meet at B_1.   The corner A moves to A_1.   The levels of B_1 and A_1 are determined in the auxiliary elevation taken in the direction of the folding line K.

The top view of the dodecahedron may now be drawn, since the locations of A_1 and B_1, and other similarly located points, are known.   The front view may then be drawn, since the levels of A_1 and B_1 are known. The side view is then readily drawn.   The pictorial view of each poly-

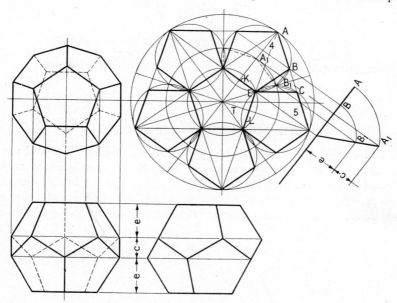

FIGURE 20. Dodecahedron and its development.

hedron shown in Figure 19 is drawn by choosing the oblique direction in which it is desired to observe the polyhedron, and then drawing its auxiliary and oblique views.   This is explained in Chapter 4, Article 2.

31. Problems.

Group 58.   Polyhedrons.

Chapter 9

SINGLE-CURVED SURFACES

CYLINDERS—CONES—CONVOLUTES

1. Ruled surfaces are generated by a moving straight line and are of three types: plane, single-curved, and warped. A *single-curved surface* is a ruled surface of which two or more consecutive, straight-line elements intersect. Since this type of surface is curved, no three consecutive elements may lie in the same plane. Since two consecutive straight-line

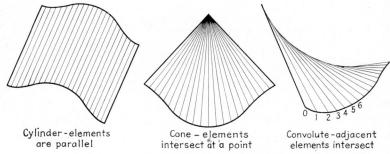

Cylinder - elements
are parallel

Cone – elements
intersect at a point

Convolute - adjacent
elements intersect

FIGURE 1. Developments of single-curved surfaces.

elements intersect and lie in a plane, all single-curved surfaces may be developed. Cylinders, cones, and convolutes are the three kinds of single-curved surfaces.

Figure 1 illustrates the geometrical relations of the elements of each kind of single-curved surface by showing a development of each. In a cylinder all elements are parallel; in a cone all elements intersect at one point; in a convolute two consecutive elements, but no three, intersect. If these developments are now curved by bending the sheet of material along the straight-line elements, the indicated single-curved surfaces will be formed. Since cylinders, cones, and convolutes may readily be made by curving sheet and plate materials, these surfaces continually are used in the design of structures.

Photographs and illustrations of typical single-curved structures are shown throughout this chapter.   Each of these structures was designed by drawing the necessary views, by determining the intersections between adjacent parts, and by developing the pattern for each part, so that the parts will fit accurately when they are formed and assembled in the shop.

Figure 2 shows the shop assembly of a welded and riveted spiral turbine casing for the Shasta Power Plant.   This casing is made from heavy steel plate cut to shape and curved to form cones and cylinders.   Each piece must fit accurately in place.

FIGURE 2. Turbine casing.   (*Allis-Chalmers Mfg. Co.*)

2. Forming the Curved Surface.   The flat plate of steel or other material is first cut to the exact outline determined by the development.   This blank is curved by bending it along each of the elements in a straight die, or brake, or by means of a roll.   Figure 3 shows a heavy steel cylinder still in place in a large roll.   The curvature of the cylinder is determined by lowering the upper roll as the rolling proceeds.   Note the indications of the straight-line bends on the surface of the cylinder.   Cones are rolled by throwing the rolls out of line as is shown in Figure 4.   Rolled cylinders and cones are shown in Figure 5.

3. Allowance for Bends.   Sheet materials bend along a straight line. A sharp bend cannot be made in cold metal without reducing the strength of the metal.   The sharp bend shown at A in Figure 6 can be made only by forging or upsetting the metal.   The bend shown at B would weaken the metal.

FIGURE 3. Rolling a cylinder.   (*Williams, White & Co.*)

FIGURE 4. Rolling a cone.   (*Williams, White & Co.*)

Bends usually are made as shown at C.   The metal is curved to some inside radius R.   The minimum allowable inside radius depends upon the thickness T and upon the kind of metal and its degree of hardness.   The amount of material that must be allowed for a bend must be calculated for any developments that are to be formed into accurately fitted parts of a

FIGURE 5. Rolled cylinders and cones.

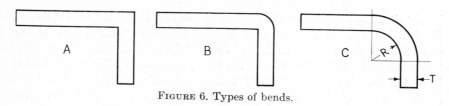

FIGURE 6. Types of bends.

structure, unless the metal is thinner than 0.032 inch.   For some particularly exacting jobs, this limit is placed at 0.022 inch.

When a piece of metal is curved, the metal near the outside of the bend is stretched, and the metal near the inside is compressed.   Tests show that the amounts of stretch and of contraction are not equal.   The following empirical formula, determined by experiment, states the amount, w, of metal that must be allowed for a given bend:

$$w = (0.01743 \ R + 0.0078 \ T) \ A$$

R is the inside radius of the bend.   T is the thickness of the metal.   A is the angle in degrees through which the metal is bent.   Tables and charts calculated from this formula are available for use by the designer who has many developments to make.

Figure 7 shows the cross section of a cylindrical tube formed to an inside radius R from metal having a thickness T.   This is a 360-degree bend. The width of the development is calculated by substituting the values of R, T, and 360 degrees in the formula given above.   The same width may

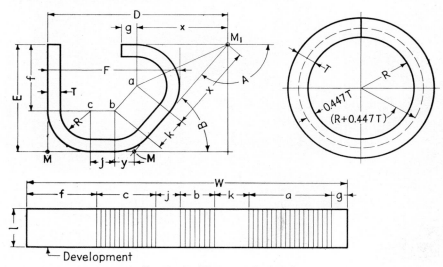

FIGURE 7. Allowance for bends.

be obtained by calculating the circumference of a circle having a radius of (R + 0.447 T).   The broken circle that determines the width of the development is not in the middle of the metal since the metal is expanded more than it is contracted during the bending process.   The coefficient of T in the formula varies slightly with the kind of metal that is used. Metals must be bent slightly beyond their final form to provide for the *spring back* of the bend.

Figure 7 also shows the cross section of a molding to be made from metal.   The following dimensions are determined by the purpose of the design: E and D, or E and F; the inside radius R of all the bends; the thickness T of the metal; and the angle A, or its supplement B.   The other dimensions, indicated by lower-case letters, and the allowance for each bend must be calculated by the designer so that he can make the development for the piece.   Some of the dimensions are calculated by simple trigonometry; others by addition or subtraction.   Obtaining the dimensions by scaling the drawing usually will not give results sufficiently accurate. The allowances c, b, and a for the three bends are calculated by the formula.

Note that the angle at M_1 is less than 90 degrees, but that the angle A through which the metal is bent is more than 90 degrees. The angle A is used in the formula when the allowance for this bend is determined.

In all the following illustrations and explanations regarding developments, only the methods of obtaining net developments are considered. The designer must calculate the necessary allowances whenever the curved metal is thicker than 0.032 inch in all cases requiring accurate fitting of parts. Folded seams or lap joints require additional allowances in the pattern.

4. Problems.

Group 59. Calculating Bend Allowances.

CYLINDERS

5. The cylinder is a single-curved surface in which the straight-line generatrix moves parallel to itself and touches a curved directrix. Since the generatrix is a straight line, the cylinder is a ruled surface. Since all the elements intersect, the cylinder is a single-curved surface, and it may be developed. The elements of a cylinder are parallel. Mathematically speaking, they are said to intersect at infinity. The proof is based on the theory of limits: If the vertex of a cone moves away from the base, the elements of the cone become more nearly parallel. When the limit is reached, the vertex is at infinity, the elements are parallel, and the cone becomes a cylinder.

6. Types of Cylinders. Figure 8 illustrates a general-type cylinder in which the directrix is an open curve. The directrix must not lie in a plane parallel to the elements.

A right circular cylinder is shown in Figure 9. The elements of a right cylinder are perpendicular to the plane of the curved directrix or base.

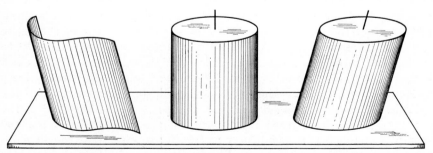

FIGURE 8. A cylinder.   FIGURE 9. A right cylin-   FIGURE 10. An oblique
                            der.   cylinder.

The right circular cylinder is also called a *cylinder of revolution,* since it may be generated by revolving the generatrix about the axis.

An oblique cylinder is shown in Figure 10.   In the oblique cylinder, the elements of the cylinder are not perpendicular to the plane of the base. The altitude of any cylinder is the distance between the parallel planes of the bases.

7. Development of a Right Cylinder.   Figure 11: The development of a right circular cylinder is a rectangle, of which one side is equal in length

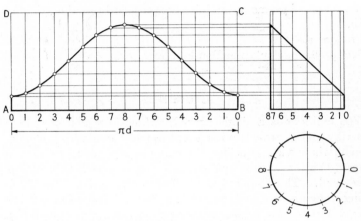

FIGURE 11. Development of a right cylinder.

to the circumference of the circular base of the cylinder, and the other side is equal to the altitude of the cylinder.   In the figure the development of the entire cylinder is the rectangle A B C D.

If a part of the cylinder of Figure 11 is cut off by a plane that is oblique to the axis, to develop the part that is left it is first necessary to divide the circular base into a number of equal parts, 16 for example.   The elements through these points are next drawn in the adjacent view, and here the true length of each element is seen.   The shortest element may be numbered 0, and the longest element 8.   In the development of the entire cylinder the circumference A B is calculated and then is divided into 16 equal parts.   Draw the elements and number the middle element 8, since it is the longest.   The other elements are then numbered consecutively as shown in the figure.   The development will be symmetrical, and the cylinder will be cut along its shortest element.   If the line A B of the development has been drawn in line with one base of the cylinder, the true length of each pair of elements may be transferred directly to the development by means of parallel lines.   Finally, the curved side of the development is drawn.

8. Intersection of a Cylinder and a Plane. In Figures 12 to 14 are illustrated three different methods of finding the intersection of a cylinder and an oblique plane. All possible methods should be understood and used as judgment dictates.

In Figure 12 the horizontal plane H cuts two elements from the cylinder, and a line K L from the given plane. In the top view the line K L is seen to intersect the elements at 2 and 4. Other points on the elliptical intersection may be found by taking other horizontal cutting planes.

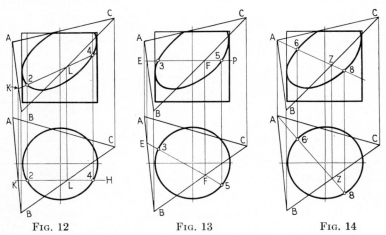

FIG. 12   FIG. 13   FIG. 14

FIGURES 12–13–14. Intersection of a cylinder and a plane.

In Figure 13 the frontal cutting plane P cuts a circle from the cylinder, and a straight line E F from the given plane. In the front view the line E F is seen to intersect the circle at the points 3 and 5. These points are transferred to the top views of the line and circle. Other points on the intersection may be found by repeating the process.

In Figure 14 any line A Z of the given plane is drawn in the front and top views. In the front view this line is seen to pierce the surface of the cylinder at the points 6 and 8. The top views of these points are next located on the top view of the line A Z. Other points on the intersection may be found by taking other lines of the given plane. Whenever it is possible to obtain an edge view of a surface, such a view will show where all lines intersect the surface.

The intersection of a cylinder and a plane also may be found by obtaining an edge view of the plane, as is shown in Figure 15. Starting with the front and top views, draw an auxiliary elevation taken in a direction parallel to any horizontal line R S of the given oblique plane Q R S. The auxiliary elevation will show the edge view of the plane. The front view of the intersection is obtained by determining the elevations of various points from the intersections in the auxiliary elevation, and then locating these points at their respective elevations in the front view. The true shape of the elliptical intersection is shown adjacent to the auxiliary elevation. The development is best drawn in line with the auxiliary elevation. The length of the development should be calculated.

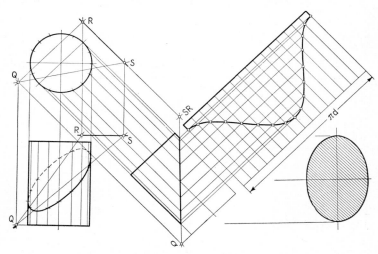

FIGURE 15. Cylinder and plane intersection and development.

9. Problems.

Group 60. Cylinder and Plane Intersections and Developments.

10. Elbows and Offsets. Sheet-metal elbows of uniform diameter are designed so that one pattern will serve for all parts of the elbow. Such a design results in an elbow satisfactory in appearance, uniform in cross section, requiring but one pattern, and reducing to a minimum the waste of material from which the parts of the elbow are cut. A 90-degree four-piece elbow is shown in Figure 16. The 90-degree angle is A C B. The ends of the pipe extend beyond the lines C A and C B. There are no seams on these lines. The least radius of the bend is r.

Note that the angle of the bend of the elbow is divided into equal angles. Each of the interior pieces of the elbow requires two of these angles, and each end piece requires one angle. The number of the equal angular divisions of the bend of the elbow is two less than twice the number of pieces in the elbow. Increasing the number of pieces in an elbow improves the appearance, decreases the internal friction, and increases the cost of the elbow. Increasing the least radius has the same effect.

The elbow consists of right cylinders cut off at an oblique angle by a plane. The development, drawn to the right of the elbow, shows how the four pieces of the elbow may be cut from a rectangular sheet of metal without waste. In addition to avoiding waste, this method of cutting the metal alternates the seams so that three seams will not come together when the parts are assembled. The allowance for seams is shown by broken lines.

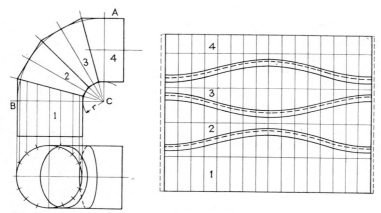

FIGURE 16. A four-piece elbow.

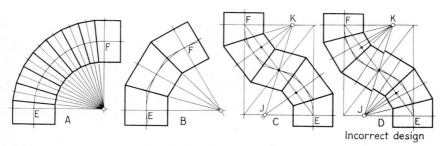

FIGURE 17. Elbows and offsets.

Figure 17: In each of the four pieces shown, the circles E and F are the given ends of pipes that are to be joined by elbows or offsets. The open ends are extended to provide for slip joints. The nine-piece 90-degree elbow shown at A gives a more gradual change in direction to whatever material flows through the pipe and has a smoother appearance than does an elbow of fewer parts, but it is more expensive to make. At B is shown a three-piece, 60-degree elbow. At C is shown an offset designed to be made of two equal three-piece elbows. The centers J and K of the bends must be on lines that are perpendicular to the line E F at its quarter points. Note that each bend angle of offset C has been divided into four equal angles. If an attempt is made as in offset D to divide the angle of the bends into five or any odd number of equal parts, neither the center line nor the pipes will meet at the middle point of the offset. An offset may be made by joining two 90-degree elbows.

11. Breeching or Y. Figure 18 illustrates several designs of a five-piece breeching or Y having uniform circular cross sections. At A are shown the given circular ends 1, 2, and 3. Next, the 45-degree center lines 5 6 and 5 7 of the two inclined sections are located so that the length 1 5 is equal to the lengths 2 6 and 3 7. This is accomplished by drawing the 45-degree line 2 4 and then taking the point 5 halfway between 4 and 1.

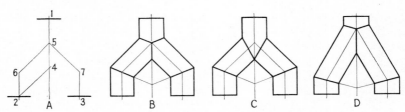

FIGURE 18. Breeching or Y. (*One design is incorrect.*)

At B, the design is completed by drawing cylinders of the given size along the determined center lines. The seams bisect the angle between the center lines. Three completed designs are shown. One of these, however, is not correct. Why is this so?

12. Problems.

Group 61.   Elbows and Branches.

13. Development of Oblique Cylinder. In Figure 19 are shown the front and top views of an oblique cylinder. To develop the cylinder, draw first an auxiliary view that shows both an edge view of the bases and a normal view of the elements. In the figure this is an auxiliary elevation taken in the direction of the arrow. Draw next an end view of the cylinder. This is shown in the figure as a crosshatched ellipse. It is a right section of the cylinder. The front and top views of the cylinder may now be ignored, and the development may be made from the auxiliary elevation and the right section.

Divide one-half of the elliptical right section into any number of parts. Preferably, these parts should be equal in length. Show the edge view of this right section at R in the auxiliary elevation. The problem now resolves itself into developing two right cylinders that have a common elliptical base at R and are cut off by two parallel oblique planes. Rectify the ellipse along the line 0 0. On this straight line step off the lengths of the parts into which the ellipse has been divided. Draw the elements. The middle element should be either 0, 10, or 5, in order to produce a symmetrical development. Let 10 be chosen as the middle element. Number the other elements consecutively in both directions. The length of each element may now be transferred directly from the auxiliary elevation to the development by means of parallel lines.   Complete the development by drawing the outline.

The circumference of an ellipse may be calculated closely only by using a formula that involves a series.   For average accuracy the circumference may be determined by stepping off short lengths.

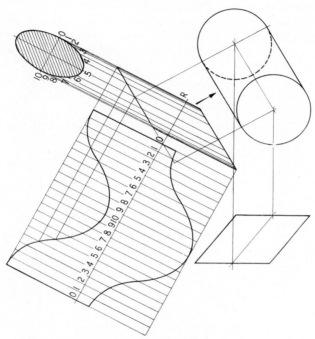

Figure 19. Oblique cylinder development.

14. Problems.

Group 62.   Oblique Cylinder Developments.

15. Intersecting Cylinders.   Several methods are available for finding the intersection of two cylinders.   The method that it is best to use in any problem is determined by the geometrical relations of the intersecting cylinders.   For the cylinders of Figure 20, where the axes of the cylinders do not intersect and the bases are in nonparallel planes, it is best to pass cutting planes parallel to the elements of both cylinders.   Such a plane will cut two lines from each cylinder, and these lines will cross at four points of the required intersection.   The operation is repeated until enough points are found to indicate the intersection definitely.

The elements of the cylinders in Figure 20 are frontal.   Frontal cutting planes will be parallel to both axes.   Pass the frontal cutting plane F. This will cut two elements from the vertical cylinder.   The elements that the plane F cuts from the inclined cylinder are best found from the circular end view of the inclined cylinder. Here the same frontal plane is shown at F_1. The distance that it is drawn in front of the axis of the cylinder is determined from the top view. It cuts two elements from the inclined cylinder. The four elements thus found cross at the points 2, 3, 4, and 5 in the front view. Pass other frontal cutting planes until enough points are found, and then draw the intersection. In the top view the intersection will show as the arc of a circle. The elements that are cut from the inclined cylinder could be determined from the ellipse in the top

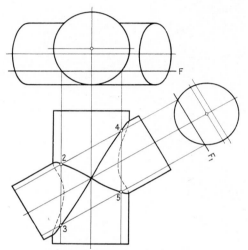

FIGURE 20. Intersecting cylinders.

view; but this is not generally advisable, since the ellipse is not likely to be drawn as accurately as the circle.

16. For finding the intersection of the two oblique cylinders of Figure 21, horizontal cutting planes could be used. Each plane would cut a circle from each cylinder, and these would intersect at two points. But this plan would involve drawing a great many circles, and only two points of intersection would be found for each pair of circles. A better plan is to pass cutting planes parallel to the elements of both cylinders. A point J, represented by its front and top views, is chosen anywhere, and lines J K and J L are drawn parallel to the elements of the cylinders. These lines determine a plane J K L parallel to the cutting planes. K L is a horizontal line of this plane.

The lower circular bases of the two cylinders lie in the same horizontal plane. In this plane a horizontal line R, parallel to K L, is drawn in the top view. This is a line of one cutting plane taken parallel to the plane J K L. This cutting plane cuts the elements 1 2 and 3 4 from the smaller cylinder, and the elements 1 3 and 2 4 from the larger cylinder. These elements intersect at points 1, 2, 3, and 4 on the required intersection.

The front views of these points are next located on the intersections of the front views of the same elements. The locations of the front views should be checked by drawing rays through the top views. The bases of the two cylinders in this figure are taken so that cutting plane Q is tangent to both. This plane cuts but one element from each cylinder, and these intersect at point 5. The cylinders are tangent at this point. Cutting plane S indicates that the larger cylinder extends behind the smaller cylinder.

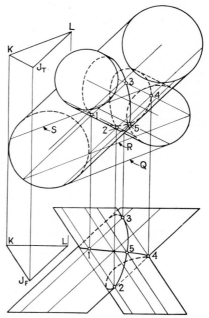

FIGURE 21. Intersecting oblique cylinders.

17. In the case of right circular cylinders with the axes intersecting, it is advisable to pass cutting spheres centered at the meeting point of the axes. Each sphere will cut two circles from each cylinder, and these circles will intersect in eight points, four points, two points, or no points that are common to both cylinders.

Figure 22 is a normal view of the intersecting axes of two right cylinders. The intersection of the cylinders may be found in this view without the

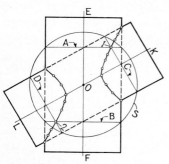

FIGURE 22. Intersection of two cylinders by sphere method.

aid of any other view. A sphere S, of any desired radius, is centered at the intersection O of the axes. This sphere cuts the circles A and B from the E F cylinder, and the circles C and D from the K L cylinder. Circles A and C intersect at point 1 on the near half of the cylinder, and at a point directly beyond 1 on the far half of the cylinder. Similarly, circles B and D intersect at 2, and at a point directly beyond it. The operation is repeated until enough points are found clearly to trace the intersection. The smallest useful cutting sphere has the same diameter as the larger cylinder. It locates the points nearest O. Four points on the extreme elements of the cylinders, in the plane of the axes, may be located immediately in the drawing.

18. Transition-elbow Design. Figure 23: The elbow here taken as an example connects two rectangular pipes that make a turn and also a twist, as is shown in the pictorial view. The right side of the elbow is plane-faced. Its shape is shown in the right-side view. The other surfaces of the elbow are planes and cylinders with elements either horizontal or vertical. The elbow is designed in the right-side and top views, and from these views the appearance of the curves in the front view may be determined. The only definite purpose that the front view serves is to show the shape of the vertical opening. The upper and lower surfaces of the elbow may be developed by considering these surfaces as right cylinders with bases in the profile plane face of the elbow. The left-hand surface of the elbow may be considered as a right cylinder having as a right section, or base, a horizontal curve shaped as shown in the top view. The upper and lower ends of the vertical elements of this cylinder are in the curves shown in the right-side view.

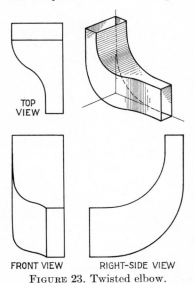

TOP VIEW

FRONT VIEW   RIGHT-SIDE VIEW

FIGURE 23. Twisted elbow.

19. Problems.

Group 63. Intersecting Cylinders.

20. Design for a Lamp Socket. The practical application of finding intersections often requires a thorough understanding of theoretical principles that are involved in determining intersections and in drawing the necessary views. This is illustrated in the design for a multiple lamp socket shown in Figure 24. The intersections are here necessary so that the actual appearance of the proposed design may be studied before the expense of manufacture is undertaken.

After the outline curves 2, 3, and 6 have been drawn, it becomes necessary to determine from these the edges 1, 4, and 5, and the curves of intersection of the right and left sockets with the middle socket. All the sockets are octagonal in cross section.

To find curves 4 and 5 of the C socket, through some chosen point F in the front view pass a plane perpendicular to the axis A C. This plane cuts from the socket the dotted octagon shown in the end view of the axis. E_x is one corner of this octagon. Its front view E, in the cutting plane, is one corner of the octagon. The location of E_1 is determined similarly. The locations of these two points should be checked with the dividers to make sure that they are equidistant from the axis. Other points on curves 4 and 5 should be located by passing other cutting planes. Points on curve 1 are found by passing horizontal cutting planes.

The curved surfaces bounded by the curves 1 and 2, 3 and 4, 4 and 5, and 5 and 6 are cylinders. In this explanation, these will be called cylinders 12, 34, 45, and 56. The first cylinder intersects the other three in

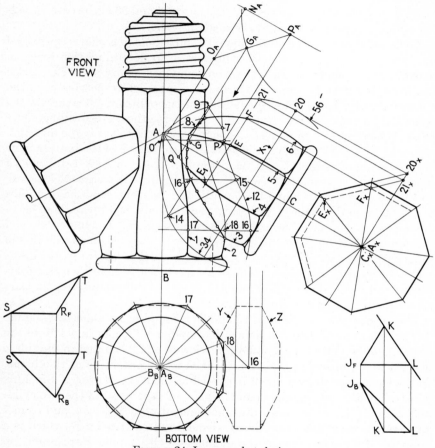

FIGURE 24. Lamp-socket design.

turn. The elements of cylinder 45 are frontal, while the elements of the other three cylinders make an angle of 45 degrees with the median plane A B C that passes through the axes of the sockets.

To find the intersections of the cylinders with inclined elements, it probably is best to pass cutting planes parallel to the elements of each pair of cylinders. As a preliminary to carrying out this plan it is advisable first to find the intersection of each cylinder with the median plane

A B C. This will provide a base for each cylinder in this one plane and will make easier the problem of passing cutting planes. Take the element from 17 to 18, for example. In the bottom view it meets the median plane at 16, and this point is then located on the same element in the front view. A series of points so found determines the curved line or base 12 in the front view. This is the base of cylinder 12 in the median plane. Similarly, from the end view of socket C, the bases 34 and 56 of the corresponding cylinders also are found in the median plane.

To find the intersection of cylinders 12 and 34, cutting planes are passed parallel to the elements of both cylinders. To determine the direction of these planes, choose the front and bottom views of any point R. Draw the front and bottom views of the line R S parallel, respectively, to the corresponding views of an element 17 18 of one cylinder. Then draw the front and bottom views of the line R T parallel to the corresponding views of an element of the cylinder 34. The front view of R T is in the direction of line 14 16. Its bottom view is parallel to the side Y of the bottom view of an octagon of socket C. In the plane R S T, the line S T is taken as a frontal line. All frontal lines of the cutting plane will be parallel to S T. In the front view draw a line 14 15 parallel to the front view of S T. This line is taken in the plane of the bases 12 and 34 and intersects these bases at points 14 and 15. Through 14 draw an element of cylinder 34, and through 15 draw an element of cylinder 12. These elements lie in the same cutting plane. They cross at point 16, which is a point on the intersection of the two cylinders. The process is repeated, and then the intersection is drawn. Owing to symmetry, a part of this intersection appears as a straight line in the front view.

The intersection of cylinders 12 and 56 is found in a similar way. Line J L is drawn parallel to the elements of cylinder 12, and line J K to the elements of cylinder 56. The bottom view of J K is parallel to the side Z of an octagon of socket C. K L is taken as a frontal line of this plane. In the front view draw a line 9 7 parallel to the front view of K L. Line 9 7 is a line of a cutting plane, and it intersects the bases of the two cylinders at 9 and 7. From 9 is drawn an element of cylinder 56, and from 7 an element of cylinder 12. These elements cross at point 8, which is a point on the intersection of the cylinders. Other points are found by repeating the process, and then this intersection is drawn.

The intersection of cylinders 12 and 45 may be found by taking an auxiliary view in the direction of the frontal elements of cylinder 45. This direction is indicated by the pointing arrow. $N_A P_A$ is the edge view of the median plane. The curve in this view is the same as curve 6, and represents the edge view of the curved face of cylinder 45. In the front view take any element P O of cylinder 12. Since this element has a 45-degree slope, the distance that O is in front of P is the same distance that

O is to the left of P. In the auxiliary view, $O_A N_A$ is made equal to this distance. All elements of cylinder 12 are parallel to $P_A O_A$ in this view, and the intersection of each element with the cylinder 45 is seen directly as at G_A in this view. From this, the front view of G is located. Other elements of cylinder 12 are drawn in this view and their intersections with

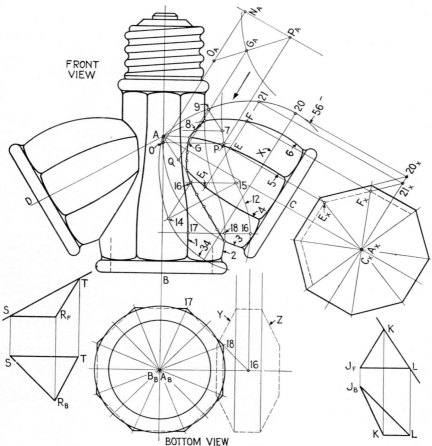

FIGURE 24. Lamp-socket design.

cylinder 45 determined. This completes the problem of finding the intersections of the three faces of socket C with the one face of socket B. On the left half of the front view is shown the intersection of two sockets without the confusion of the lines used in determining the intersection. The design now may be studied, and changes made as seem desirable.

21. Structures with Cylindrical Faces. A variety of structures, of which the cross sections are symmetrical polygons and of which the faces

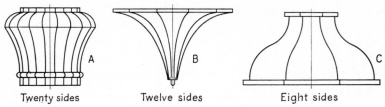

Twenty sides   Twelve sides   Eight sides

FIGURE 25. Structures having cylindrical faces.

or sides are cylinders, occur frequently in engineering designs. Examples of these are shown in Figure 25. Each object is designed first by drawing the right and left contour lines which also are edge views of two of the cylindrical faces. A number of polygonal sections are drawn in the end view, and the corners of each polygon are then located on its edge view. The curves drawn through each series of points represent the intersection of adjacent cylindrical faces of the structure. Points must be symmetrically disposed about the center line, otherwise the appearance of the drawing will not be satisfactory.

22. Problems.

Group 64. Cylindrical-faced Objects.

CONES

23. The cone is a single-curved surface in which the straight-line generatrix traverses a fixed point and intersects a curved directrix. The fixed point is the vertex, and the curved directrix is the base of the cone. All elements of the cone intersect at the vertex. Since the generatrix is a straight line, the cone is a ruled surface. Since all elements intersect, it is a single-curved surface and is developable. The generatrix may extend through the vertex, in which case two nappes of the cone are generated. The altitude of a cone is the perpendicular distance from the vertex to the plane of the base.

24. Types of Cones. In Figure 26 are shown three types of cones. The general type has for its directrix an open curve that may be either a

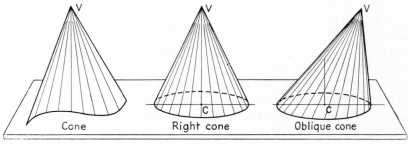

Cone   Right cone   Oblique cone

FIGURE 26. Cones.

single- or a double-curved line.   The ruled elements indicate successive positions of the generatrix.

The axis V C of the right cone is perpendicular to the plane of the circular base.   The axis of the oblique cone is not perpendicular to the plane of its base.   The right circular cone is also a cone of revolution, since it may be generated by revolving the generatrix about the axis.   The base of a right cone may be an ellipse or other symmetrical figure.

Right and oblique cones find frequent use in structures, as is illustrated throughout this chapter.   Figure 27 illustrates a few applications.   In the transition, the surface connecting the open ends of the pipe consists of four triangles and four oblique cones.

25. Development of a Right Circular Cone.
Figure 28: Visualize the development of the cone as if the surface were unrolled or unwrapped from the cone.   The elements of the right circular cone are equal in length and intersect at the vertex.   The development will be a sector of a circle having a radius equal to the length of the elements.   The arc of the development sector will be equal in length to the circumference of the base of the cone.

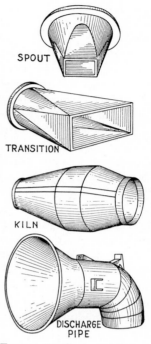

FIGURE 27. Conical objects.

Divide the circular base of the cone into any number of equal parts, not less than 12 or 16.   The true length of the elements, or slant height of the cone, is seen at V 4 in the front view.   Using this length as a radius, draw

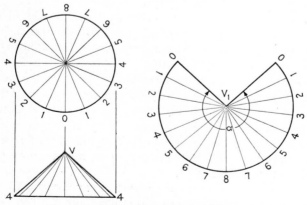

FIGURE 28. Development of a right cone.

a circle with center V_1 in any convenient location. On this circle, step off parts equal in length and number to the parts into which the base of the cone is divided. Care must be taken to obtain these distances accurately, since any error is multiplied in the development by the number of divisions taken. Complete the development by drawing the two radii V_1 0. The elements of the cone may be shown in the development. Care must be taken to see that there are as many equal parts in the development as there are in the base of the cone.

A fairly accurate development may be obtained by the method just described. If an accurate development is required, calculate the angle a of the development sector, and measure it on the development with an accurate protractor; or calculate the length of the chord. The angle a, in degrees, may be determined from the proportion:

$$\frac{a}{360} = \frac{2\pi r}{2\pi s} = \frac{r}{s},$$

in which r is the radius of the base of the cone, and s is the slant height of the cone.

The cone is formed from the development by bending the sheet material along the straight-line elements. Near the vertex, these elements are so close together that it is difficult to form this part of the cone. When possible in a design, this part is eliminated as is illustrated in Figure 5. If desired, a solid metal point may be substituted to provide a point for the cone.

26. Intersection of a Cone and a Plane. A plane will intersect a right circular cone in a point, two straight lines, a circle, an ellipse, a parabola, or a hyperbola. The ellipse, parabola, and hyperbola are called *conic sections*. Oblique cones with circular bases have similar plane sections. The intersection of a cone and a plane may be found by passing cutting planes, or by obtaining an edge view of the plane.

27. Development of a Truncated Cone. The right circular cone of Figure 29 is intersected by the vertical plane R shown in the top view. The truncated cone is the part of the cone that is included between the circular base and the elliptical section. The crosshatched section is a normal view of the ellipse. Before starting the development, it should be noted that this truncated cone is divided symmetrically by a horizontal plane through the vertex. The shortest line of the development is the element at the right of the cone. The development should be cut on this line. The middle line of the development is the line at the left of the cone. Since the development will be symmetrical, it should be started at the middle and developed both ways.

Divide the circular base into any number of equal parts, 16, for example, and number the parts in both directions from 8 to 0. Begin the development with the middle element V 8, and first develop the entire cone as shown at the right.

To develop the truncated cone, it is necessary to find the true distance

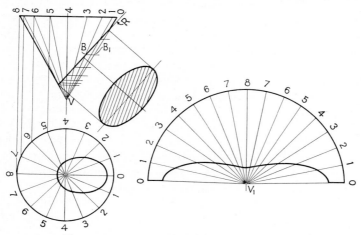

FIGURE 29. Development of a truncated cone.

from the vertex of the cone to the point of intersection of each element with the plane R.   This is done best in the top view by revolving the cone about its axis.   For example, re-volve the point B, on the element V 2, to B_1.   The true length of V B is $V B_1$.   In the top view find the true distance from V to the inter-section of the element V 8 with the plane R, and mark this distance on V_1 8 in the development.   Next, find in the top view the true length for V 7, and transfer this length to each of the elements V_1 7 in the development.   Take each pair of elements in turn.   Complete the solution by drawing the boundary of the development.   The ele-ments V_1 0 are not in a straight line.

28. Slip Joints.   When a cylin-drical pipe is to be made from several lengths with slip joints, it is necessary to make the sections conical so that the end of one section will slip inside or outside the end of the adjoining section.   Cylindrical sec-

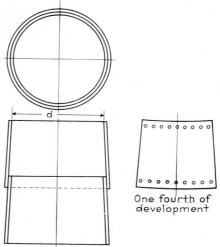

FIGURE 30. Slip joints.

tions of pipe of uniform diameter cannot be forced to telescope in this manner, unless the ends are enlarged or reduced. Conical sections are illustrated in Figure 30. One-fourth of the development of a conical section is shown. In developments of this kind it is generally best to calculate the slant height of the cone by means of a simple proportion.

29. Problems.

Group 65.   Development of Right Circular Cones.

Group 66.   Cone and Plane Intersections and Developments.

30. Tapered Elbows.

Uniformly tapered elbows find considerable use in engineering designs; for example, elbows for connecting two pipes of different diameters; spouts for discharging various materials; intake pipes for pumps to increase gradually the velocity of the water or air; exhaust pipes to decrease the velocity gradually; ship ventilators; and snail cases for turbines as illustrated in Figure 2.

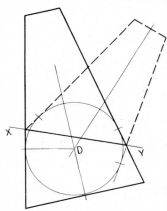

FIGURE 31. Two-piece tapered elbow.

The two-piece tapered elbow of Figure 31 illustrates the geometrical principles on which the design of tapered elbows is based. X Y is a plane section of a right cone. Since this section is a symmetrical ellipse, the part of the cone above X Y may be turned to the position indicated by broken lines, and in this position it will form a perfect joint with the lower part. The axes of the two parts will intersect at D, which point may be taken as the center of a sphere to which both parts of the tapered elbow are tangent. Tangent spheres are an aid in designing tapered elbows of more than two pieces.

Figure 32 illustrates the design of a uniformly tapered four-piece elbow. When the design is begun, only the size and location of the end circles centered at K and M are known. A freehand sketch may indicate to the designer that a four-piece elbow would be satisfactory.

The designer proceeds as follows: The axes K L and M L of the end circles are drawn. These intersect at L. The bisector L P of the angle K L M is then drawn. Some point P on this bisector is chosen as a suitable center for the curve of the bend, and the arc through E and F is drawn. The arc E F is divided into a number of equal parts. The number of these divisions is determined by observing that each end piece of the elbow requires one of the equal divisions, and each of the other pieces requires two of the equal divisions. For a four-piece elbow, the total number of divisions of the arc is six. The arc E F and the angle E P F are now divided into six equal parts.

Tangents K 1, 1 2, 2 3, and 3 M are drawn at alternate divisions of the arc. These tangents are the axes of the four conical sections of the elbow. The lengths of these tangents are now laid off along a straight line from K to M in Figure 33. The circles K and M are added, and these become the ends of the frustum of a right circular cone. Spheres centered at 1, 2, and 3 are drawn tangent to the cone; and spheres of corresponding size, each centered at its similarly numbered point, are drawn in Figure 32.

The following cones now are drawn in Figure 32: A cone having axis K 1 and tangent to the sphere centered at 1. As an aid in drawing accu-

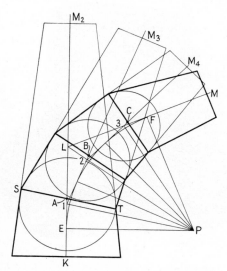

FIGURE 32. Four-piece tapered elbow.

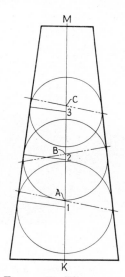

FIGURE 33. Elbow cone.

rately, the axis is extended to M_2 and the sides of the cone are drawn through the ends of the diameter of the larger circle centered at K, and of the smaller circle centered at M_2. Next, is drawn a cone having axis 1 2 and tangent to the spheres centered at 1 and 2. As an aid in drawing accurately, the axis of this cone is extended from 1 to M_3, which length is obtained from Figure 33. A third cone having axis 2 3 and tangent to the spheres centered at 2 and 3 is now drawn, with the aid of the axis extended to M_4. Lastly, a cone having axis 3 M tangent to the sphere centered at 3 is drawn.

In Figure 32 the edge view of the elliptical intersection of the first and second cones is now drawn by connecting the points S and T where the outside contour lines of the two cones meet. This straight, edge view should check as parallel to the radius P 1. The two remaining intersections through B and C are similarly drawn, and these should be parallel, respectively, to the radii P 2 and P 3.   This completes the design of this uniformly tapered elbow.

The developments of the four parts of the tapered elbow are determined from the right cone of Figure 33.   Here, the distances 1 A, 2 B, and 3 C are equal to the similarly lettered distances of the preceding figure.   The cuts, indicated by broken lines, make the same angles with the axis as they do in the design drawing.   As a final check, the straight contours of each conical part must be equal in the two figures.   This frustum is cut

FIGURE 34. Draft-tube liner for a large turbine.   (*Allis-Chalmers Mfg. Co.*)

apart in the planes A, B, and C, and then the four parts are assembled and welded to form the required four-piece tapered elbow.

Twisted elbows may be designed by imagining that one of the conical sections is cut apart around a circular section, and then one part is revolved on the other through any desired angle.   When the four parts are now assembled, a twisted tapered elbow will result.   It thus is possible to design tapered elbows for connecting any two given circular openings.

Accurate developments of the parts of a tapered elbow are readily made and checked when these are parts of a right cone; and work is saved, since each curve of the development serves as an edge of two parts.   Also, costs of manufacture are lowered when it is possible to cut one curved edge of two parts at a single cut.

The large draft tube shown in Figure 34, having the upper end circular and the larger opening rectangular with half-circular ends, may be regarded as a tapered elbow split into right and left halves.   These halves are spaced apart, and the area between is enclosed by plane sheets of steel. The designer must determine the development and the shape of each curved plate.

31. Problems.

Group 67.   Tapered Elbows.

32. Intersecting Cones.

The choice of the method to be used when finding the intersection of two cones depends upon the geometrical relations of the cones. The intersection of cones, right or oblique, generally may be found by passing cutting planes. Each plane should be passed so that it cuts either one circle or two straight lines from each of the two cones.

In Figure 35 the intersection of the two cones may be found by passing cutting planes parallel to the horizontal circular bases of the cones. Plane 4, for example, cuts a circle from each of the cones. In the top view these circles intersect at two points. The front views of these points are next located on the front views of the circles. The process is repeated until a sufficient number of points are found. The curve of intersection is then drawn, and the hidden parts of the cones are either dotted or erased.

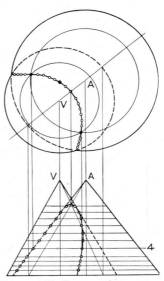

FIGURE 35. Intersecting cones.

The intersection of any two cones may be found by passing cutting planes that cut two lines from each cone. To do this, draw a line connecting the two vertices. A cutting plane passed through this line will cut two lines from each cone, and these lines will cross at four points. One or more of these points, however, may be outside the limits of the cones.

In Figure 36 the bases of the two intersecting cones do not lie in parallel planes. To find the intersection, first draw the line V A connecting the vertices. Any plane passed through this line, within certain limits, will cut two lines from each cone, and these lines will determine four points of the intersection. Extend the line V A until it meets the plane of the base of the horizontal cone at P, and the plane of the base of the vertical cone at H. The line P H coincides with the line V A. All cutting planes pass through this line. In the top view assume a horizontal line H K. This determines a cutting plane H K P. The line H K intersects the horizontal circular base of the vertical cone at 3 and 5. The elements V 3 and V 5 are cut from the vertical cone and may now be located in all views. Next, locate the points K and P in the side view, and draw the line K P. This line is a line of the same cutting plane H K P, and it intersects the circular base of the horizontal cone at 2 and 4.   The elements A 2 and A 4 are cut from the horizontal cone and may now be drawn in all views.   The two pairs of elements thus found intersect at four points that should be independently located in each view.   The accuracy of the locations of these points should be checked by means of rays connecting adjacent

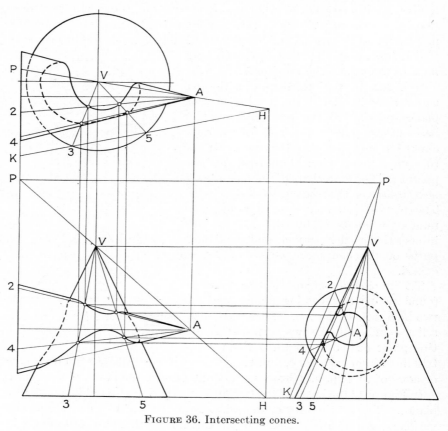

FIGURE 36. Intersecting cones.

views.   The above process is repeated until enough points are found, and then the curve of intersection is drawn.

Usually, the intersection of two cones may be found more quickly by passing cutting planes through the vertices, but it often is desirable to cut circles from the cones.   At times both methods are useful in a single problem.

33. If a sphere has its center on the axis of a right circular cone, the sphere will cut two circles from the cone.   When the axes of two right circular cones intersect, this point of intersection may be taken as the center of cutting spheres. Each cutting sphere will cut two circles from each cone. Each circle of one cone will intersect two, or one, or neither of the two circles of the other cone, and the number of points of intersection found for each cutting sphere will be eight, six, four, two, or zero. This is a rapid method when the conditions are as specified. The cutting spheres must be drawn in a view that is a normal view of the intersecting axes.

As an example take the two right cones of Figure 37. The frontal axes intersect at O in the front view. All cutting spheres are centered at O. A radius is chosen and a cutting sphere is drawn in the front view. This

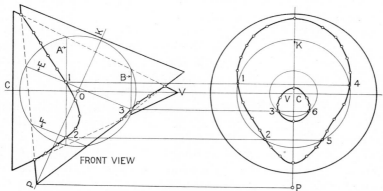

FIGURE 37. Intersection of right cones by sphere method.

sphere cuts from the V C cone the two circles A and B, and from the P K cone it cuts the two circles E and F. The circle E of one cone intersects the circles A and B of the other cone at points 1 and 3 on the front half of each cone, and at points 4 and 6 on the rear half. The circle F intersects the circle A at point 2 on the front half, and point 5 on the rear half. Circle F does not intersect circle B. Six points thus are found on the intersection of the two cones. More points are located by passing cutting spheres of different sizes. All are centered at O. The right-side view is an end view of the V C cone and shows the hole that must be cut into this cone to fit the P K cone. The top view of the two cones is not shown.

34. Problems.

Group 68. Intersecting Cones.

35. Cylinder and Cone Intersections.

Two general methods are available for finding the intersection of any cylinder and cone: Cutting planes may be passed through the vertex of the cone and parallel to the elements of the cylinder, or the intersection of the elements of the cone with the cylinder may be determined directly in a view that is an end view of the cylinder.

The first general method is similar to that explained in Article 16 for finding the intersection of two cylinders.   For finding the intersection of a cone and cylinder, each cutting plane is passed through a line that is drawn through the vertex of the cone and parallel to the elements of the cylinder.   Two lines are cut from each surface, and these intersect at four points.   The second general method is of practical use mainly when the

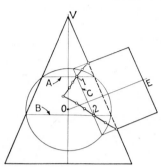

normal or edge view of the circular base of the cone is seen in the view that shows the end view of the cylinder.   This is illustrated in Chapter 8, Figure 8.   Cutting planes may be passed so as to cut circles from both surfaces only when the circular bases lie in parallel planes.

For the special case when the cone and cylinder are right circular with axes intersecting, the readiest method is to pass cutting spheres as illustrated in Figure 38.   The axes intersect at O.   The sphere, centered at O, cuts from the cylinder the circle C, and from the cone it cuts the circles A and B.   The

FIGURE 38. Intersection of a cylinder and a cone by sphere method.

latter circles intersect circle C at points 1 and 2 on the near half of the cone and cylinder, and at points directly behind these on the far half. The process is repeated until a sufficient number of points are found.

36. Problems.

Group 69.   Intersecting Cylinder and Cone.

37. Oblique Cones.   Since oblique cones are so frequently used in structures, it is advisable for the student of engineering to observe their various applications and to learn how to represent and develop them.

Figure 39 shows a tank car for transporting molten steel.   The ends of the tank are oblique cones, and the middle part is a cylinder.   The oblique cones here serve to lower the center of gravity.

Figure 40 is a photograph of a heavy welded-steel offset connection for

FIGURE 39. Hot-metal transfer car.   (*Koppers Company.*)

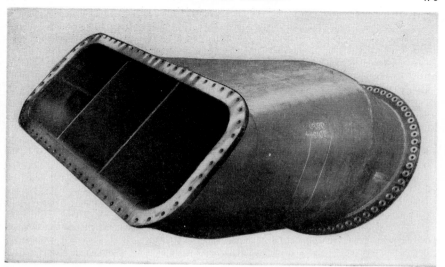

FIGURE 40. Welded-steel water connection for a large condenser. (*Allis-Chalmers Mfg. Co.*)

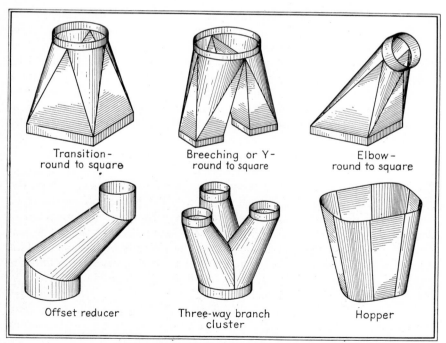

FIGURE 41. Oblique-cone transitions.

a large condenser.   One end of this transition is circular, and the other end is rectangular with rounded corners.   The surface is designed by combining planes, cylinders, and cones.

Figure 41 offers pictorial drawings of a variety of transitions in which oblique cones and parts of oblique cones are used.   Transitions similar to these find frequent use in many large and small structures.

38. A Common Type of Transition.   Figure 42 is an example of a transition designed for connecting a square opening with a round opening.

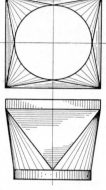

Since the transition is to be made from sheet metal, it must be designed so that it is composed of surfaces that may be developed; that is, plane and single-curved surfaces.   In the transition shown, there are four triangles and four oblique cones.   The vertex of each triangle is a point on the circle, and its base is one side of the square.   The vertex of each oblique cone is at one corner of the square, and its base is one-fourth of the circle.   In making the development for a transition piece, care should be taken not to reverse the developments of the triangle and the adjacent cone.   Short connecting collars are added to the ends of the transition.

FIGURE 42. Transition.

39. Development of an Oblique Cone.   The oblique cone frequently is used in sheet-metal work.

The elements of an oblique cone vary in length, so that the development will not be the sector of a circle.   The development of an oblique cone is shown in Figure 43.   To produce a symmetrical development, a plane should first be passed through the longest and shortest elements of the cone.   In the figure this is the vertical plane V 0 6.   It divides the cone symmetrically.   V 0 is the shortest element of the cone, and the development should be cut on this line.   The center line of the development should be the longest element V 6.   Beginning at 0, divide the base of the cone into twelve or more equal parts. These are numbered consecutively on one-half of the base.   Since the cone is symmetrically divided, the points on the other half need not be numbered.   The lengths of the elements may be found as explained in Chapter 8, Article 28.   In the top view of Figure 43 draw the arc A centered at C and having a radius equal to the altitude of the cone.   This arc and its center are in the plane of the base of the cone.   To find the length of any element V 1, draw the right-angled triangle V 1 1.   The distance from 1 to 1 is the true length of the element V 1.   It is necessary only to locate the third corner of each triangle on the arc A.   The sides and hypotenuse of the triangle need not be drawn.

To start the development, determine the true length of the longest element V 6, and draw this at V_1 6 in the development.   Next, set the compass to the true length of the element V 5; then center the compass at V_1 and draw two arcs at 5 and 5.   Set another compass to the constant distance 6 5, 5 4, etc., and retain this setting throughout the solution of the problem.   Center this compass at 6 in the development and draw arcs that cross the previously drawn arcs at 5 and 5.   In a similar manner locate each pair of points in turn.   Draw the two elements V_1 0, and complete the development by drawing a smooth symmetrical curve through the numbered points.   This curve should be perpendicular to the shortest element at 0.   Right cones having noncircular bases are developed in the same way that oblique cones are developed.

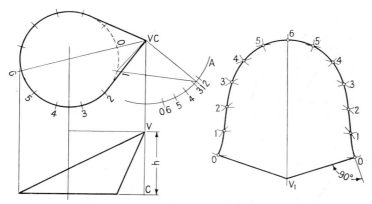

FIGURE 43. Oblique-cone development.

The length of the curved outline of the above development should be equal to the circumference of the base circle of the cone.   A ribbon of metal or paper may be bent around the curved outline to check its length, or a measuring wheel may be used.   Any error in setting the compass to the length of one spacing on the base is here multiplied by twelve in the development.   This compass setting is the length of chords of arcs having various radii in the development, and this introduces errors.   Also, sharp intersections of arcs are not wholly dependable for locating points.   Certain structures, aircraft for example, require exact fitting of parts; and inaccurate developments cannot be tolerated.

40. A second method for finding the lengths of the elements of an oblique cone is here explained in connection with the construction diagram of Figure 44.   The front and top views of the frustum of an oblique cone are shown at the left.   The cone should be divided symmetrically about a plane that passes through the vertex and the centers of the bases.   Each circle is here divided into 12 equal parts.

The length of any element of the cone, V 4 for example, is equal to the hypotenuse of a right-angled triangle of which one leg is equal to the altitude of the cone, and the other leg is equal to the horizontal distance K 4 which may be measured from K_T to 4 in the top view.

The true length of V 4 is found in diagram 1. Here, $V_1 K_1$ is equal to the altitude of the cone, and K_1 4 is equal to K_T 4 of the top view. The hypotenuse V_1 4 is the required true length. The true length of V 4' is the distance V_1 4' on the line V_1 4 in the diagram. The construction diagram is not a view of the cone.

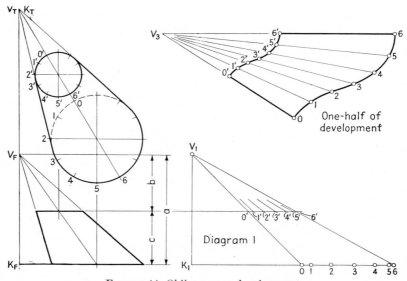

FIGURE 44. Oblique-cone development.

One-half of the development of the frustum is shown. The numbered points are located by using the method explained in the preceding article. Both curved contours of the development must meet the elements V 0 and V 6 at right angles. All chords of arcs, 4 5 and 4' 5' for example, must be parallel. Additional checks are described in the preceding article.

41. Problems.

Group 70. Development of Oblique Cones.

Group 71. Oblique-cone Transitions.

42. Noncylindrical and Nonconical Transitions. It is necessary to distinguish whether certain transitions having curved ends are cylindrical, or conical, or neither.

A, in Figure 45, is first taken as an oblique cone having as its base a circle centered at D, and its vertex at V. An inclined section of this cone taken at E is an ellipse. This may be proved analytically, or graphically, by finding the true shape of the section, as is here indicated by the broken

line.   The only circular sections of this cone are parallel to the base circle.
Two unequal circles determine a cone only if the circles lie in parallel
planes.

Next D and E are taken as the circular ends of a transition.   The surface of this transition cannot be a cone.   Only two straight lines of the
surface can be drawn through V to intersect the given circles.

At B in Figure 45 are shown circles of equal size lying in nonparallel
planes.   These two circles cannot here determine a cylinder, since the

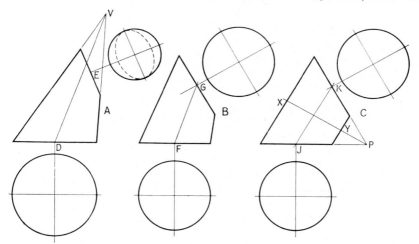

FIGURE 45. Transitions.   Cylindrical and conical.

contour elements are not parallel to the axis F G.   Nor, can this be a
cone, since the straight contour lines do not intersect the axis F G at the
same point.   There is, however, a special limited case: At C in the same
figure, two equal circles are centered at J and K, which points are here
equidistant from P where the planes of the circles intersect.   The elements are now parallel to the axis.   This cylinder may be considered as
the frustum of a right cylinder having the elliptical right section X Y as a
base.   Hence, this particular transition may be designed and developed
as a cylinder.   Two circles in nonparallel planes cannot be used as the
ends of either a cylindrical or a conical transition, with the exception of
the special case shown at C in Figure 45.

43. Development by Triangulation. Any curved surface may be
approximated by dividing the surface into triangles.   Since triangles are
planes, the triangles should be conceived not as lying on the curved surface, but rather as undercutting the curved surface.   The smaller the
size of the triangular divisions, the nearer will the actual surface be
approached.   In the development, adjacent triangles are joined.

Curved surfaces that are not single-curved often are developed by triangulation. But surfaces formed from triangulated developments generally will not be smoothly curved, *fair*, or *streamlined*. The formed surfaces likely will have the appearance of being divided into triangles.

Transitions designed and developed as convolutes have a smoother appearance than do those designed by triangulation. The convolute method is described in Articles 45 to 53.

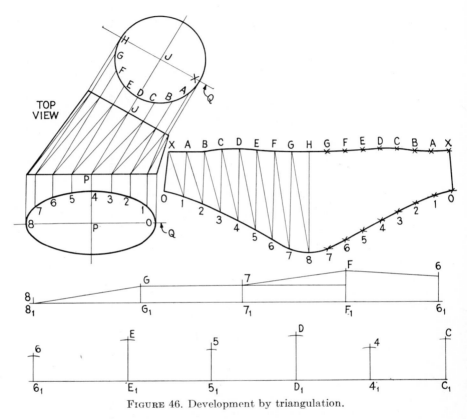

FIGURE 46. Development by triangulation.

The triangulation method is here explained. It should be understood by engineers, since it is much used by sheet-metal workers. Figure 46 shows a transition having a circular and an elliptical end. Unnamed surfaces of this type frequently are used in piping. This surface is neither a cylinder nor a cone.

The horizontal plane Q passing through the axis J P divides the transition symmetrically. The development should be cut on the shortest line X 0 of the surface. Divide the circle and the ellipse into the same number of equal parts. These may be numbered consecutively on the ellipse and lettered on the circle. The surface of the transition may now be divided into triangles, as shown in the top view.　Developing the transition consists in finding the true lengths of the sides of these triangles and in building up the development line by line.　The middle line of the development will be H 8.　Since it is horizontal, its true length is seen in the top view. Draw H 8 in the development.　Determine the true lengths of the lines H G and G 8, and draw the triangle H G 8 in the development.　A similar triangle is drawn on the other side of H 8.　Now, find the true lengths of the sides of the triangle G 8 7, and add one of these triangles to either side of the development.　In turn, find the true lengths of the sides of the triangles G F 7, F 7 6, etc., and add these triangles to either side of the development.　The completed development is shown in the figure.

The true lengths of the longer sides of the triangles may be found by means of the construction diagram shown below the development in Figure 46.　On a horizontal base line mark off in succession the lengths of the top views of the lines 8 G, G 7, 7 F, etc., as indicated at 8_1 G_1, G_1 7_1, 7_1 F_1, etc.　At each of these lettered points, draw a perpendicular to the base line, and on this perpendicular mark the distance that the point itself is above the median plane Q.　The true lengths of the lines may now be measured at 8 G, G 7, 7 F, etc., in the construction diagram.

Proof: The true length of 7 F in the diagram is the hypotenuse of a right triangle, of which one leg is equal in length to the top view of 7 F, and the other leg is equal to the distance that F is above 7.　In the diagram it is unnecessary to draw the true lengths.　These may be obtained from the lower diagram.　Time is saved in developing the transition piece by using three compasses: set one compass to the true length of the equal parts of the circle; set another compass to the true length of the equal parts of the ellipse; and use the third compass for determining the lengths of the longer sides of the triangle in the construction diagram.

44. Problems.

Group 72.　Developments by Triangulation.

CONVOLUTES

45.　Convolute surfaces are being used more and more in engineering structures.　Convolutes are smoothly curved and developable.　This surface is used as a covering for airplane fuselages and wings, seaplane pontons, automobile bodies, ships, piping, and transitions.　Convolutes should be understood by engineers, since they may be used to advantage in many designs.

When the design of a structure requires that the space between two curved ribs or openings is to be closed by bending some sheet or plate material to form a smoothly curved or *fair* surface, this surface must consist of cylinders, cones, or convolutes, or some combination of these.

Double-curved surfaces are also used for this purpose, but these usually are more expensive to manufacture than are single-curved surfaces.

Cylinders, cones, and convolutes are the three types of single-curved surfaces. All three may be developed. Cylinders have parallel straight-line elements. Those of the cone intersect at a point. In the convolute, two consecutive, but no three, elements intersect.

46. Geometry of the Convolute. Figure 47 shows two developments of a convolute, and also the convolutes that are formed by bending these developments along the straight-line elements.

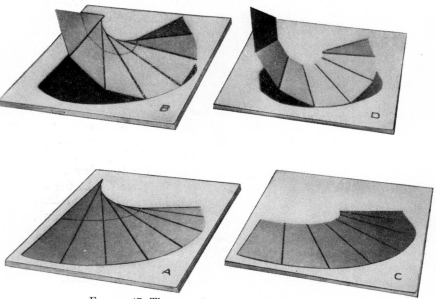

FIGURE 47. The convolute and its development.

The flat development of a convolute lying on a plane surface is shown at A. The theoretical distance between consecutive elements is here greatly exaggerated. At B is shown the curved convolute that is formed when development A is bent along the straight-line elements. Any two consecutive elements of the surface now intersect, but no three elements intersect.

At C, a part of the development is cut away. This illustrates a typical development for some actual engineering design. When this development is bent along the elements, the surface shown at D is formed. The end curves of this convolute are here clearly noticeable. These end curves are ordinarily determined by the requirements of the design of the structure. After any two curves of the surface are determined, the next problem is to locate the straight-line elements so that the enclosing sur-

face will be a smoothly curved convolute.   The geometry of the problem
is relatively simple.

At D in Figure 47, one elemental plane area of the convolute is in the
plane D.   When the two straight elements of the surface in plane D are
imagined to be an infinitesimal distance apart, plane D then becomes
tangent to the convolute along the entire length of an element.   The key
to locating individual elements of the convolute is to pass a plane tangent
to the surface and then to locate the line of tangency that determines one
element of the surface.   This operation is repeated until enough elements
are found fully to represent the surface.   The use of the convolute in
engineering structures and the methods of drawing and developing the
surface are explained in the following articles.

47. Fuselage or Transition.   When the end curves in any design lie in
parallel planes, the drawing for the convolute covering may be made as

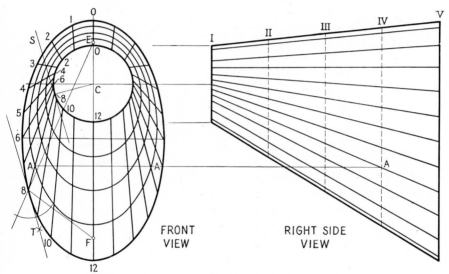

FIGURE 48. Convolute design of a fuselage or transition.

illustrated in Figure 48.   The front circle and the rear ellipse first are
determined by the requirements of the design.   A series of points is
located on the ellipse.   At point 8, for example, tangent T is drawn to
bisect the angle between the focal radii E 8 and F 8.   The radius C 8 of
the circle is then drawn perpendicular to the tangent T, and the tangent
S to the circle may be drawn perpendicular to the radius.   Tangents S
and T are parallel lines of a plane that is tangent to the convolute along
the line 8 8, and this line becomes an element of the convolute.   The
other numbered elements of the convolute surface are similarly found.
Tangents to the circle need not be drawn.

The shapes of intermediate curved ribs may be determined by first choosing their spacing in the side view, and then transferring the intersection of each element with the plane of the rib to the front view of the element, or better, by dividing the front view of each element proportionally. In the drawing the five ribs are equally spaced in the side view. In the front view, the intermediate ribs will pass through the quarter points of each element.

48. Development of the Convolute. Several methods are here described. The accurate development of the convolute on the drawing

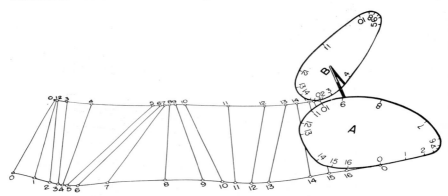

FIGURE 49. Development of a convolute.

board offers several difficulties. The four-sided area between closely spaced consecutive elements is a plane area that may be developed by triangulation. Each elemental area requires finding the true lengths of six lines. Extending two consecutive elements until they meet may often be an aid, except that these lines usually intersect at a sharp angle and their intersection cannot be located accurately. When all the elements of a convolute surface are extended, the envelope of these lines is a curve called the *edge of regression*. This curve is at times an aid in developing the surface.

A skeleton, or mockup, of any convolute surface may be constructed full scale by providing curved end and intermediate ribs formed to the shapes indicated in the design, or by providing straight-line members at the locations determined for the elements, or by providing both curved ribs and elements. A sheet of easily curved material may then be rolled over this skeleton, and the edges of the pattern and the locations of the elements or bending lines are then marked on the pattern.

Another method for obtaining an accurate development is to roll the end curves of the convolute on a plane, instead of curving the plane around the curves. Figure 49 shows thin sheet material cut to the form of the end curves. These camlike forms are fixed to a rod. When this assembly is rolled on a plane, the numbered points on curves A and B come into contact in turn with the correspondingly numbered points in the plane. In each position, the plane is tangent to both curves, and the straight line joining the points of tangency is an element of the convolute. The figure drawn on the plane becomes the development of the convolute surface of which A and B are the end curves. For any position of the rolling curves, the tangent points may be determined quite closely by using a light to cast a shadow of the curves onto the flat surface.

When thin sheet material is used to form the convolute surface, it will readily bend to form the surface. When thick material is used, the elements must be marked on the blank, and the material is curved by setting the bending rolls or brake to curve the material along the elements.

49. Convolute and Cone Transition. Figure 50 illustrates the need for frequently combining convolutes and cones in the design of transitions.

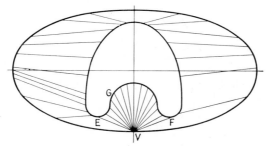

FIGURE 50. Convolute and cone transition.

The two given curved ends are in two parallel planes. If a tangent is drawn at G, there is no possibility of drawing a parallel tangent to the other curve in this area of the transition. The tangent at V on one curve is parallel to the common tangent at E and F on the other curve. The lines V E and V F are limiting edges of the convolute surface. The point V is taken as the vertex of an oblique cone of which the base is the reverse curve between the points E and F. The cone and the convolute form the enclosing walls of this transition.

50. Oblique Transition. Figure 51: The covering is to be designed as a convolute. The curved ends do not lie in parallel planes. The true shape of the ellipse is shown in a bottom view, and the circle is shown in an auxiliary view.

The straight-line intersection of the two planes of these curves is a horizontal line of which the end view is seen at P. The bottom view of this line is $P_B K_B$, and its auxiliary view is $P_A K_A$. The ellipse is divided into a number of approximately equal parts. A tangent to the ellipse is drawn at 2, for example. This tangent intersects P K_B at T_B, a distance *t* rearward of the point Q.   T_A is now located the same distance rearward of Q in the auxiliary view.   From T_A a line is drawn tangent to the circle, and the point of tangency is located at B.   The two tangents determine a plane tangent to the surface, and the line 2 B in the front view is an element of the convolute surface.   Note that 2 and B must both be located on the front half of the surface.   Additional elements now are located.

The solution of this problem may be somewhat simplified by drawing the auxiliary view of the ellipse, in the same view with the circle.   The

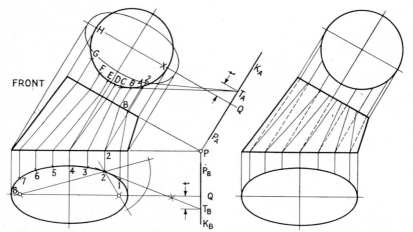

FIGURE 51. Transition.   Convolute design.   FIGURE 52. Comparison of convolute and triangulation design.

tangent to this ellipse at 2 is extended to T_A, and from this latter point a tangent to the circle is drawn.   B is the point of tangency, and B 2 is an element.

Figure 52 offers a comparison of the results of designing the oblique transition as a convolute and again by triangulation.   The solid lines are elements of a convolute, while the broken lines are the straight lines determined by triangulation.   The two methods give decidedly different locations for straight lines of the surface.   The convolute design ensures a smoothly curved surface, while the triangulated design will show kinks in the formed surface.

Figure 53 shows a photograph of a typical convolute transition of which the end curves are in nonparallel planes.   Elements of the convolute are represented by wires.   Some of the pairs of adjacent elements intersect at a considerable distance beyond the larger end of the transition, and other pairs intersect far beyond the smaller end.   Theoretically, the double-curved line along which adjacent elements intersect is useful in

drawing the development. Practically, this curve of regression is generally of little value, since it frequently is an exceedingly irregular curve.
The development of the transition may be drawn by finding the true
lengths of the four sides and of the two diagonals of each quadrilateral
area between each pair of adjacent elements, but this requires finding the
true lengths of 80 lines for the 16-
element model. Likely a better
method would be to make a model
of the two curves, fixed together in
their proper relation, and then obtain the development either by
rolling the curves on a plane or by
curving sheet material around the
model.

**51. Fuselage or Ponton Cover-
ing.** Figure 54 illustrates the
method of designing a convolute
covering when the end curves or
ribs are in nonparallel planes. For
the upper part of the body, the
given curves are the vertical curve
S R A and the horizontal curve P C
on one side, and a similar curve P G
on the other side. The lower part
is divided into two similar right and
left halves. The given curves for
the right lower half are the vertical
curve K D and the horizontal curve
P C. The body will come to a
point at P. The problem is to
design a smoothly curved surface
to fit the given curves. The sur-

FIGURE 53. Model of a convolute transition.

face is to be developable so that it may be formed from sheet material by
bending, but not stretching, the material. In addition, the shapes of
intermediate ribs are to be determined. The general plan for designing
this convolute covering is to determine elements of the surface by drawing
planes tangent to the surface.

To locate an element, take any point A on the curve R A. The tangent
A B to this curve is one line of a plane that is tangent to the required sur-
face. The point B is taken in the plane of the other given curve, P C.
From B is drawn a tangent to this curve. C is the point of tangency.
The plane A B C now is tangent to the required surface. Note this plane
in the pictorial insert, and in the front and top views. A and C are points

of tangency and, since the plane must be tangent along an element, the straight line A C becomes an element of the surface. It is drawn in both views. Other elements of the convolute are found by repeating this process, and a number of elements of the surface are drawn. The tangent at P in the top view is P Q. The corresponding tangent in the front view is Q R. The element P R is a limiting element of the convolute surface. The surface P R S is an oblique cone.

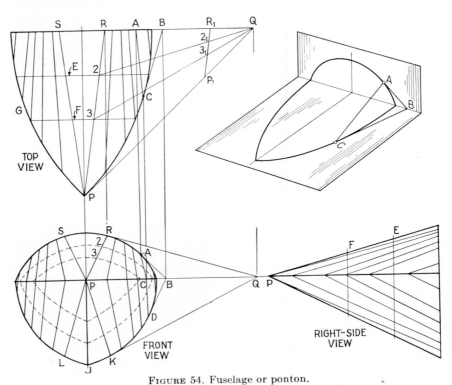

FIGURE 54. Fuselage or ponton.

On the bottom half a similar method is used. B C D is a tangent plane of the surface, and C D is the element of tangency. The plane P Q K determines the limiting element of the convolute. The surface P K L is an oblique cone.

One of the problems in designing structures of this type is to determine the shapes of intermediate ribs or supports so that a smoothly curved surface will fit all of them. The elements of this surface have just been found. The ribs may be located at E and F in the top view, and the intersections of the elements with the ribs carried to the front view. Since the rays intersect the ribs at a very sharp angle in the front view, it is better either to draw the side view of the surface and to carry the points of intersection of the ribs and elements from the side view to the front view, or to determine the front views of the points as follows: In the top view, an element of the convolute, P R for example, intersects the rib planes at 2 and 3. The element is thus divided into three parts, each of which has a certain proportion to the whole. In the top view of the triangle P R Q draw a line $P_1 R_1$ parallel to the top view of P R, but equal in length to the front view of P R. The lines Q 2 and Q 3 will divide P_1 R_1 into its proper proportions. From this the front views of 2 and 3 may be located. The broken lines in the front view indicate the shapes that must be given to the ribs so as to support the convolute surface.

The development of this surface might be undertaken by determining the shape of each quadrilateral that is bounded by adjacent elements, and assembling these on a flat sheet. Another way that is possible in some cases is to extend adjacent elements until they meet and then to develop the corresponding triangles side by side. A practical way in the shop is to set up all the ribs and end curves and then to curve a sheet of metal or other material to fit these supports. The necessary shape for the pattern can then be scribed on the sheet metal.

52. Helical Convolute. Three helical convolutes are shown in the photograph, Figure 55. The straight-line elements of each convolute are

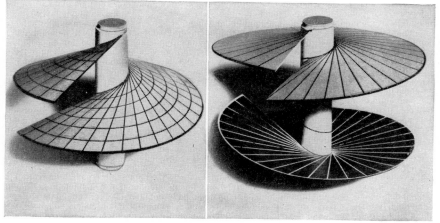

FIGURE 55. Helical convolutes.

tangent to a helix. The helix at the left has a lead twice that of the helices at the right. Right-hand and left-hand convolutes are shown at the right. The helical convolute is used in conveyers, augers, and pumps. The helical convolute is developable. It should not be confused with the helicoid, a warped surface, which is described in the next chapter.

Figure 56 shows a pictorial drawing of a helical convolute. The straight-line elements tangent to the helix are shown extending in both directions from the point of tangency, thus forming two nappes, or sheets of the convolute. Each part may be developed if the two are separated along the line of the helix. Each spiral-shaped curve represents the intersection of the convolute with a plane perpendicular to the axis of the helix. This curve is an involute of the circular base of the cylinder of the helix.

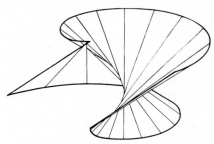

FIGURE 56. Helical convolute.

The front and top views, and the development of a helical convolute, are shown in Figure 57. One turn of the helix on the cylinder is taken as the directrix. The generatrix is here taken as a straight line of limited length. Its upper end is tangent to the helical directrix, and its lower end will trace another helix larger in diameter.

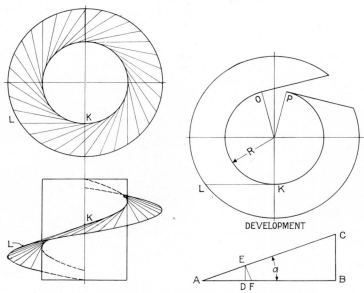

FIGURE 57. Helical convolute and its development.

To draw the helical convolute, first choose and draw the helical directrix. Next draw the element K L. It is tangent to the helix at its front point. The direction for drawing K L is determined from the triangle A B C. The side A B is made equal to one-half of the circumference of the cylinder on which the helical generatrix is wound. The side B C is made equal to one-half of the lead of the helix. The hypotenuse A C shows the slope and the half length of the helix. All lines tangent to the helix will have the same slope. In the front view, draw K L parallel to A C. In the top view, draw K L tangent to the circular top view of the helix. The length of K L may be chosen as desired. The point L will trace another helix of the diameter indicated in the top view, and the lead of this helix will be the same as the lead of the helical generatrix. In the top view, beginning at K and L, divide the circular view of each of the two helices into the same number of equal parts. Transfer these division points to the respective helices in the front view. Straight lines joining corresponding points will be elements of the convolute. The intersection of the convolute with a plane perpendicular to the axis is an involute. Why is this so?

53. Development of the Helical Convolute. The development of the convolute may be visualized by imagining that the convolute, as shown in the front view, is pressed downward until it lies in a flat plane. Since the curvature of the helix is constant, the helix will become a circular arc in the development. The radius of curvature R of a helix is equal to $\dfrac{r}{\cos^2 a}$, in which r is the radius of the cylinder of the helix, and a is the angle of slope of the helix. The formula is developed by the aid of calculus. The radius of curvature may be calculated from the formula just given, or the formula may be solved graphically as follows: In the triangle A B C, Figure 57, make A D equal to r. Draw D E perpendicular to A B, and then draw E F perpendicular to A C. The distance A F is equal to the radius of curvature R of the helix. Prove that the distance

$$\text{A F} = \frac{r}{\cos^2 a}.$$

In the development draw a circle of radius R. At K draw a tangent to this circle, and make K L equal in length to the front view of this line. Draw the outside circle through L. Make the arcs K P and K O each equal in length to the straight line A C. The length of the arc O K P is now the same as the length of the helical directrix. At P and O draw tangents to the inner circle. The completed development represents one turn, or flight, of the convolute. The ring of the development might be cut radially instead of tangentially at the points O and P, but the radial cuts will be slightly curved when the convolute is formed from the development.

54. Problems.

Group 73. Convolute Surfaces.

Chapter 10
WARPED SURFACES

HYPERBOLIC PARABOLOID—CONOID—HELICOID—
HYPERBOLOID OF REVOLUTION—CYLINDROID—WARPED CONE

1. A warped surface is a ruled surface in which the consecutive straight-line elements do not intersect. In surfaces of this type, the motion of the straight-line generatrix usually is determined by two curved- or straight-line directrices and a plane director. The generatrix intersects the directrices and remains parallel to the plane director. If the surface has three linear directrices, no plane director is required.

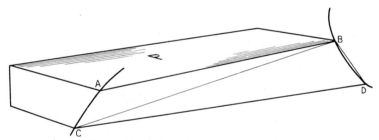

FIGURE 1. Elements of a warped surface.

Figure 1 illustrates two consecutive elements A B and C D of a typical warped surface. The elements are straight lines that do not intersect. In the illustration, the lines A C and B D are curved-line directrices of the surface, and a plane P is the plane director. The two elements intersect the directrices and are parallel to the plane director. Either one or both of the directrices may be straight.

Only the most commonly used warped surfaces are described in this chapter. These are the hyperbolic paraboloid, the conoid, the helicoid, the hyperboloid of revolution, the cylindroid, and the warped cone. All these surfaces have definite uses and are relatively easy to construct if the geometry of the surfaces is understood. They could, to advantage, be used more generally.

2. Warped Surfaces Not Developable. A warped surface cannot be developed. Such a surface, however, may be approximated by triangulation, and the approximate form may be developed.

The typical warped surface, shown in Figure 1, cannot be developed or unrolled into a plane, because the consecutive elements A B and C D do not intersect. The straight line B C does not lie in the warped surface even when the directrices are straight lines, but it is not very far from the surface. Hence, the triangles A B C and B C D approximate the surface, and this approximate surface may be developed by triangulation. If B C were a line of the surface, the surface would then be single-curved.

HYPERBOLIC PARABOLOIDS

3. The hyperbolic paraboloid is a warped surface having two straight-line directrices and a plane director. Since the surface is warped, it is a ruled surface and the generatrix is a straight line.

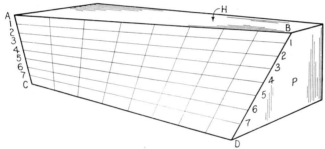

FIGURE 2. A hyperbolic paraboloid.

This surface is illustrated in Figure 2. A C and B D are the straight-line directrices, and H is the plane director. A B and C D are elements of the surface. Other elements are shown parallel to the plane director. The hyperbolic paraboloid may be doubly ruled. The elements A B and C D of the first generation may be taken as directrices of the surface. The plane P, parallel to the directrices A C and B D of the first generation, becomes the plane director of the second generation. Other elements parallel to the plane P are shown. The elements of both generations form the same surface. Plane sections of the surface are straight lines, hyperbolas, and parabolas.

4. To Draw the Hyperbolic Paraboloid. Figure 2: The problem may be stated as follows: A C and B D are the directrices of a hyperbolic paraboloid. A B and C D are two elements of the surface. Draw the front, top, and left-side views. The plan of drawing various elements of the surface is based on the fact that, if planes parallel to the plane director are passed through the surface, these planes will divide the directrices into proportional parts, and equally spaced planes will divide each directrix into equal parts.

First locate the views of the directrices, and then divide each directrix into the same number of equal parts.   Draw the element A B, and then, in turn, draw the elements connecting consecutive points on the two directrices.   Time is saved by numbering the division points of each directrix consecutively from A and from B, in the different views.   Each straight-line element is then drawn through the two points that have the same number.

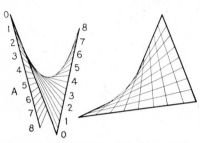

FIGURE 3. Doubly-ruled hyperbolic paraboloids.

The surface may be doubly ruled by dividing the elements A B and C D— which are now taken as the directrices of the second generation—into the same number of equal parts, and then connecting the corresponding points by straight lines.   It is not necessary to divide both pairs of directrices into the same number of equal parts, but the two directrices of a single generation must have the same number of divisions.   Pictorial views of doubly ruled hyperbolic paraboloids are shown in Figure 3.

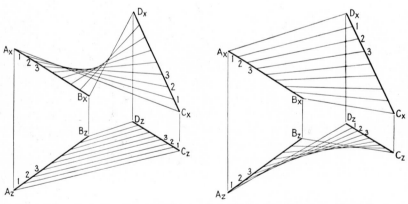

FIGURE 4. Two hyperbolic paraboloids having the same directrices.

Figure 4 illustrates the possibility of obtaining two entirely different hyperbolic paraboloids when two directrices are given.   At the left, A B and C D are the directrices and A C and B D are elements of the surface. Each directrix is here divided into eight equal parts.   At the right, the same directrices A B and C D are given, but A D and B C are taken as elements.   The two surfaces are entirely different.   It may also be noted that the boundary lines of the surfaces are the respective quadrilaterals A B D C and A B C D. The plane directors are not shown. For the surface at the left, the plane director is parallel to the elements, and it may be found by locating the plane parallel to the elements A C and B D. For the surface at the right, the plane director would be parallel to the elements A D and B C. Both surfaces may be doubly ruled.

5. Uses of the Hyperbolic Paraboloid.

The fact that this surface may be doubly ruled makes it possible to construct strongly braced curved surfaces of straight cross timbers, as in a roof or in a form for concrete. The timbers follow the directions of the elements of each generation. The surface

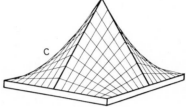

FIGURE 5. A warped roof.

is used for the wing walls of dams, for abutments, bridge piers, roofs, bows of ships, pilots of locomotives, and forms for concrete. Figure 5 shows a roof, and Figure 8 an abutment, or pier, of which the surfaces are doubly ruled hyperbolic paraboloids.

Figure 6 is a photograph of a proposed roof for a residence. Two hyperbolic paraboloids are joined to form the roof. The roof surface is built up of two crossed layers of thin plywood sheets cemented and nailed

FIGURE 6. A design project for a roof. (*By Professors Donald Dean and Willard Strode, University of Kansas.*)

together. And the sheets also are cemented and nailed to the rafters, thus forming an unusually stiff structural unit. Only seven rafters are required. The entire roof is supported on three piers. The three top points of the roof require no support. This model is on the campus of the University of Kansas.

Figure 7 shows the layout of the seven rafters. For the left half of the roof, the rafters 1 2, 2 5, 5 6, and 6 1 are the straight-line directrices of one of the hyperbolic paraboloids. The straight-line edges of the rectangular plywood sheets may be considered as straight-line elements of the doubly ruled surface. Note that the plan view of the roof is rectangular.

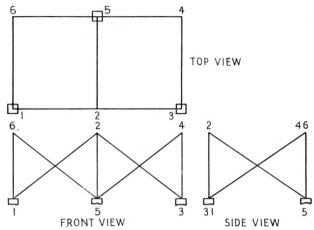

FIGURE 7. Rafters and supports of the roof.

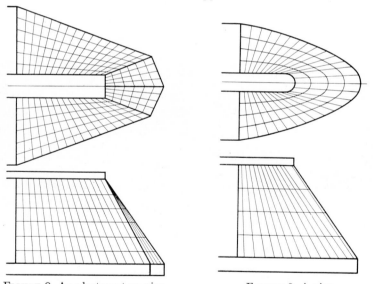

FIGURE 8. An abutment or pier.   FIGURE 9. A pier.

Figures 9 and 10 illustrate some uses of warped surfaces of a general type having one or both directrices curved. These cannot be doubly ruled. In one roof of Figure 10 the horizontal sections are equilateral triangles, and in the other roof the horizontal sections are squares. Each roof has a horizontal plane director.

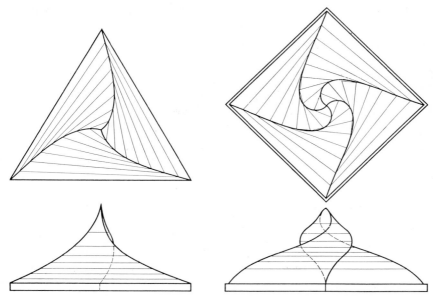

FIGURE 10. Curved roofs having warped surfaces.

6. Problems.

Group 74.   Hyperbolic Paraboloids.

CONOIDS

7. The conoid is a warped surface having a straight-line directrix, a curved directrix, and a plane director.   Since it is a ruled surface, the generatrix is a straight line.   The surface is warped and cannot be developed except approximately by triangulation.

8. Right and Oblique Conoids.   In the right conoid the straight-line directrix is perpendicular to the plane director.   The common form of a right conoid is illustrated in Figure 11.   The elements of the surface are

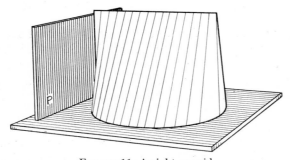

FIGURE 11. A right conoid.

parallel to the plane director P and intersect the straight-line directrix and the circular directrix. The surface cannot be doubly ruled. Plane sections parallel to the circular base are ellipses. An oblique conoid is shown in Figure 12. The straight-line directrix is not perpendicular to the plane director T.

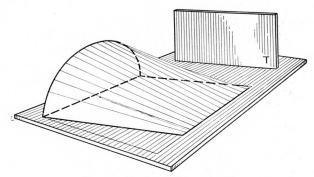

FIGURE 12. An oblique conoid.

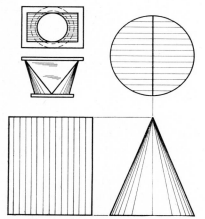

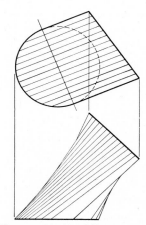

FIGURE 13. A right conoid.   FIGURE 14. An oblique conoid.

The front, top, and left-side views of a right conoid are shown in Figure 13. Since all the elements are frontal, the plane director is frontal. The equally spaced elements are drawn in the top view and then in the front and side views. Inserted in the figure are the front and top views of a cast-iron pipe connection. The surfaces of this casting are conoidal and triangular.

The front and top views of an oblique conoid are shown in Figure 14. The elements of the surface appear parallel in the top view; hence the plane director must be a vertical plane parallel to these elements. The elements themselves are not parallel, as is shown by the twisted appearance of the oblique conoid in the front view.

9. Uses of the Conoid. The conoid is used for connecting a flat surface with a curved surface, for example, when connecting a flat veiling or wall with an arch, or when changing the cross section of a flume or pipe from rectangular to circular. The conoid also is used as a pilot on the rounded ends of some railway cars. The surface cannot be doubly ruled. Transition pieces that are to be made by curving sheet material should not

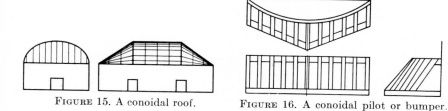

FIGURE 15. A conoidal roof.   FIGURE 16. A conoidal pilot or bumper.

be designed as conoidal surfaces, since the surface cannot be developed. Figures 15 and 16 illustrate two applications of the conoid.

10. Problems.

Group 75. Conoids.

HELICOIDS

11. The helicoid is a warped surface having a helical directrix, a straight-line directrix, and a plane or a cone director. It may be cisualized as a surface that is generated by a moving straight line, which intersects a helix and its axis, and keeps a constant angle with the axis. If the generatrix remains perpendicular to the axis, a right helicoid is generated; this is the surface of a square-threaded screw. If the generatrix makes a constant oblique angle with the axis, an oblique helicoid is generated; this is the surface of a screw having V-threads. The right helicoid has a plane director; the oblique helicoid, a cone director. The generatrix may not intersect the axis of the helix, but this type of helicoid is unusual. The surface of the helicoid is warped; hence, it is not developable except by approximation. It cannot be doubly ruled.

The helicoid may also be visualized as generated by a straight line that intersects an axis at a fixed angle, that rotates around the axis and at the same time moves along the axis at a uniform rate. It is an inclined plane, or wedge, curved around an axis.

12. Representing the Helicoid. One flight, or turn, of a right helicoid is shown in Figure 17. The elements are perpendicular to the axis and intersect the helix and its axis.   The surface is here represented as a right-hand right helicoid with the elements ruled on the upper side of the surface.   In the top view the elements are spaced at equal angles around the axis; in the front view they are spaced at equal distances measured parallel to the axis.   The lead of a helix is the distance traveled in one turn, measured parallel to the axis.   The lead of the helix in the front view is divided into the same number of equal parts as is one turn of the helix in the top view.   The leads of all helices of a helicoid are the same; but their

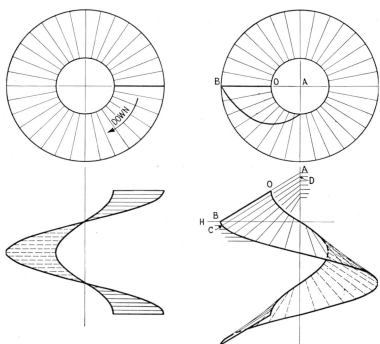

FIGURE 17. A right helicoid.   FIGURE 18. An oblique helicoid.

diameters are different, and the helix of smaller diameter has a steeper slope than the one of larger diameter.

An oblique helicoid is shown in Figure 18.   The elements intersect the axis at a constant oblique angle.   The surface is here represented as one flight of a left-hand oblique helicoid with the elements ruled on the upper side of the surface.   In the top view the elements are shown equally spaced around the axis.   As the generatrix revolves around the axis and at the same time moves parallel to the axis, each point of the generatrix traces a helix.   All of these helices have the same lead.

To draw the oblique helicoid of Figure 18, the limiting helices should first be shown in the top view, and the equally spaced radial elements drawn.   The larger helix, of the required lead or pitch, should now be plotted and drawn in the front view.   One of the normal elements, A B, may now be drawn.   The given angle that it makes with the axis is seen at A in the front view.   As the generatrix A B moves, the point O traces the smaller helix.   This helix has the same lead as has the larger helix. A B is the first element of the surface.   As the lower end B is rotated and lowered to the next position C on the helix, the upper end A is simultaneously lowered an equal vertical distance to D on the axis.   The vertical distance A D is equal to the difference in level between B and C.   The other elements are drawn in a similar fashion.   The intersection of the oblique helicoid with a plane H that is perpendicular to the axis is an Archimedean spiral.   This intersection is at times useful in drawing or representing the surface.

13. Uses of the Helicoid.   The helicoid is used more frequently than any other warped surface.   It is the surface of screw threads, of "spiral"

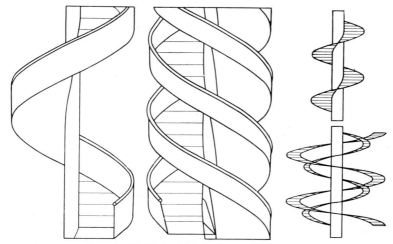

FIGURE 19. Helicoidal chutes and conveyers.

springs of square cross section, of screw propellers, of "spiral" chutes, of screw conveyers, of helical cams.

Since the surface may be approximated and developed by triangulation, it is useful in designing pipe bends and transitions that are to be built from sheet metal.   Attention is here called to the convolute, a single-curved surface that also is known as the "developable helicoid."   It is described in the chapter on Single-curved Surfaces.

Helicoidal chutes and conveyers are illustrated in Figure 19.   Chutes are used for conveying material from one level to a lower level by the force of gravity.   At the left, a single right-hand chute is shown.   To the right of this is a double left-hand chute that is used for delivery to different levels. The screw conveyers, illustrated at the right, are set in a trough and turned by power for forcing material along the trough. The lower ribbon conveyer consists of a right-hand helicoid and a left-hand helicoid mounted on the same shaft. It mixes the materials as they are being conveyed.

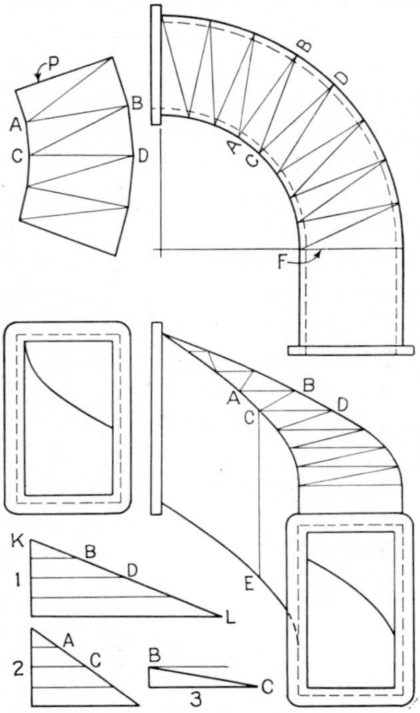

14. Rectangular Ducts. The refinement of processes for welding heavy plate, as well as the use of older methods of joining sheet metal, offers possibilities in the design of special structures. Figure 20 illustrates a design for an exhaust-pipe connection of uniform rectangular cross section. The connection starts at one level, rises at a uniform rate to a higher level, and then continues to rise at the same rate while making a 90-degree turn. This connection is designed to be made from steel plates welded together. If the bend is to carry pressure or a high vacuum, ribs are welded to the outside surface to give added strength. The edges of the bend are helices, the upper and lower surfaces are right helicoids, and the vertical surfaces are cylinders. The part of the connection forward of the line F is designed as

FIGURE 20. An exhaust connection.

an oblique prism, the edges of which have the same slope as the outer helix. Near the inner end of line F, there is a slight bend.

After the pipe connection is designed in the front, top, and side views, equally spaced elements are drawn on the upper helicoid. A B and C D are two of these elements. The surface of the helicoid is thus divided into approximately plane areas of equal size and shape. The development of one-half of the upper helicoidal surface is shown at P. The area A B C D is divided into two triangles. The equal lengths of A B and C D are obtained directly from the top view, since they are horizontal lines. The distance from B to D may be determined accurately by developing the helix. This is done in diagram 1. The horizontal base of this diagram is equal in length to one-half of the 90-degree circular arc through the top view of B D. The vertical line of diagram 1 is equal to one-half of the rise of the 90-degree bend. B D is the slope of the helix with the horizontal, and the true length of B D is here shown.   This length is used in the development.

Diagram 2 gives the slope of the inner helix and shows the true length of A C which may be used in drawing the development.   The length of diagonal B C may be found from diagram 3.   Here, the horizontal line is equal in length to the top view of B C, the vertical line is the difference in level between B and C, and the hypotenuse is the true length of B C. This last is used in drawing the development.   One trapezoidal area of the development is now completed.   Three similar areas are added, and this completes the development of one-half of the upper helicoidal surface. The lower helicoidal surface is the same shape as the upper one.

The vertical faces of the bend are cylinders.   Each will require its own development.   The development of the cylinder of larger radius will be a parallelogram.   The vertical sides will be equal in length to the line C E in the front view.   The sloping sides of the parallelogram will have the slope of the line B D of diagram 1, and the lengths of these sides will be twice the length of K L.   To the development of the cylinder must be added its continuation as a plane surface to the front end of the bend. The entire development of this outside face will be a parallelogram.   The development of the inner cylinder is another parallelogram of which the sloping lines will have the slope of A C in diagram 2.   To this is added the inner plane face of the front end.   It is a parallelogram having a slope equal to that of K L.   The angle, where the sloping lines meet, may be faired with a curve.

15. Problems.

Group 76.   Helicoids.

16. Screws and Springs.

These are such common articles that there is no need to describe their uses.   We are here primarily concerned with visualizing them accurately and also with representing them accurately in drawings, whenever an exact drawing is needed.   Conventional methods of representing screws are illustrated in engineering drawing textbooks.

The threads of screws are of different shapes, depending upon the use to which the screw is to be put.   Threads are normally made right-handed, but the requirements of design at times make it necessary to use a left-hand thread.   Threads may be single or multiple; that is, one or more threads may be cut in a cylinder.   Single threads are used when a screw is to act as a fastening or when the screw is to exert great pressure. Multiple-threaded screws are used for increasing the travel per turn and for power-transmission purposes.   The *lead* of a thread, or screw, is the travel in one turn.

The screw shown in Figure 21 has a right-handed, single, sharp V-thread. The angle of the V is 60 degrees.   The surfaces of the thread are oblique helicoids.   The curved edges that limit the surfaces are helices.   The

screw is represented by drawing these helices and the profiles of the
V-thread.   Threads are shown conventionally by drawing the helices as
straight lines, eliminating the V-profile, and showing the outline of the
cylinder.

A left-hand, single, square-threaded screw is shown in Figure 22.   The
thread is drawn by showing the visible parts of the four helices.   These

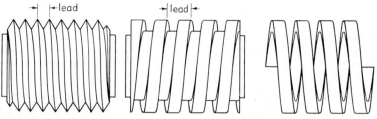

FIGURE 21. A right-   FIGURE 22. A left-hand,   FIGURE 23. A spring,
hand, single, V-thread.   single, square thread.   wound right-handed.

may be considered as being traced by the four corners of a square.   The
working surfaces of the thread are right helicoids.   The lead of the thread
is indicated.   The size of the square is one-half the lead.

A right-hand spring made from square stock is shown in Figure 23.   It
is a square thread with the cylindrical core removed.   It may be made by
winding a square metal wire around a cylinder.   Other methods of manufacture also are used.   The surfaces bounding the spring are cylinders and
right helicoids.   Springs made from round stock are double-curved
surfaces.

17. Multiple Threads.   The possibility of cutting more than one
thread on a cylinder is illustrated in Figure 24.   The lead of the left-hand

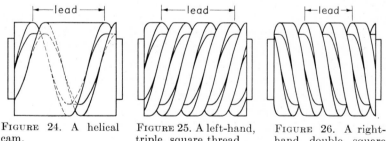

FIGURE 24. A helical   FIGURE 25. A left-hand,   FIGURE 26. A right-
cam.   triple, square thread.   hand, double, square
                                                     thread.

square helical groove is here taken as six times the width of the groove.
Two other similar, equally spaced, left-hand, helical grooves could be cut
in the cylinder between the turns of the first groove.   When this is done,
the left-hand, triple, square-threaded screw, illustrated in Figure 25, is
produced.   The "pitch" of this triple thread is one-third of the lead.   On

machine drawings, the number of threads per inch usually is specified. This is the reciprocal of the lead. Another screw, having a right-hand, double, square thread, is shown in Figure 26.

To determine the size of a square thread, a profile similar to that shown at A in Figure 27 may be sketched. If the thread is to be a single thread, the lead will be from 0 to 1 and the size of the square will be one-half of the lead. If the thread is to be a double thread, the lead will be measured from 0 to 2 and the size of the square will be one-fourth of the lead. If the thread is to be triple, the lead will be measured from 0 to 3 and the size of the square will be one-sixth of the lead. The size of the square of any multiple thread may be determined in this way.

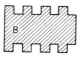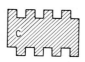

Size of square

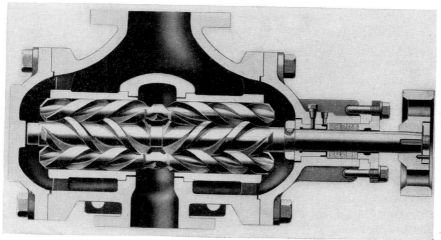

Even number threads   Odd number threads

FIGURE 27. Square thread profiles.

When it is necessary to draw the profiles of a square thread, care must be taken to see that the profiles of the opposite sides of the cylinder are properly related. At B in Figure 27 is shown the relation between the profiles when the screw is to have an even number of threads, and at C is shown the correct relation for an odd number of threads. At B, the val-

FIGURE 28. Section of oil pump. (*DeLaval Steam Turbine Co.*)

leys of the threads are opposite; at C, the thread is opposite a valley. These relations may be determined by the fact that the thread travels one-half of the lead in one-half of a turn.

Multiple-threaded screws are used when a rapid traverse per turn is required, as in planers, grinding machines, steering gears, and for worm drives of many kinds. Multiple-threaded screws are more efficient, within certain limits, than are single-threaded screws. Self-locking mechanisms—those that can be driven from one end only—always are of low efficiency.

The cross section of an oil pump shown in Figure 28 illustrates an unusual application. Propellers for use in liquids and in air are parts of multiple-threaded screws with modified helicoidal surfaces. The airplane propeller is an air screw. One blade and its sections are shown in Figure

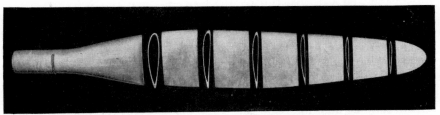

FIGURE 29. Airplane propeller blade. (*Curtiss-Wright Corp.*)

FIGURE 30. Turbine runner. (*Allis-Chalmers Mfg. Co.*)

29. A propeller-type turbine runner with adjustable blades is illustrated in Figure 30. The twist of the helicoidal surfaces is clearly seen.

18. Problems.

Group 77. Screws and Springs.

HYPERBOLOIDS OF REVOLUTION

19. The hyperboloid is a warped surface generated by a straight line revolving about an axis that it does not intersect. The revolving line maintains a fixed relation to the axis. This surface may also be defined as a warped surface having three coaxial circular directrices. Ordinarily two of the circles are the same size, and the third and smallest circle is halfway between them. The surface may be doubly ruled, but it is not developable.

20. Drawing the Hyperboloid of Revolution. Figure 31 shows the front and top views of a hyperboloid of revolution. If the upper and lower circles and the middle, or gore, circle are given, any number of equally spaced elements may first be drawn in the top view, where they appear tangent to the gore circle and terminate in the upper and lower

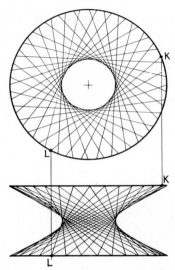   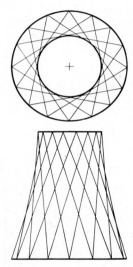

FIGURE 31. Hyperboloid of revolution.   FIGURE 32. Hyperboloid of revolution.

circles. The elements do not lie in the plane of the gore circle. Every element intersects each of the circular directrices at a single point. One end of the element K L, for example, is at K on the upper circle, and the other end is at L on the lower circle. These points are located in the front view, each on its respective circle, and then the front view of the element is drawn.

In each view of Figure 31 all the elements of a single generation, or ruling, are shown. The elements of the second generation may be drawn by reversing the elements of the first generation, for example, by locating the point K on the lower circle, and the point L on the upper circle in the front view.

If the axis and the generatrix K L of the surface are given, the elements may be drawn as described above, after the circles generated by the points K and L and the gore circle are drawn. The gore circle is generated by the point on the generatrix that is nearest the axis. The intersection of the surface of the hyperboloid of revolution with a plane passed through or parallel to the axis is a hyperbola.

In Figure 32 is shown the lower part of a hyperboloid of revolution.   In the top view the elements of two generations are shown.   In the front view the elements of both generations that lie on the front half of the surface are shown.

21. Uses of the Hyperboloid of Revolution.   The doubly ruled hyperboloid of revolution, built from straight steel members, is a stiff, light-weight structure.   It is used for observation towers, cooling towers, and ventilating fans.   Elliptical hyperboloids are used in some designs. Incidentally, the surface appears in latticework and in reed furniture.

22. Skew Gears.   When two nonintersecting and nonparallel shafts are to be directly geared together, skew gears are used.   The rolling sur-

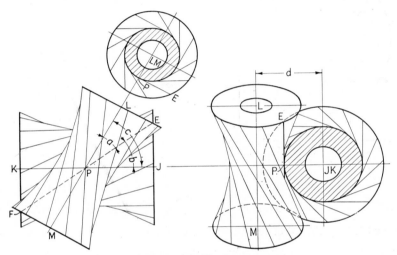

FIGURE 33. Skew gears.

faces, taken at the pitch diameter, must be hyperboloids of revolution. This is illustrated in Figure 33.

J K and L M are the center lines of the shafts.   The distance between the shafts is d.   The difference in direction of the shafts is indicated by the angle c.   The line E F is the element of contact between the rolling hyperboloids.   The direct ratio of the diameters of the gore circles does not determine the gear ratio, since there is a certain amount of inherent slip between the gear teeth in contact as the gears revolve.   The design of these gears is complicated by this fact.   The gear ratio is proportional to the sines of the angles a and b, and the diameters of the gore circles are proportional to the tangents of the same angles.   Once these angles and diameters are obtained, the gears may be drawn as is indicated in Fig. 33.   This is a specialized job in gear design.

23. Problems.
   Group 78.   Hyperboloids of Revolution.

CYLINDROIDS

24. The cylindroid is a warped surface having two curved directrices and a plane director. The surface is used for connecting two curves in nonparallel planes and at different levels, as in a skewed arch. The front and top views of a cylindroid are shown in Figure 34. The directrices are two ellipses A and B. The plane director is frontal. The ellipse B appears as a circle in the front view and is here divided into a number of equal parts. Through the top views of these points, frontal elements are

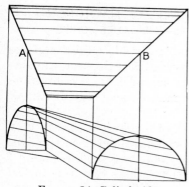

FIGURE 34. Cylindroid.

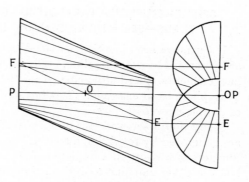

FIGURE 35. Warped cone.

drawn. These intersect curve A at points that are carried to the front view of this curve. In the front view, the elements of the surface connect corresponding points.

WARPED CONES

25. The warped cone, *corne de vache*, or cow's horn, is a warped surface having two curved and one straight-line directrix. Normally, the curved directrices are equal circles in parallel planes, and the straight-line directrix passes through the mid-point of the line joining their centers. The surface has its principal use in an oblique arch. This is illustrated in Figure 35. The semicircles centered at E and F are the curved directrices, and the line O P is the straight directrix. The right-hand view is an end view of O P. Here all the elements, when extended, will pass through O P, but they terminate in the circles. The ends of each element are located on the edge views of the circles, and then the elements are drawn in this view.

26. Problems.

Group 79. Cylindroids and Warped Cones.

Chapter 11

DOUBLE-CURVED SURFACES

SPHERE—ELLIPSOID—PARABOLOID—SURFACES OF REVOLUTION—
TORUS—SERPENTINE—GENERAL TYPES—AIRPLANES—SHIPS

1. Surfaces are classified as ruled or double-curved. Ruled surfaces are generated by a straight line. Double-curved surfaces have no straight-line elements. A double-curved surface is curved in every direction. The sphere is an example. Modern design makes use of a great variety of double-curved surfaces.

Many double-curved surfaces are surfaces of revolution; that is, they are generated by revolving a curved line around a straight line as an axis. Surfaces of revolution are easily made. They may be turned or spun on a lathe or other machine tool, formed on a potter's wheel, cast from turned patterns or in turned molds, or shaped by turned dies. A view of a surface of revolution taken in the direction of the axis shows circles only; a view taken perpendicular to the axis shows the outline contour, or silhouette, of the surface. Ruled surfaces of revolution are the cylinder, cone, and hyperboloid, but these are single-curved surfaces.

Many double-curved surfaces of a general type follow no definite geometrical law. These are represented by drawing single-curved *contour lines* of the surface taken in planes at uniformly spaced intervals. These contours represent the intersection of the planes with the double-curved surface. The topography of land and the curved surfaces of aircraft, ships, and irregularly curved structures are all represented by curved contours. Examples of these are illustrated in this and the following chapter.

A double-curved surface cannot be developed, but it may be approximated by enclosing it in sections of cylinders or cones. The latter, being single-curved surfaces, may be developed. Double-curved surfaces made from sheet metal are formed to shape by stretching the metal.

SPHERES

2. A sphere is a double-curved surface generated by revolving a circle about one of its diameters as an axis. All points of a spherical surface are

equidistant from the center. Every view of a sphere shows a contour great circle of the sphere.

3. Uses of Spheres. Small and large spherical steel balls for ball bearings are forged, ground, and lapped to size, and are true spheres within very close limits. Spherical ball-and-socket joints find frequent use. Large structures, tanks and domes, approximating a spherical shape more or less closely, are made from thin and thick metal sheets. Figure 1

FIGURE 1. A welded sphere. (*Chicago Bridge and Iron Co.*)

shows a Horton tank 62 feet in diameter, designed for holding water at 60 pounds per square inch. The heavy steel plates are forged to shape, and the seams are welded. For a given volume, a spherical tank requires less material than does a tank of any other shape and generally affords a more economical use of the tensile strength of the steel plates than do other shapes.

4. Development of the Sphere. Two methods of making an approximate development of a sphere are commonly used: the meridian development illustrated in Figures 1 and 2, and the zone development illustrated in Figure 3.

For development by the meridian method, the spherical surface is approximated by enclosing the sphere in similar sections of a right cylinder. The design and the development are shown in Figure 2. The top view of the larger sphere shows the correct way to draw the tangent cylinders so that the extreme contour in the front view will be a great circle that represents the edge view of two of the cylindrical sections. The

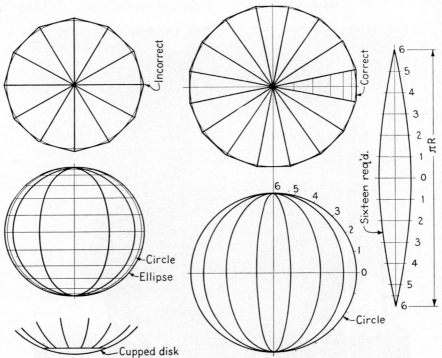

FIGURE 2. Meridian development of spheres.

views of the smaller sphere show a less desirable way to draw the sections, since the extreme contour in the front view must here be an ellipse. The development of one of the 16 equal cylindrical sections of the larger cylinder is shown, and the method of drawing the development is indicated. A large number of seams meeting at the poles should generally be avoided by substituting a flat or cupped disk as is indicated in the figure. The greater the number of sections, the nearer will the true shape of the sphere be approximated. But at the same time, the number of pieces to be cut to shape and the total length of the seams are increased.

The tank shown in Figure 1 was developed by the meridian method. Since the sections are here formed by stretching the metal, the development is drawn just inside, instead of outside, the sphere.

Figure 3 illustrates the zone development of the sphere.   The spherical surface is approximated by enclosing the sphere in sections of right circular cones.   The development of the conical sections is shown.   It is more difficult to form conical sections to shape than to roll cylindrical sections. The surface of a sphere may also be approximated by surrounding the sphere with one of the regular polyhedrons.

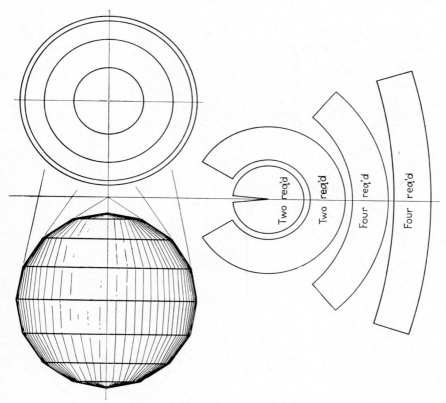

FIGURE 3. Zone development of sphere.

5. Sphere and Plane Intersection.   Every plane section of a sphere is

a circle.   Several methods for determining this intersection are explained in connection with Figure 4.   The given sphere is centered at S.   The given plane is J K L.

Pass horizontal or frontal cutting planes.   Each plane cuts a circle from the sphere and a straight line from the given plane.   The line and circle will intersect at two points of the required intersection.   Pass the frontal plane F.   This plane cuts from the sphere a circle of which the edge view and true diameter are seen in the top view.   The front view of this circle is then drawn. Plane F intersects line J K at E. All frontal lines of plane J K L are parallel to the frontal line K L. Through the front view of the point E draw a line parallel to K L. This parallel intersects the previously found circle at points 5 and 6. The top views of these two points are now located on the top views of the line and circle. The points 5 and 6 are on the line, on the circle, and on the surface of the

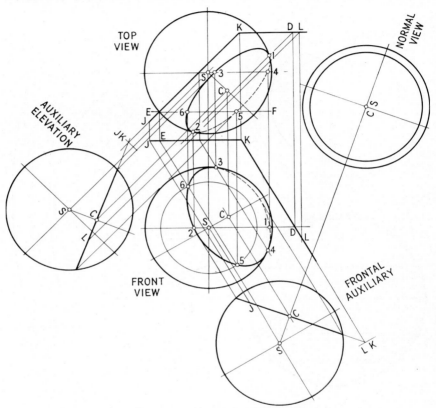

FIGURE 4. Intersection of sphere and plane.

sphere. This operation is repeated until a sufficient number of points are found.

It is essential to determine where the views of the intersection change from visible to invisible. Pass a frontal plane through the center S to locate the points 3 and 4 on the great circle in the front view. That part of the required circle that is behind the points 3 and 4 will be invisible in the front view. Also, the elliptical view of the circle will be tangent to the frontal great circle at 3 and 4. Similarly, with the aid of a horizontal cutting plane passed through S in the front view, the points 1 and 2 are located on the great circle in the top view. Below points 1 and 2 the required circle is invisible in the top view. These critical points should always be located.

The intersection of the sphere with the plane J K L may also be determined as follows: Draw a frontal-auxiliary view taken in the direction of the frontal line K L of the given plane. In this view, the edge view and the true diameter of the required circle are seen. The center is C. The line S C is perpendicular to the given plane. It may now be drawn in the front and top views, and the views of C located in these views. The minor axis of the elliptical front view of the circle is next determined by rays from the auxiliary view, and the major axis is made equal in length to the diameter of the circle as found in the frontal-auxiliary view. To determine the minor axis of the elliptical top view, draw an auxiliary elevation taken in the direction of the horizontal line J K of the given plane. From this view, the length of the minor axis in the top view is determined. A trammel may then be used to plot the curves. The normal view of the required circle may be drawn if desired.

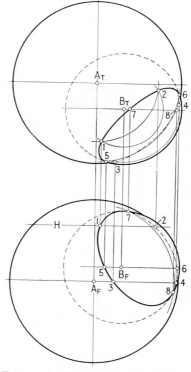

6. Intersection of Spheres. Figure 5: Pass horizontal, frontal, or profile cutting planes. Each cutting plane

FIGURE 5. Intersection of spheres.

will cut a circle from each of two spheres, and each pair of circles will cross at two points common to both spheres. The operation is repeated until the intersection is indicated by a series of points.

Since center B is above center A in the figure, the visible part of the curve in the top view will be above points 5 and 6 which are determined by passing a horizontal cutting plane through B in the front view. And since B is in front of A, the visible part of the curve in the front view will be in front of the points 7 and 8 which are determined by passing a frontal cutting plane through B in the top view.

7. Problems.

Group 80. Development of Spheres.

Group 81. Sphere and Plane Intersections.

ELLIPSOIDS—PARABOLOIDS—SURFACES OF REVOLUTION

8. An ellipsoid is a double-curved surface of revolution generated by revolving an ellipse about its major or its minor axis.

Figure 6 shows pictorial views of a prolate ellipsoid and an oblate ellipsoid. The axes of revolution are indicated. The circles and ellipses drawn on these surfaces aid in visualizing the curved form of each surface and indicate how the surface could be divided when it is to be constructed

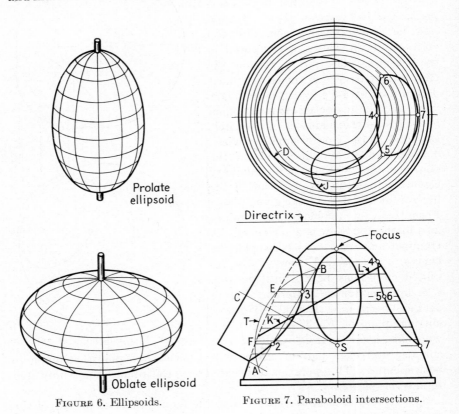

FIGURE 6. Ellipsoids.   FIGURE 7. Paraboloid intersections.

from steel plates. Large tanks and domes often are designed as ellipsoids or spheroids. Elliptical shapes may be turned on a lathe by making use of a slotted mechanism based on the principle of the trammel.

The intersection of an ellipsoid with a plane, and with some other surfaces, may be found by passing cutting planes perpendicular to the axis of revolution. In many situations, cutting spheres expedite the solution of the problem of finding intersections. This method is explained in Article 10.

9. Paraboloids. Figure 7: The directrix and focus of the generating parabola are indicated. The paraboloid is generated by revolving the parabola about its axis.

Any plane inclined to the axis, K L for example, intersects the paraboloid in an ellipse that appears as a circle in the end view. This leads to the conclusion that any circular cylinder having its axis parallel to the axis of the paraboloid, cylinder J for example, will intersect the paraboloid in an ellipse as shown in the front view, and this ellipse is a plane section of the cylinder and of the paraboloid.

In the front view, 4 5 7 is the end view of a cylinder. Its intersection with the paraboloid is readily found by passing horizontal cutting planes. Points 5 and 6 are thus located in the top view, and other points are similarly located.

10. Use of Cutting Spheres for Finding Intersections. The intersection between any two surfaces of revolution when the axes of revolution intersect may readily be found by passing cutting spheres centered on the point of intersection of the axes. Each cutting sphere cuts one or two circles from each of the surfaces of revolution, and these circles intersect at two, four, six, or eight points of the required intersection. This method also is explained in the chapter on Single-curved Surfaces.

Figure 7: The axis of a right circular cylinder is C S. This axis intersects the axis of the paraboloid at S. The arc T is a contour circle of a cutting sphere centered at S. A B is the edge view of the circle that is cut from the

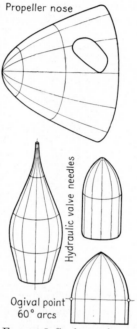

FIGURE 8. Surfaces of revolution.

given cylinder by this cutting sphere. Through E and F are drawn the horizontal circles that are cut from the paraboloid by the cutting sphere. The three circles, determined by the cutting sphere, intersect at points 2 and 3 and at two points directly behind these points. Other points on the required intersection are similarly located by passing larger and smaller cutting spheres until an adequate number of points are found. If the top view of this intersection is needed, points may readily be located on top views of the horizontal circles.

Figure 8 illustrates some of the double-curved surfaces that are used in the problems.

11. Problems.

Group 82.   Ellipsoids and Paraboloids.

Group 83.   Surfaces of Revolution.

ANNULAR TORUS

12. The annular torus, or anchor ring, is a double-curved surface of revolution which is generated by a circle revolving about an axis that lies in the plane of the circle. It also may be visualized and drawn as the envelope of all spheres of a given size that are centered on a given circle. Figure 9 is a pictorial view of an annular torus. Sections of the torus taken in the plane of the axis are circles of equal size. A plane perpendicular to the axis intersects the torus in two circles.

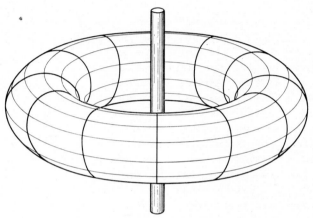

FIGURE 9. Annular torus.

The intersection of the torus with other surfaces may be found by passing cutting planes perpendicular to the axis, or by passing cutting spheres centered on the axis. The torus cannot be developed, but it may be approximated by enclosing the surfaces in sections of cylinders. A pipe bend is a torus.

13. Torus Intersections. Figure 10 illustrates a pipe bend joined to a cylindrical casing, as in a steam turbine. A cutting plane perpendicular to the axis of the bend cuts two circles from the torus, and a straight line from the cylinder. These intersect at four points. The operation is repeated until sufficient points are located to determine the intersections accurately.

A steam trap with a cylindrical Y-connection is shown in Figure 11. The bowl of the trap consists of parts of two torii and a cylinder. The axes of all of these surfaces intersect at S. A cutting sphere centered at S is indicated in the drawing. This sphere cuts circle K from one torus, and circle L from the cylinder. These two circles intersect at point 2 on the near half of the trap and at a point directly beyond 2 on the far half.

Cutting spheres of different diameters are passed until enough points are located to determine the intersection.

Figure 12 shows the intersections of a torus and five different planes. In the front view, the edge views of planes C, D, and E are assumed. The similarly lettered intersections in the top view indicate the intersection of

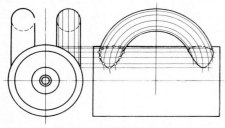

FIGURE 10. Turbine pipe.

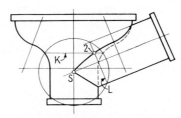

FIGURE 11. Steam trap.

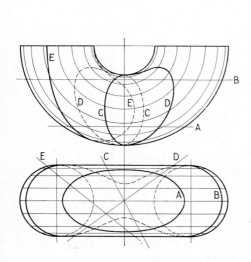

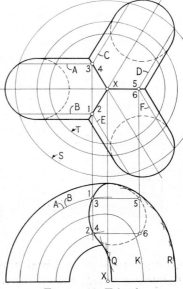

FIGURE 12. Intersections of torus and planes.   FIGURE 13. Tripod.

each plane with the torus. These intersections are determined by passing cutting planes perpendicular to the axis of the torus. In each cutting plane, two circles of the torus intersect a line of the inclined plane at two or four points. The intersections of the frontal planes A and B are shown at A and B in the front view.

14. Three Intersecting Torii. Figure 13: This tripod or pipe connection consists of parts of three equal torii. The three axes intersect at X. At S is shown the horizontal great circle of a cutting sphere that is centered at X. This sphere cuts two circles from each of the given torii. At A and B in the top view are seen the edge views of two of these circles, and other pairs are seen at C and D and at E and F. These intersect at points 1, 3, and 5 in the top view. In the front view, circles A and B are drawn, and the front views of points 1 and 3 are located on these circles and in line with their rays from the top view. Point 5 in the front view is located at the same level as points 1 and 3, and on its ray. Points 2, 4,

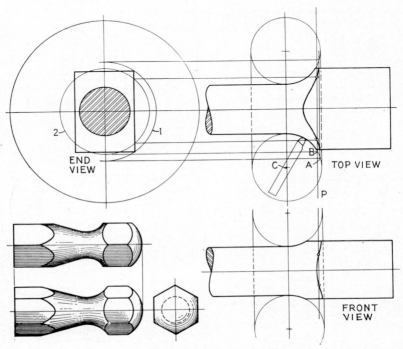

FIGURE 14. Connecting rod.

and 6 are then located with the aid of cutting sphere T. Other cutting spheres are taken, and additional points are determined.

Curve K in the front view is the circular path of the center of the generating circle of the forward torus. Spheres having the same radius as the generating circle of the torus are centered on curve K, and arcs of great circles are drawn as indicated. Contours Q and R of this torus are then drawn tangent to these arcs to complete the front view.

15. Connecting Rod. The stub end of a connecting rod is shown in Figure 14. This piece is formed from a rectangular bar of metal by turning a part of the bar cylindrical. A circular fillet joins the two parts. A sharp corner here would tend to start a crack in the metal. The bar turns in the lathe, and the point of the lathe tool forms the fillet when the tool is rotated about the center C.

To complete the appearance of the front and top views, it is necessary to determine the curved lines that are generated by the point of the lathe tool as it enters and leaves the flat faces of the rectangular bar. Geometrically, the surface of the fillet is an annular torus, and the problem is to find the intersections of the torus with the plane faces of the bar. The torus is indicated in the three views of the figure.

When the point of the lathe tool is set at B, for example in the top view, it is turning the circle 2 shown in the end view. This circle intersects the plane faces of the bar in eight points. These points are next located on the edge views of the circle in the top and front views. When the point of the lathe tool is set at A, it is just nicking the edges of the bar as is indicated by circle 1 in the end view. These four points are then located in the front and top views. The points where the tool enters the middle of each face are next determined, and enough other points are found to indicate the true shape of the two curves. Note that there are two reversals in each curve.

The insert in Figure 14 shows a hexagonal bar turned with a curved fillet merging into a taper. One end of the bar is spherical. The resulting intersections with the flat faces of the bar must be accurately determined and drawn if the views are to have a natural appearance.

16. Problems.

Group 84.   Annular Torus.

SERPENTINES AND SPRINGS

17. The serpentine is a double-curved surface that is generated by a sphere which moves so that its center follows a helix. This surface may be visualized and drawn as the envelope of all spheres of a given size that have their centers on a given helix as in Figure 15. Surfaces of this kind are called *tubular*. The annular torus also is a tubular surface.

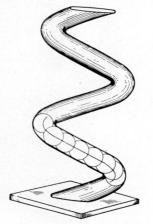

FIGURE 15. Serpentine.

The serpentine is the surface of helical springs that are made from round rods. When the ends of these springs are ground flat to take the thrust, the appearance of the end view may be determined by finding the circular sections, with the end plane, of a number of generating spheres. A curve drawn tangent to these circles shows the shape of the end of the spring.

Figures 16 and 17 show the use of serpentines in a pump and in a blower.

FIGURE 16. Pump rotor. (*Robbins & Myers, Inc.*)

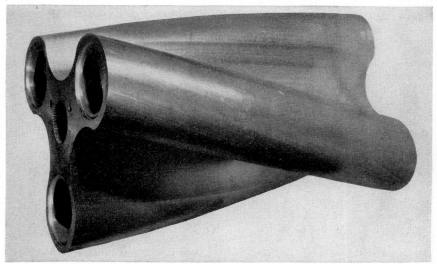

FIGURE 17. Blower rotor. (*General Motors Corp., Diesel Engine Division.*)

The surfaces of these rotors are accurately machined. The serpentine also is used as an architectural ornament. The surface cannot be developed, but it may be approximated by enclosing the serpentine in sections of cylinders.

18. Problems.

Group 85. Serpentines and Springs.

GENERAL TYPES OF DOUBLE-CURVED SURFACES

19. Airplanes, automobiles, and ships have streamlined double-curved exterior surfaces that cannot be designated by any particular geometrical name. Many other articles of manufacture are designed with double-curved surfaces of entirely general types. Also rolling and mountainous lands are irregular double-curved surfaces.

Double-curved surfaces are represented in drawings by showing curved lines, or contours, of the surface. Contours usually are taken as parallel plane sections of the surface, spaced at uniform intervals. Land contours are explained in the next chapter.

Small-scale design drawings of large structures, and all drawings that must remain accurate, are drawn on metal sheets, since drawings on paper change considerably in size with changes in humidity.

20. Airplane Drawings. The designer of aircraft works in a highly specialized field. He must have a thorough understanding of aerodynamics, and he must know how to represent curved surfaces of intricate shapes. The principles explained in this textbook provide the foundation for drawing structures of every possible shape.

Figure 18 shows the lines of a fuselage in five principal views. It should be noted that the view to the right of the front view is taken from the right, but that it is here called the *left-side view*, since it shows the side of the plane that is to the left of the passenger as he sits in the plane. Chapter 2, Article 12.

The pictorial insert in Figure 18 shows three reference or base planes: vertical, horizontal, and transversal, from which all points are measured. With the exception of minor details, the fuselage is symmetrical about the vertical reference plane, so that it is necessary to show only one-half of the fuselage in the views.

The designer first locates the three reference planes in each view where the edge view of these planes is seen. The planes are here indicated respectively as V-R-P, H-R-P, and T-R-P. Next, three sets of planes are drawn parallel to the three reference planes. In the top, bottom, and in both end views are shown the edge views of four vertical planes parallel to and spaced at the indicated inches, 5, 10, 15, and 20, from the V-R-P. In the left-side, front, and rear views, are drawn horizontal *water planes* spaced at the indicated plus and minus inches above and below the zero H-R-P. In the top, left-side, and bottom views are drawn transversal planes spaced at the indicated inches, 0 to 340, behind the zero T-R-P. These locations are known as *stations*. See Chapter 13, Figures 1, 14, and 15 for pictorial views of stations and frames.

When the designer is ready to draw the lines of the fuselage, he proceeds somewhat as follows: The extreme upper and lower contours in the central

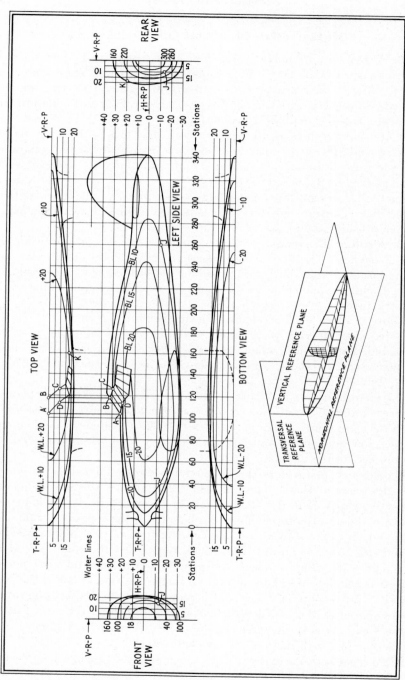

FIGURE 18. Airplane contours.

vertical reference plane are drawn in the left-side view. All curves must be fair. Next, the extreme horizontal contour at level zero is drawn in the top and bottom, or half-breadth, views. These three curves determine the general shape of the fuselage and also the height and width of each transversal section at each station.

The transversal sections in the front and rear views are drawn next. As an example take station 160. The height and width of this section are determined from the curves previously drawn. In the end views, the curved shape of this section is drawn to suit the requirements of the design. The transversal sections of station 160 and of the stations forward are here shown in the front view; and those of station 160 and rearward are shown in the rear view. The transversal sections determine the outlines of the frames of the fuselage.

In the left-side view, the curved *buttock lines*, marked B L, are now determined by locating in the front and rear views the points of intersection of each frame line with each of the several planes parallel to the central V-R-P. For example, point J in the rear view is the intersection of station or frame 260 with vertical plane 10. In the left-side view, J is now located at its proper level in station 260. J is a point on buttock line 10. All points on the buttock lines are similarly located in the left-side view, and smooth curves are drawn through the points of each buttock line. For the sake of clearness, buttock line 5 has not been shown in the figure.

Horizontal *water lines* of the fuselage are determined in a similar way. Point K, for example, is first taken in the rear view at the +20 level, on frame 160, and its distance from the V-R-P is noted. These data determine its location in the top view. Points on the plus water lines are located at each station in the top view, and then the smoothly curved water lines are drawn. The zero water line and those below it are shown in the bottom view.

If any of the buttock lines or water lines are found to be not fair curves, it then is necessary to make changes in the curves of the transversal sections until all lines of the surface are fair. An additional graphical check of the fairness of a curved surface is explained in connection with Figure 20.

21. Airplane Intersections. The intersection between any two parts of an airplane may be determined by the usual method of passing cutting planes. Each cutting plane cuts a contour line from each part, and these lines cross at one or more points of the required intersection.

The intersection of the flat windshield of the plane shown in Figure 18 is to be determined. A B is taken as the straight sloping center line of the windshield in the central V-R-P. B C is taken as the straight upper edge of the windshield. A B C is a plane surface. Straight buttock lines of this plane are drawn parallel to A B in each of the buttock planes 5, 10, and 15.　One point D of the required intersection is found at the point where B L 10 of the fuselage intersects B L 10 of the windshield.　Other points of intersection are located, and then the curved line A D is drawn. This is the required intersection of the lower edge of the windshield with the fuselage.　If the windshield is cylindrical, a view taken in the direction of the elements of the cylinder is needed to determine the intersection. And, if double-curved, the curved contours of the windshield surface must be drawn to represent the surface and to determine intersections.

22. Streamlining.　The exact shapes of aircraft and of all double-curved surfaces are designed by drawing curved contour lines of the surface.　The exact streamlining of the surface and of each contour line of objects that travel at high speed cannot generally be determined with sufficient accuracy by graphical means.　Equations of lines and analytical calculations are used to make certain that two curves meeting at a common point have a common tangent, and the same curvature, radius, and center at the point where they meet.　This geometrical requirement for fairness is checked by calculations for a number of points on each contour. These calculations make use of analytical geometry and calculus.

23. Lofting Floors.　Large structures are first designed in drawings that are much smaller than the actual structures.　If a scale of $\frac{1}{4}$ inch to

Figure 19. A lofting floor.

1 foot is used, an error of about one-fiftieth of an inch in the drawing becomes an error of 1 inch in the full-scale structure. To avoid such errors, the lines of airplanes and ships are drawn full size on lofting floors.

Figure 19 is a photograph of a ship lofting floor, which is in effect a large drawing board hundreds of feet in length. The lines of the ship or plane are drawn directly on the floor. Coordinates are measured for different points on each line of the original small-scale design drawing, and many coordinates are determined from calculations. Tables of these coordinates, or offsets, are made for use in scaling the location of points on the lofting floor. Thin wooden battens are smoothly curved through the points on the lofting floor, and with their aid the contour lines are drawn on the floor. Other battens are then curved to fit the lofting-floor lines and are nailed together to provide templates like those shown in Figure 19. The templates are taken to the shops where they are used for laying out the exact shapes of the frames and plates of the ship. The lines of airplanes are determined with great accuracy on similar lofting floors.

24. Ship Drawings. The lines of the forward, or bow, section of a ship are shown in Figure 20. The particular names of the different views as used by ship designers are given in the drawing. The horizontal water lines are here indicated by letters, and their true curved shapes are shown

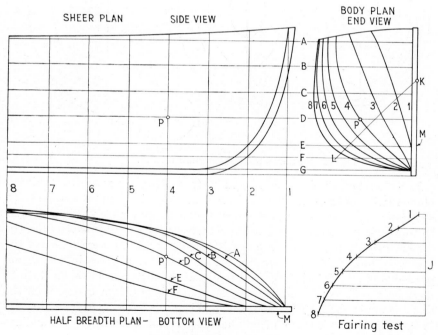

FIGURE 20. Lines of a ship.

in the bottom view. The transversal stations are numbered. The true shapes of these station lines, or frame lines, are shown in the end view. Any point P in the side view in station 4 and at level D must be located in the end view on frame line 4 and at level D. And in the bottom view, P must be on water line D and in station 4. The location of each point in each view must be in agreement with its location in the other views.

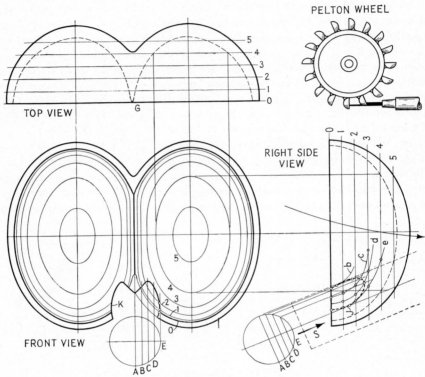

FIGURE 21. Pelton wheel bucket.

Tests of the fairness of a curved surface often are made by taking a plane section of the surface, such as K L in the end view of the ship shown in Figure 20. Test sections are best taken approximately perpendicular to the surface. Also, it is best to contract the curve by shortening the distance between stations in order to exaggerate any irregularities of the curve. The fairing test shown in the figure is a view taken in a direction perpendicular to the plane K L, except that the distances between stations have been reduced. The distance of each point of intersection from the line J is made equal to the distance of this point from K in the end view. If the fairing test indicates that the curve is not smooth, the frame lines should be redesigned.

Common and nautical terms may be related by grouping the short and the long words: (left, port, red) and (right, starboard, green).

25. Pelton Wheel Bucket. Figure 21: The small inserted sketch shows a Pelton wheel having a number of cupped buckets fastened to its rim. A high-pressure stream of water from a nozzle impinges against the buckets, revolves the wheel, and generates power.

Three views of one cupped bucket are shown in the figure. The arrow S and the cylinder indicate a stream of water. The ridge in the middle of the bucket splits the stream, and the curved cups force the water to make a U-turn so that nearly all of its energy is used in turning the wheel. A slot is provided in each bucket, as is shown in the front view at K, so that the stream from the nozzle may have a clear passage to impinge squarely on the preceding bucket. As the bucket shown in the figure continues to revolve with the wheel, the stream is progressively cut off from the preceding bucket until the next bucket receives the full force of the water.

The double-curved surface of each cup is shown by contours. To show the appearance of the slot in the bucket, determine the intersection of the cylindrical stream with the inner surface of the bucket. Equally spaced profile cutting planes, B to E, are drawn. Each plane cuts two straight lines from the cylinder, and a curved line from the bucket. These straight lines and the curved lines, b, c, d, and e, are shown in the side view, their points of intersection are here located, and the curve J is drawn. The points of intersection are now transferred to their respective cutting planes in the front view, and curve K is drawn.

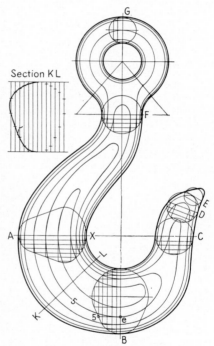

FIGURE 22. Crane hook.

26. Crane Hook. Figure 22: This forging is represented by drawing cross sections and contours. The size and the shape of the cross sections determine the load capacity of the hook. For each revolved cross section, planes are shown at equally spaced distances from the central contour plane, points of intersection are found, and from these the contours are located. For example, in cross section B point 5 is on the outline of the section and in the fifth plane from the central contour plane. In the edge view of section B, point 5 is located at *e*, which is a point on contour line 5 of the crane hook.   For each section, a point in plane 5 is located, and through these points contour 5 is drawn.   The true shape of section K L, shown in the insert, is determined by reversing this process.

27. Problems.

Group 86.   Double-curved Surfaces.

Chapter 12

TOPOGRAPICAL AND
MINING PROBLEMS

1. Engineers in many different fields encounter topographical and mining problems dealing with land contours, underground and surface workings and surveys, roads, railways, bridge piers, dams, foundations, retaining walls, excavations, underground and surface water supplies, drainage, irrigation, geological formations, rock strata, oil wells, mines, tunnels, veins of ore, dumps, layout of grounds, landscaping, and structures built into the ground and on the surface of the ground. All engineers should be able to read and make drawings of structures of these types.

The methods used in solving mining problems may be applied to the solution of similar problems in other fields. Mining and topographical problems, although seemingly difficult of solution, may be solved quickly and accurately by applying the methods and principles of the geometry of engineering drawing.

Figure 1 is a typical drawing of an engineering project built above and below and on the surface of the ground. Each crooked land contour represents the irregular surface of the ground at a single level. The walls of the canyon are rough and steep. Each smoothly curved contour of Hoover Dam merges with the land contour at the same level. Note the power intake towers and tunnels, the powerhouse, and the road down the mountain sides and across the dam. Study and visualize this illustration in connection with the other illustrations of Hoover Dam shown on the first pages of this book.

2. Definitions. Strata of rock, beds of coal, and veins of ore were deposited on the surface of the earth or in the earth's crust. Owing to upheaval, these deposits may lie in any position and may be regular or irregular in shape. Within limited areas, strata and veins often are tabular in form, bounded by two approximately parallel plane faces, and nearly

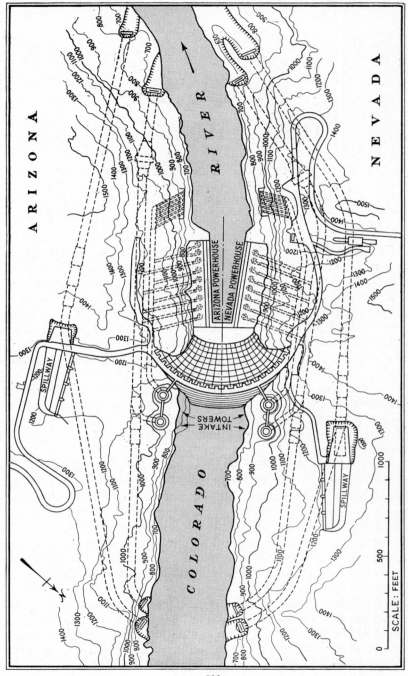

FIGURE 1. Hoover Dam contours. (*U. S. Bureau of Reclamation.*)

uniform in thickness.   Some veins are sheared or faulted, and others are folded.

The *strike* or trend of a stratum or vein is the direction of any horizontal line of the vein.   The strike may be taken in the center of the vein or in either wall, and it may be taken at any level.   The direction or bearing of the strike is specified, for example, as N 42° E, or N 77° W.

The *dip* of a vein of ore or stratum of rock is the average angle that the vein makes with a horizontal plane.   It is the slope of the steepest line in the vein.   The dip should be indicated as an angle measured below the horizontal.   The location of a vein may be completely specified by showing its strike at a given level and by stating the dip of the vein.   For example, if the strike is N 42° E, the dip may be stated as 35 degrees to the N.W.; or if the vein slopes the other way, 35 degrees to the S.E.

The lower surface on which the vein or stratum rests is the *foot wall*, since it is the wall on which the miner stands.   The surface above the vein is the *hanging wall*.

In mining problems, as in land surveying, directions are measured in relation to some base line that usually is taken as a north and south line. Elevations or levels are measured from some horizontal reference plane. The zero level may be taken at sea level, or otherwise, as desired.   Levels in a mine often are indicated by the distance in feet below the surface.

Veins of ore usually are discovered through surface indications or *outcrops* of the ore in places where erosion has uncovered the vein.   After the vein is discovered, it may be developed by removing the overburden or by excavating a tunnel, incline, or shaft.   A *tunnel* is a horizontal or nearly horizontal passage having one opening at daylight and extending across the country rock to the vein.   A *shaft* is a vertical or nearly vertical passage from the surface of the ground.   An *incline* is an entry that follows the dip of the vein or seam.   A *drift* is a horizontal passage that follows the vein.   The *grade* of a tunnel or of a road is stated, for example, as 7 per cent.   This means that there is a vertical rise of 7 feet in a distance of 100 feet measured horizontally.   A *shoot* is a rich streak of ore in a vein.   Enrichment of ore may be expected where two veins intersect.

3. Angle of Repose.   Any loose material that is dumped in a pile approximates the shape of a right cone.   The angle of slope, or base angle of the cone, varies with the moisture content, the size of the particles, and the nature of the material.   This angle is called the *angle of repose*, the natural slope, or the angle at which the material hangs up.   It may be stated in degrees above the horizontal, or specified as a slope ratio.   The angle of repose of rock varies from 36 to 54 degrees.   Sand stands up at 34 degrees, and gravel and earth at 37 degrees.   The approximate angle of repose of any material, for any locality and conditions, may be obtained by measurement of rock slides or dumps.   It is necessary to know the angle of repose of the material concerned when designing mine dumps, ore bins and chutes, retaining walls, foundations, dams, roads, and cuts and fills for every kind of excavation.

4. Contours and Profiles. Structures of all kinds are represented by drawing lines of the structure. Irregular surfaces are represented in a drawing by curved *contour* lines of the surface taken at regularly spaced intervals.

In Figure 2, the upper half of the figure shows a contour map of a hilly country. The contours are obtained from surveyors' topographical notes,

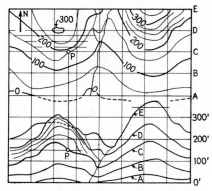

by the use of a plane table, or from photographs taken from an airplane. The contour map is the top view of the country. Each contour line is a line of the ground surface at the indicated level. The contour line represents the intersection of the ground surface with a horizontal plane. In the front view, and in all views observed in a horizontal direction, each contour appears as a horizontal line. The elevation of each 100-foot contour is marked on the map of Figure 2. Intermediate

FIGURE 2. Contours and profiles.

50-foot contours also are shown. In the N.E. area a few contours at 25-foot intervals have been interpolated. Where contours crowd together, as near P, the hill rises rapidly in a short horizontal distance. Here, the hill is steeper. Where contours are farther apart, the country becomes more nearly level. On the map, a creek and its branch are shown. An arrow indicates the north direction. The country represented by a contour map should be visualized by the reader of the map. He should note the valleys, ridges, and hills, and changes in slope, and picture these in his mind.

Profiles are intersections of the ground surface of the country with vertical planes. The direction in which these vertical sections may be taken is not limited to profile planes, but the intersections are called *profiles*. On the lower half of Figure 2 are shown five profiles of the country that is represented by contours on the map of the upper half of the figure. These profiles are here obtained by determining the intersection of the ground surface with the frontal planes A, B, C, D, and E. For example, the point P on the map is on the 150-foot contour and in the plane C. In the front view P is located in line with its ray and at the 150-foot level. Other points in plane C are found similarly, and the profile C is drawn through them. The different profiles give a good picture of the front view or elevation of the country. North of P additional profiles have been determined. These bring out the details of this section of the hills.

5. Locating Veins of Ore. A section of mountainous country above the 10,000-foot level is shown in Figure 3. Twin peaks appear on the map, and a valley runs toward the north. The section has been pros-

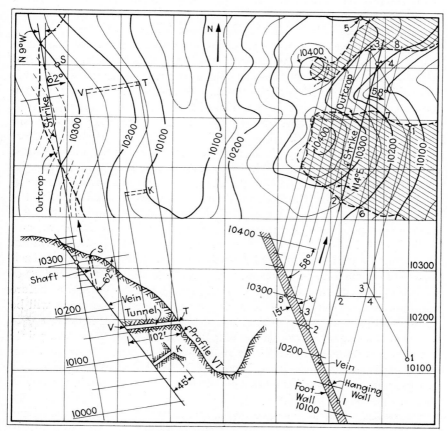

FIGURE 3. Veins and outcrops.

pected, and outcrops or traces of a vein of ore have been found at points 1, 2, and 3 in one wall of a vein, and at 5 in the other wall of the same vein. If the geology of the country indicates that the vein is probably not distorted, then the necessary information on which to base mining operations is determined as explained in the following paragraphs.

6. To Find the Strike and Dip. After the country has been surveyed and the map of Figure 3 made, the points of outcrop 1, 2, 3, and 5 are located on the map. The points 1, 2, and 3 lie in one plane face of the vein. The strike of the vein may be found by drawing any horizontal line of this plane. Locate the three points of the plane in the front view, each at its correct elevation as determined from the contour, and then draw a horizontal line through the point 2. This line intersects the line 1 3 at 4 in the front view. Next, locate 4 on the line 1 3 in the top view. Draw the line 2 4 in the top view. This is the strike or trend of the vein of ore. It is a horizontal line in one wall of the vein. The strike bears N 14° E and here is taken at the 10,250-foot level.

The dip of the vein is obtained by drawing an edge view of the plane face of the vein. Since the angle of dip is the angle that the vein dips below the horizontal, the necessary edge view must be an auxiliary elevation taken in the direction of the strike. In this auxiliary elevation each 100-foot level is shown, and the points 1, 2, 3, and 5 are located, each at its proper level. The points 1, 2, and 3 will fall in one wall of the vein and 5 will be in the other wall. The edge view determines that the first three points are in the hanging wall and that 5 is in the foot wall. The sectional view of the vein is section-lined. The thickness of the vein may now be measured and is found to be 15 feet. The angle of dip of the vein is measured as the dip below the horizontal and is found to be 58 degrees to the eastward. The dip should now be indicated on the map by drawing a short arrow perpendicular to the strike, pointing to the eastward, and marked with the angle of dip. When the strike and dip of the vein are shown on the map, the general direction of the vein may be visualized.

7. To Find the Line of Outcrop. A vein of ore will meet the surface of the ground along a line of outcrop. This line should be determined before mining operations are begun, so that the extent of the ore body will be known and an economical plan of operations may be outlined.

When the country shown on the map of Figure 3 was prospected, points of outcrop in the hanging wall were found at 1, 2, and 3. Other points on the probable line of outcrop are found as follows: Take any horizontal line in the hanging wall in the edge view of the vein, for example, the line at the 10,200-foot level. On the map this line appears as the line 6 8 parallel to the strike. It is at the same level, and in the same horizontal plane, with the 10,200-foot contour line. These two lines cross at the points 6, 7, and 8 within the limits of the map. These three points are in the vein and on the surface of the ground and hence are points of outcrop. The vein usually will be found near the points indicated. The points of outcrop found at the 10,350-foot level near the south peak are rather far apart, and no outcroppings are here indicated at the 10,400-foot level. It becomes necessary to sketch in the 10,375-foot intermediate contour and to determine points of outcrop at this level. Interpolation of additional contours frequently is necessary to find the course of a line of outcrop, particularly where the contours are nearly parallel to the strike. A series of points of outcrop is thus found, and the line of outcrop is drawn through them.

The complete line of outcrop of the hanging wall of the vein is shown by broken lines in the figure. For a thick vein it may be desirable to find the outcrops of both walls of the vein. In the country lying between the points 7 and 8 there is a valley running east and west that carries no ore.

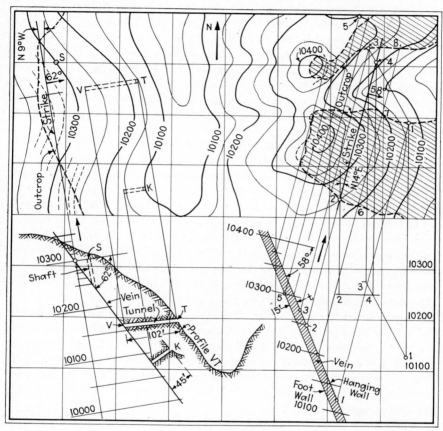

FIGURE 3. (*Continued.*)

Here, the land has been eroded, and the ore carried downstream. All of the ore lies within the two loops formed by the line of outcrop and is indicated on the map by shaded areas. The extent of the ore body is now known. Its tonnage may be calculated, and the best methods of mining it determined.

8. Tunnels and Shafts. On the western half of the map of Figure 3 are indicated the strike, dip, and outcrop of a thin vein of ore. To find this outcrop it is necessary to draw a number of intermediate contours. The auxiliary elevation taken in the direction of the strike is shown below the map. A tunnel is to be started at T on the 10,150-foot level. The tunnel is to be on a 5 per cent upgrade, so that it will drain readily and so that the loaded mine cars will roll out of the mine. Also, the tunnel is to be as short as possible. The direction of the tunnel will be perpendicular to the strike, as shown on the map. The grade of the tunnel and its length, 102 feet, are shown in the auxiliary elevation. A short tunnel from K is shown perpendicular to the vein, but it would not drain. A shorter upgrade tunnel could be run from K to the vein than from T. The location of the entrance to a tunnel or shaft on an actual job is governed by many factors. A vertical shaft is shown at S. It would have to be about 50 feet deep to reach the vein. The profile taken on the section V T and shown in the auxiliary elevation aids in visualizing the relation of the vein to the surface of the ground above and below the tunnel. The amount of overburden is here shown.

9. Mine Dumps. Adequate space must be provided for dumping the refuse of a mine. Property boundaries, legal restrictions, and the slope of the land often limit the possible size of a dump and, hence, the extent to which the mine can be worked.

On the map of Figure 4 a shaft mouth is located at S at the 325-foot level. Mine refuse having an angle of repose of 42 degrees is to be dumped from this point. The surface of the dump will take the form of a cone. In the front view, S is shown, at the 325-foot level, as the vertex of a right cone having a base angle of 42 degrees. The problem is to find the intersection of this cone with the surface of the hillside. As usual, pass horizontal cutting planes. A cutting plane at the 200-foot level, for example, will cut from the cone a circle of radius X Y; and from the hillside the cutting plane will cut the 200-foot contour line. On the map, or top view, the circle and the contour line will cross at points 2 and 3. The dump at this level will lie between these points. Outside these points the circle runs underground. At the different levels, a series of points on the edge of the dump is found in a similar manner. The outline G of the dump is drawn through them.

When mine refuse is dumped directly from the shaft mouth, or shaft collar, S, the dump is found to be rather small. The capacity of the dump can be increased considerably by dumping material at increasing radial distances until a flat area is formed around the shaft mouth. In Figure 4, such an area is taken as a circle of 72-foot radius. In the front view, the top of the cone now becomes a circle of 72-foot radius S A. The radius of the dump at the 200-foot level is now X Z. In the top view the circle of this radius intersects the 200-foot contour at points 4 and 5. These are points on the enlarged dump. It should be noted that the circle of the conical dump at the 150-foot level intersects the 150-foot contour at four

points.   Between the points 7 and 8 the contour line is outside the circle.
This means that there is a shoulder at this point that cannot be covered
by the dump.   Other points on the shoulder are found by plotting points
on intermediate contours at 12½-foot intervals.   The area at F, found in
this manner, will not be covered by the dump.   After a sufficient number

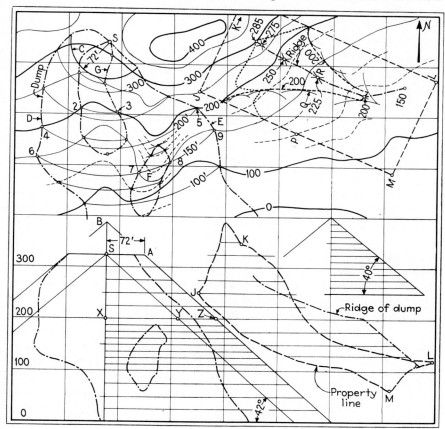

FIGURE 4. Mine dumps.

of points are found, the outline of the larger dump may be shown.   If
desired, the front view of the dump also may be drawn as is shown in the
figure.

When a mine dump must be kept within certain limits or boundaries,
it becomes necessary to determine the points from which material may
be dumped so as to keep the dump within this area.   The capacity of the
dump may then be calculated in advance of mining operations.

In Figure 4, mine refuse from the 300-foot level is to be dumped within
the property limits of the rectangular claim J K L M.   The ridge along

which rock may be dumped is to be determined. The natural slope of the mine refuse is found to be 40 degrees. A cone of 40-degree base angle is first drawn in the front view, and circles at each $12\frac{1}{2}$-foot level of the cone are shown. Next is to be found a line, at some chosen level, along which the material may be dumped to reach just to the property limits. The 200-foot level is here chosen. Points on this line are found as follows: Take P on the boundary line. It is at the 125-foot level. The difference between 125 feet and the chosen 200-foot level is 75 feet. Set the compass to the radius of the cone circle that is 75 feet below the vertex. This radius is the horizontal distance that the 200-foot level on the dump must be from P. Center the compass at P and scribe the arc Q of a circle. Take other points along the boundary lines and go through the same process. A line tangent to the arcs thus found will be a line on the dump at the 200-foot level. It is the 200-foot contour line of the dump, and it is shown on the map as a short-dash line. The area within the V of this line is level. The problem now is to find a ridge along which additional material may be dumped so as just to cover this level area. The point R on the ridge at the 225-foot level, for example, is 25 feet above the 200-foot contour of the dump, and its horizontal distance from each of the two branches of this contour is equal to the radius of the cone at the 25-foot level below its vertex. The point R, then, is found as the intersection of two lines that are drawn parallel to, and at the stated horizontal distance from, the two branches of the 200-foot dump contour. Other points on the ridge at higher and lower levels are found in the same way, and the ridge of the dump is drawn through them. The drawing indicates that the highest level from which mine refuse may be dumped is on the ridge at the 285-foot level, and that any material dumped from the 300-foot level will flow beyond the property line. It is impossible to cover the entire property with the dump. The dotted line indicates the upper limit of the base of the dump. The lower limits follow the property lines downhill. The corner L will not be filled unless the ridge of the dump is extended to the 150-foot level to the point shown on the map. The corners of a dump always are rounded to a conical surface.

The irregular outline of the property on the mountain side is shown in the front view, and the ridge of the dump is shown. The capacity of the dump may now be calculated, and the effect of its limitations on future mining operations taken into consideration.

10. Cuts and Fills. Level areas for landing fields, building sites, railways, roads, and other earth-moving operations require planning to determine where excavations or cuts are to be made and where fills are necessary.

Figure 5 shows a level rectangular field excavated on a hillside. The four edges of the field are taken at the 300-foot level. The view taken in the direction of the arrow A is an auxiliary elevation showing the edge view of one of the cuts, with the slope indicated as 1 to 1. From this view, the horizontal lines of the cuts at each 12½-foot level are determined for three sides of the field in the plan view. The horizontal lines of the cuts at the 325-foot level, for example, intersect the 325-foot contour of the hillside at points 1, 2, 3, and 4. These are points where the

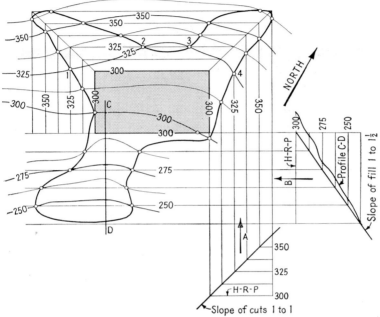

FIGURE 5. Cuts and fills.

plane surface of the cuts meets the curved surface of the hillside. Other points are located for each level, and through these points the curved limiting lines of the cuts are drawn.

A view taken in the direction of arrow B shows the edge view of the fill for a slope of 1 to 1½. From this view the horizontal lines of the fill are determined for each 12½-foot level in the plan view. Here, the intersections of each of these lines with the contour at the corresponding level are determined, and through these points the limiting line of the fill is drawn.

Figure 6 shows a better and more economical plan than the design of Figure 5. Note that rounding the corners of the cuts considerably reduces the yardage to be excavated. The curved surface of each rounded corner is an inverted cone.

Additional engineering calculations are necessary to determine the volume of material to be excavated in the cuts and placed in the fill. The areas of equally spaced sections are measured. For example, the profile through C D in the plan view is here shown in auxiliary view B. The area

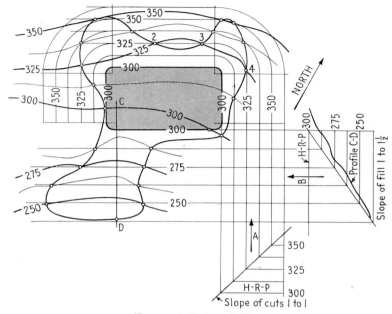

FIGURE 6. Cuts and fills.

between this profile and the edge of the fill is found graphically, or with the aid of a planimeter. From the areas of similar sections and the distance between them, the total volume is calculated. The vertical dimensions of profiles in relatively flat land often are exaggerated to magnify the differences in elevations.

The level field in Figures 5 and 6 may also be regarded as a limited length of a railway bed or roadway, the cuts and fills of which are determined by the methods just explained.

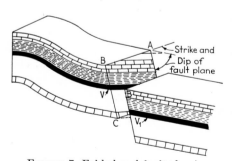

FIGURE 7. Folded and faulted vein.

11. Folded and Faulted Veins. The walls of strata of rocks and of veins of ore generally are plane surfaces only within rather limited areas. Movements in the crust of the earth cause veins to be folded and faulted. In Figure 7 a short section of folded or curved strata is shown in the left half of this pictorial illustration. In the right half of the figure the strata have retained their original plane form, but one part has slipped in relation to the other part. This slip produces a fault in the strata. The surface of the fault is usually a plane, within limited areas, and is called the *fault plane*. The strike and dip of the fault plane are indicated in the figure. They are independent of the strike and dip of the strata of rocks. When strata are faulted, scratches or striations often are left on the faces of the rocks in the fault plane. These indicate the direction of the relative movement of the two parts. Any possible movement may take place in the formation of a fault. If the two parts separate, a fissure is formed.

By applying the methods and principles of the geometry of engineering drawing, veins of ore that have been folded, or that have been lost through faulting, may be located. The problems may seem to be complex, but their solution is based on simple principles.

12. Outcrops of Folded Veins. On the map of Figure 8, the land contours are shown as solid lines. A folded vein underlies parts of this area. It is desired to find the lines of outcrop of the vein so that the extent of the vein may be known and plans may be made for mining it. Since the vein is folded or curved in various directions, it becomes necessary definitely to locate a number of points in the vein, and from these to determine the approximate location of other points in the vein. When a sufficient number of points are found, contours representing the irregular curved surface of the folded vein may be drawn. Points on the required line of outcrop are then located at the intersections of the land and vein contours.

The area that is shown on the map is prospected both on the surface and with a core drill. A few points in the vein are thus found as outcrops on the surface, and other points in the vein are located with a drill at definite distances below the surface of the ground. The location of each point so found and its elevation are marked on the map. The points 10 and 15, for example, are at the 700-foot elevation and they also are on the 700-foot contours. This means that these are points of outcrop of the vein, and they have been located without drilling. Point 2, for example, is a drill hole. Here, the elevation of the surface of the ground is 785 feet, and the drilling records show that the vein was found at a depth of 160 feet. The vein at this point is therefore at an elevation of 625 feet, and this elevation is marked on the map.

Twenty-one points in the ore vein have been located on the map; but at this stage the contours of the vein have not been located. A study of the elevations of these points indicates that there is a depression or low area in the vein near the points 2, 3, 5, and 11, and that there is a ridge near point 21. The 21 points are not sufficient for determining the contours of the vein. Additional points in the vein are determined by

assuming that the vein is straight for limited distances. These points
are located as follows: Take the points 1 and 2, for example. Draw a
straight line connecting these points, and assume that it lies in the vein.
This line slopes upward from the point 2 to 1, from the 625-foot level to
the 740-foot level, in a horizontal distance that may be measured from 2 to

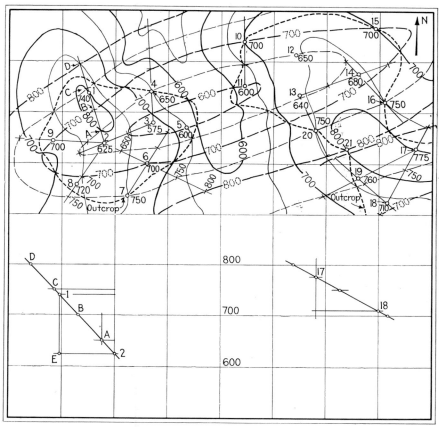

FIGURE 8. Outcrop of folded vein.

1 on the map. Visualize this. The slope of this line is now shown in a
drawing below the map. First, the 600-, 700-, and 800-foot elevations
are marked. The point 2 is taken somewhere on the 625-foot level; and
the point 1 is at the 740-foot level, but to one side of the point 2 a horizontal distance 2 E equal to the horizontal distance between the points 2 and
1 on the map. A sloping line is now drawn through these points. This
construction drawing is not a front view. It is a misplaced normal view
of the line 1 2. Points A, B, C, and D are now located on this slope at
each 50-foot interval. The horizontal distance of each of these points

from point 2 may now be measured and transferred to the line 1 2 on the map. The points A, B, C, and D on the 50-foot interval contours of the vein are thus located on the map. The elevation of each point so found may be conveniently marked as has been done on the line through 2 and 6, and 2 and 8. Other points that have been found by this method also are shown on the map. Care must be taken not to run a straight line across a depression or ridge of the vein. The contours of the vein should not be drawn until enough points are found definitely to determine each contour. The vein contours are indicated on the map by long-dash lines. The vein-contour elevations are indicated by dotted figures to distinguish them from the land-contour elevations. Richer ore usually is found in the troughs of folded veins.

Points of outcrop of the vein are found as follows: The 700-foot contour of the vein, for example, lies in the same horizontal plane as the 700-foot contour of the land surface. These two contours intersect at a number of points that are in the vein and on the surface of the ground and, hence, are required points of outcrop. Other points of outcrop are found at each contour level, and the lines of outcrop, indicated by the short-dash lines, are drawn through them. Wherever the contour of the vein is above the surface of the land, the vein has been eroded. The map indicates that the vein will be found within the closed outcrop line on the west half, and within the loop of the outcrop on the east half. The extent of the folded vein is now determined.

13. Faulted Veins. When a vein is faulted in a mine, the vein will end suddenly against a wall of rock, and the rest of the vein is lost. The problem for the mining engineer is to find the lost part of the vein. Surface and underground indications may give some hint as to the direction in which the lost vein may be found. The principal difficulty is to obtain sufficient field data. Since this is a highly specialized problem requiring knowledge of mining and geology, the solution is not here shown. Those who are interested will find a solution in the second edition of this textbook.

14. Problems.

Group 87. Topographical and Mining Problems.

Chapter 13

PICTORIAL VIEWS

PRODUCTION ILLUSTRATIONS—ORTHOGRAPHIC PICTORIAL VIEWS—
FREEHAND SKETCHES—PERSPECTIVE VIEWS—PHOTOGRAPHIC
METHODS—ISOMETRIC VIEWS—SHADES AND SHADOWS

1. The engineer designs structures by drawing principal, auxiliary, and oblique views. Those who are not trained in reading such orthographic views often have difficulty in visualizing the appearance of the structure from the views. Pictorial views avoid this difficulty. They readily are understood by everyone and are coming into greater use in industry. Freehand pictorial sketches are a considerable aid to the engineer in working out his own ideas and in explaining his ideas to others.

Pictorial views are observed by looking at an object in a chosen direction, or by looking at it from a chosen point of view. Care must be used to choose a direction or a point of view so that the resulting pictorial view will afford a satisfactory picture of the object.

2. Production Illustrations. The use of pictorial production illustrations often increases the output of a factory considerably beyond the output obtained when orthographic front, top, and side views are used. Figure 1 is an example of a production illustration used to expedite the assembly of the forward compression compartment of an airplane. The parts of this structure are readily assembled by observing their relative locations in the production illustration.

Figure 1 is a perspective drawing. It is first drawn as a line drawing and is then shaded until the finished picture appears almost as if it were a photograph of the object. Methods of making orthographic pictorial drawings and of making perspective line drawings by freehand, by drafting board, and by photographic methods are explained in this chapter.

3. Pictorial Orthographic Views. An orthographic pictorial view of an object often is just as satisfactory for many uses as is a perspective view; and the orthographic view requires much less work to draw. As explained in Chapter 4, an oblique view of an object may be obtained by first drawing a complete auxiliary view and by transferring measurements of the adjacent principal view to the oblique view. This plan is useful if the object is relatively simple. But a considerable amount of work is required if the object is at all complicated. The intermediate steps may be almost entirely eliminated by the method here described.

A casting for a drilling jig is chosen as an example. This object is first visualized in the mind of the designer and then its three principal views are drawn as shown in Figure 2. The best direction in which to take the

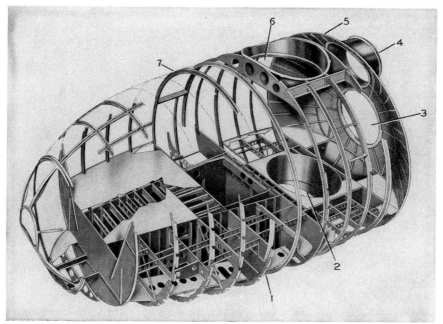

FIGURE 1. Production illustration. (*Boeing Aircraft Co. and Aero Digest.*)

pictorial view is chosen, and this direction is fixed by drawing the views of the pointing arrow. Careful choice of the direction and slope of the arrow is probably the surest way of determining in advance that the pictorial view will show the details it is desired to show. The slope of this arrow is not nearly so steep as it appears to be in the front view. The actual slope is a little less than is indicated by the arrow in the side view.

The explanation of the method of determining the directions of the lines of the object in the pictorial view is simplified by first considering any horizontal rectangle of the object. The rectangle A B C D at the level of the center line is here used.

Consider first the top view in Figure 2. The observer notes that the corners of the rectangle are spaced to one side or the other of the arrow. The four points should be visualized as being in vertical planes parallel to the arrow. The edge views of these planes are represented by the fine lines drawn parallel to the arrow. Since the pointing arrow is not horizontal, these planes are not considered as rays. The horizontal spacings of the planes and of the points, indicated by h, are measured perpendicular to the arrow. These spacings are independent of the slope of the arrow. The spacings here observed will be seen, and may be measured, in the required pictorial view. Hence points in the pictorial view may be

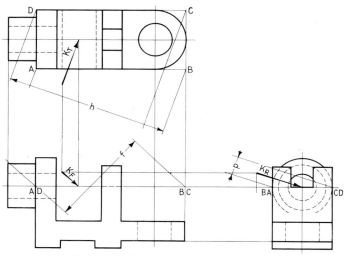

FIGURE 2. Principal views of a drill jig.

located in line with their top views by extending the edges of these parallel spacing planes.

Similar observations are made in the front view. The frontal spacings, indicated by f, of the points in the receding planes parallel to the arrow will appear in the pictorial view. And the profile spacings in the side view, indicated by p, also will appear in the required pictorial view. To avoid the work of measuring these spacings in the pictorial view, the principal views of the object are placed in certain predetermined positions relative to each other, as is done in Figure 3. These locations are determined by first drawing a pictorial view of the horizontal rectangle A B C D of the object. Tracings or prints of the principal views may be used to avoid redrawing these views.

Figure 3: The top view of the casting is located so that view K_T of the arrow points north. The resulting pictorial view will then be right side up. Vertical spacing planes parallel to the arrow are extended toward the observer. One of the four corners of the pictorial view of the rectangle A B C D will be in each of these planes. To determine the locations of these corners, it is necessary first to determine the exact slope of the pointing arrow by drawing a normal auxiliary elevation of the arrow in which the edge view of the rectangle also is seen. In this view, shown to the right of the top view, spacing planes are drawn through the corners of the rectangle and parallel to arrow K_A. These spacings, indicated by x, will be seen and may be measured in the required pictorial view. Spacings x are perpendicular to spacings h, and the two sets of spacing planes are perpendicular. Visualize these relations.

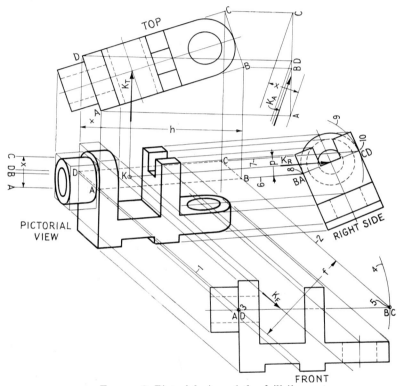

Figure 3. Pictorial view of the drill jig.

Measurements x and the spacing planes are now transferred to the indicated location below and to the left of the top view. Here, measurements x are perpendicular to the h measurements and the two sets of spacing planes are perpendicular. The spacing plane of each point is extended to intersect the corresponding spacing plane of the top view, and each intersection is lettered with the name of the point. The pictorial view of the rectangle, here represented by four dash lines, is now drawn.

It should here be definitely understood that the pictorial view of the rectangle is not observed in a horizontal direction. The normal procedure for drawing adjacent views is here violated.   Care must be taken not to reverse the order in which the spacing planes to the left of the pictorial view are lettered.   Point A is the corner of the rectangle nearest the observer who looks in the direction of the arrow K.   Hence point A must be nearest the observer in the pictorial view.

In the pictorial view of the rectangle A B C D, the spacing f between edges A D and B C will be equal to spacing f, Figure 2.   And spacings p in the two figures will be equal.

In Figure 3, the locations of the front and top views of the rectangle, and of the object, are determined from the pictorial view of the rectangle. Spacing planes 1 and 2 are drawn through the pictorial views of A D and B C.   The compass is set to the true length of A B in the front view.   A center is chosen at some point 3 on spacing plane 1, and arc 4 is drawn to intersect spacing plane 2 at 5.   Points 3 and 5 determine the end views of A D and B C, and this front view of the rectangle determines the location of the front view of the object.   This front view is not horizontal. To determine the location of the right-side view of the rectangle and of the object, set the compass to the true length of B C, choose a center 8 on spacing plane 6, and draw arc 9 to locate point 10 in spacing plane 7. The side view of the rectangle, and of the object, is then drawn.

Note that the front view K_F of the arrow must be parallel to the spacing planes 1 and 2.   And arrow K_R must be parallel to spacing planes 6 and 7.

The required pictorial view is now readily completed by drawing spacing planes from each corner or point in each of the principal views, and by locating the pictorial view of that corner at the intersection of the three spacing planes.   The pictorial view of any point may be located from any two principal views, but determining the locations of points from three principal views serves as a useful check.   Circles may be boxed with a square, and also the major and minor axes of their elliptical views readily may be determined.   Intersections of any two surfaces of the object may be found in the pictorial view by passing cutting planes without reference to any principal view.

Principal views must be accurately located, otherwise the locations of points will not be correct and the resulting pictorial view will be a disappointment.   Much time is saved in accurately drawing the parallel spacing planes by fixing to the drawing board short straightedges perpendicular to the spacing planes, so that these planes may readily be drawn by using these straightedges in turn as guides for a triangle.

When choosing the direction in which an object is to be viewed, it may be desirable to select the top view of the arrow, and then its slope in the normal auxiliary elevation.   These two views will then determine the front and right-side views of the arrow.

A pictorial view drawn by the method just described often serves its required purpose fully as well as would a perspective view, which is much more difficult to draw.

4. Problems.

Group 88.   Orthographic Pictorial Views.

5. Freehand Pictorial Sketching.

The engineer who trains himself in the art of readily making freehand perspective sketches finds frequent use for this ability.   Pictorial sketches are a considerable aid in developing his own ideas and in explaining his ideas to others.   Freehand perspective sketches having a satisfactory appearance are readily drawn by training the eye and the hand and by observing a few simple geometrical relations.

A habit of making neat and correct sketches should be cultivated. Visualizing in advance each line that is to be drawn will avoid much erasing and will save time.   Poor work and fuzzy lines should not be tolerated.   The use of mechanical aids, such as straightedges, vanishing points, and ruled papers, is not advisable in connection with freehand drawings, since these limit the freedom inherent in freehand methods.

A pictorial drawing generally is more satisfactory when the object is viewed in a slanting direction not too far from the horizontal and from a point not too close to the object; and since the drawing offers a pictorial view of the object, the drawing is best viewed in the same general direction and from the same distance.   At times, it is desirable to show views taken in unusual directions.   A common fault, however, is to draw the object so that it has the appearance of being tilted forward, as in isometric drawings. A plan for basing sketches on a view of a horizontal circle, as explained below, offers a ready foundation on which to build a satisfactory sketch.

Figure 4: Two right circular cylinders are shown at A.   One cylinder has a vertical shaft or axis, and the other has a horizontal, or an inclined, axis.   In both cylinders, the major axis of the elliptical view of each circle is drawn perpendicular to the shaft line or axis of the cylinder.   Perpendicular-line principles apply here: All diameters of a circle are perpendicular to the axis of the circle.   The major axis is the normal view of one of the diameters.   Hence according to the perpendicular-line principle, the major axis must be drawn perpendicular to the axis of the circle.   And the minor axis is perpendicular to the major axis.   The minor axis represents a diameter of the circle and is never considered as coinciding with the axis of the circle.

The incorrectly drawn right circular cylinders shown at B illustrate a type of error that is all too common in technical and other pictorial illustrations.   Distorted drawings never are satisfactory.

When a horizontal circle is viewed in a slanting direction inclined approximately 15 to 20 degrees below the horizontal, the elliptical view will show about a 1 to 3 ratio of the minor to the major axis.   Views taken at steeper angles generally are not so satisfactory in appearance.   Sketch

C shows a view of a horizontal circle. The axis of every horizontal circle is vertical. Hence the major axis is horizontal, and the minor axis is perpendicular to the major axis.

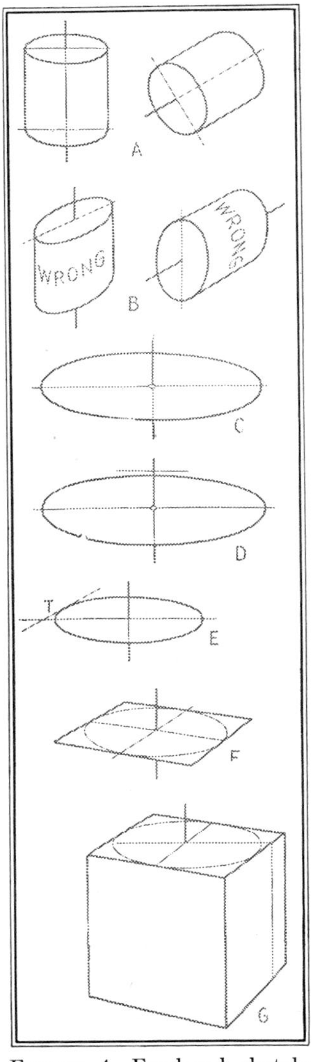

FIGURE 4. Freehand sketching.

View C is drawn as a true ellipse, while view D is a true perspective view of a circle in which the far half of the diameter represented by the minor axis is slightly shorter than the near half. This difference is indicated by the short horizontal line. This difference may be observed in the sketches if desired.

With the aid of a horizontal circle, a horizontal square is readily drawn, as is illustrated in sketches E and F. A tangent is drawn at any chosen point T. Next, a diameter is drawn through T and the center of the circle. The tangent and the diameter represent two perpendicular horizontal lines in the picture, and they indicate the directions in which the sides of a square may be drawn. The completed square is shown in sketch F. When drawing perspective sketches, parallel lines are drawn to appear parallel when the entire sketch is viewed as a picture. These lines actually converge and meet at a point. If parallel lines are drawn actually parallel, they appear to diverge. There is no advantage in locating vanishing points when making freehand perspective sketches.

The horizontal square just drawn is used as the upper face of a cube in sketch G. The height of the cube, indicated by the fine vertical line, may be determined by making this line equal in length to, and in the same frontal plane with, the major axis. Vertical lines are here drawn vertical, and the other parallel lines are drawn to appear parallel.

Using the view of a cube as a basis for determining directions of lines and proportions of parts, the sketcher is able to draw rectangular structures of any degree of complexity.

The picture of the cube in sketch G illustrates the need for the reader to view each perspective sketch from the proper point of view. Sketch G should be viewed with the page held vertically, and with the eye a few inches above the sketch and at a normal distance from the page. If viewed offhand, the cube will appear too tall and somewhat distorted. Careless sketching and careless viewing of a true sketch will give a distorted picture of the object.

6. Sketching an Angle Plate. A method of building up the pictorial sketch of the angle plate J of Figure 5 is here described. The rounded end is first drawn as a complete cylinder K having a vertical axis. At L, parallel straight lines are drawn tangent to the circular disk. These may be drawn in any desired direction as indicated, for example, by either the solid or the broken lines. In sketch M, tangent points T are located, and the diameter T T is drawn. This represents a line perpendicular to the tangents. In sketch N, all cross lines are now drawn to appear parallel to line T T. The sketch is now completed by adding the screw holes and accenting the lines of the finished drawing as shown at J. The correct geometrical relations have been maintained, and parallel lines have been drawn to appear parallel in this perspective view.

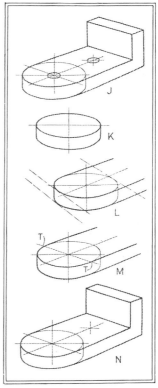

FIGURE 5. Sketching an angle plate.

7. Sketching a Bearing. Figure 6: The shaft line or axis of cylinder Q is drawn in any desired direction. The major axis is perpendicular to the shaft line. The ratio of the lengths of the minor and major axes may be taken as desired. In sketch R, vertical lines are drawn tangent to the front end of the cylinder, and tangent points T and T are located. These points are at the same level as the center of the circle. The cross line T T is a horizontal line of the bearing. The lines through T and T and parallel to the axis of the cylinder are halfway up on the cylinder. In sketch S, vertical lines of the base are drawn. Note how the location of the vertical line at the left is determined. The pictorial view is now completed by drawing the cross lines of the base so that they appear parallel to the horizontal line T T, and the shorter lines are drawn to appear parallel to the shaft. The height of the bearing may be judged by the vertical height of the circular ends. The major axes of the bolt holes and of the oil hole must be horizontal. The completed drawing is shown in sketch P.

8. Sketching Objects in Any Position. The appearance of a finished sketch will be satisfactory if the correct geometrical relations and the relative proportions of all parts of the object are maintained in the sketch.

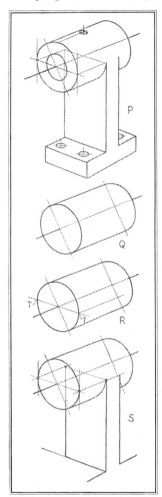

The directions of three mutually perpendicular lines may be correctly determined in pictorial drawings by the methods explained in connection with the bearing illustrated in Figure 7. Some ingenuity is required at times to locate certain points and lines. At all times it is necessary to be critical of the appearance of the object shown in the sketch.

To draw the pictorial view of the bearing shown in Figure 7, the procedure may be as follows: Draw the axis of the cylinder in any desired direction. The major axis is perpendicular to this, and the ratio of the minor axis to the major is taken as desired. The view of the cylinder is then completed. Parallel tangents A and B to the ellipse are drawn in any desired direction. The tangent points determine the direction of the cross line C. The directions of three mutually perpendicular lines of the object are now fixed. Parallel lines of the object are now drawn to appear parallel. The major axes of the small bolt holes are perpendicular to tangents A and B.

FIGURE 6. Sketching a bearing.

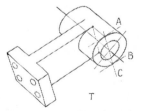

FIGURE 7. Bearing in oblique position.

9. Avoiding Common Errors. Concentric circles divide all radii of the largest circle into proportional parts. In the circular disk or washer of Figure 8, if the diameter of the hole is two-thirds the diameter of the outside circle, then the smaller circle passes through the two-thirds point of every radius of the larger circle. The radial distances between the two circles are not drawn equal in the pictorial view.

Circles frequently are incorrectly shown in pictorial sketches. In sketch V of a rectangular block, lines 3, 4, 5, and 6 are horizontal edges of a horizontal plane face. It is incorrect to assume that these lines determine either the major or the minor axis of the elliptical view of a horizontal circle. Vertical lines 1 and 2 determine the direction of the shaft line or axis of the horizontal circles 1 and 2. Likewise, lines 4 and 6 determine the direction of the axes of circles 4 and 6; and lines 3 and 5 determine the direction of the axes of circles 3 and 5. And each axis of a circle determines the perpendicular direction of the major axis of its elliptical view. The application of simple geometrical principles prevents many errors that so commonly are found in pictorial drawings.

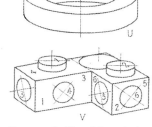

FIGURE 8. Sketching circles.

10. Problems.

Group 89. Freehand Perspective Sketches.

11. Perspective Drawings.
Anyone who looks at an object sees a perspective view of it. The observer, having two eyes, sees two different perspective views. These are merged, in his brain, into one view that conveys to him some idea of the depth of the picture. This is called *binocular vision*. The considerable difference in the pictures seen by each of the two eyes may be observed by looking first with one eye and then with the other at a group of objects at fairly close range. The apparent shifting of the objects will be readily noticed. Two photographs taken with two lenses of a stereoscopic camera convey the idea of depth in a picture when they are viewed through a stereoscope. A single photograph appears flat in comparison.

The simplest idea of a perspective view may be had by imagining that with one eye the observer looks at an object through a windowpane. Rays of light are reflected by the object to the eye of the observer. The intersections, with the windowpane, of the various rays of light that meet at the eye of the observer trace the perspective view of the object on the window glass. The plane on which a perspective view is drawn is called the *picture plane*. The point where the eye of the observer is located is called the *station point*, or *point of sight*. A perspective drawing is made on a picture plane by finding the intersections with the picture plane of the straight-line rays of light that extend from the points of the object to the station point. Usually, the picture plane is taken vertical, but it may be located in any position. The truest perspective is obtained by taking the picture plane perpendicular to the central line of sight. Perspective drawings are made at times on cylindrical and on spherical surfaces.

Only the basic methods of making perspective drawings are explained in this chapter. Many short cuts are available to those who will use their ingenuity to discover them, or who will study a textbook that explains various methods. Perspective drawings may be classified as drawn in either parallel perspective or angular perspective.

12. Parallel Perspective. In Figure 9 are shown the front, top, and right-side views of a rectangular box. The front and rear ends of the

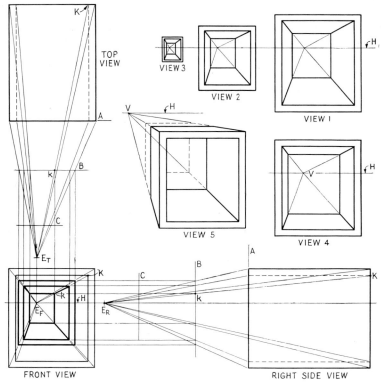

FIGURE 9. Elements of parallel perspective.

box are open and frontal. The eye of the observer is located at E. A frontal picture plane, parallel to the open ends of the box, is located at B. In each view are shown the converging rays of light that connect each corner of the box with the eye of the observer. The point of intersection of each ray with the picture plane, as seen directly in the top and side views, is transferred to the front view of the ray. The perspective view may now be completed by drawing the straight-line edges of the object, as indicated by the broad lines within the front view.

The perspective view just drawn is a parallel-perspective drawing of the rectangular box. In the parallel-perspective view it should be noted that all vertical lines of the object remain vertical in the picture; all horizontal-frontal lines of the object are horizontal in the picture; all receding lines of the object converge and meet at E_F in the perspective view. This meeting point is called the *center of vision*. The perspective view may be found with the aid of either the top or the side view. Both are here shown to give a better idea of the theory of perspective, and both may be used when it is desired to check the locations of points in the picture.

In Figure 9 three picture planes are shown at A, B, and C. As the picture plane moves nearer the station point, the resulting perspective view becomes smaller. Views 1, 2, and 3 show the perspective drawings for the picture planes A, B, and C. View 1 shows the view taken from the station point E, while view 4 is taken at a distance twice as far from the box. In view 5 the center of vision has been moved above and to the left of the box. In this view the dash lines indicate the addition that is made to the view when the observer moves from his first position to a station point only half as far from the front face of the box.

13. Selecting the Station Point. To obtain a satisfactory picture, judgment must be used in selecting the location of the station point. It must be neither too near the object nor too far away. Its elevation, in the case of large structures that stand on level ground, should usually be chosen at the level of the average person's eyes. In parallel perspective, the location of the station point may be taken slightly to one side of the center of the object. If taken too far to one side, the resulting drawing becomes a pseudo, or imitation, perspective.

A perspective drawing is best viewed from the station point that was selected by the draftsman or artist when the drawing was made. The eye of the reader should be directly in front of the front view of the station point. The picture is more satisfactory if viewed from this point than when viewed at random.

14. Circles in Parallel Perspective. When all circles of an object are in parallel planes, a perspective drawing of the object is readily made by taking a picture plane parallel to the circles. In the perspective drawing, all circles will then be drawn as circles.

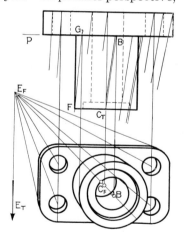

FIGURE 10. Circles in parallel perspective.

In Figure 10 the picture plane P is taken to coincide with the front face of the rectangular part of the casting. The front view of this face then becomes a part of the perspective view.   The front view E_F of the station point is shown in the figure. E_T is not shown, but it is here taken at a distance of about 8 inches in front of the picture plane.   In the perspective view, E_F is the center of vision, and all lines parallel to the axis of the cylinders will converge at E_F.   The center C of the front circle is located in the edge view of the picture plane at B in the top view.   The perspective view of B is on the line E_F C_F.   The point F at one end of the horizontal diameter of the same circle is found to be at G in the picture plane. B G is then the radius of circle C in the perspective view.   Centers and radii of other circles not in the picture plane are similarly found.   The perspective drawing of Figure 10 should be viewed with the page vertical and from a point about 8 inches from the page and directly in front of E_F.

15. Problems.

Group 90.   Parallel Perspective.

16. Angular Perspective.

The stepped block, of which the front and top views are shown in Figure 11, is taken as an example.   The details of making an angular perspective view of the steps may be explained as follows: The top view of the steps, turned so as to make a suitable angle with the frontal picture plane, is redrawn to the right of the original top view. The picture plane is here taken through the front corner of step 1.   The locations of the front and top views of the station point S are chosen as desired.   The top view of S has here been taken rather too close to the object, in order that all lines of the drawing may come within the limits of the page; and S_T is taken below S_F to keep the front and top views reasonably close together.   The rays that converge at S_T may now be drawn in the top view.   These rays need to extend only from the corners of the object to where they meet the picture plane.

Draw a horizontal line through S_F.   It is on a level with the eye of the observer and is called the *horizon*.   In the perspective view, all lines that represent the parallel horizontal lines of the object will converge and meet at vanishing points that are on the horizon.   In the steps there are two sets of parallel horizontal lines.   To find the vanishing point for one set of lines, draw S_T K_T parallel to the shorter horizontal edges of the steps. The front view of this line is S_F K_F.   The line S K meets the picture plane at K_T in the top view.   The front view of K is at K_F or V_1 on the horizon. V_1 is the vanishing point of one set of parallel lines.   All the lines of the steps that are parallel to S K will converge and meet at V_1 in the perspective view.

To find the other vanishing point, draw S_T L_T parallel to the longer edges of the steps.   It meets the picture plane at L_T.   The vanishing point is on the horizon at V_2.   All the edges of the steps that are parallel to S L will converge and meet at V_2 in the perspective view.

The front view of the steps shows the height of the steps.   The different levels may be measured in the picture plane by extending to the right a horizontal line from the level of each step.   The front vertical edge 1 of the steps is in the picture plane.   In the perspective drawing this edge appears in its true length at 1'.

The longer vertical-plane risers of the steps 2 and 3, Figure 11, are extended in the top view until they meet the picture plane at M and N. Here these risers intersect the picture plane in the vertical lines shown, respectively, at 2' and 3'.   The lines 2' and 3' represent the actual height of the steps in the picture plane.   Similarly, the shorter risers of steps 2

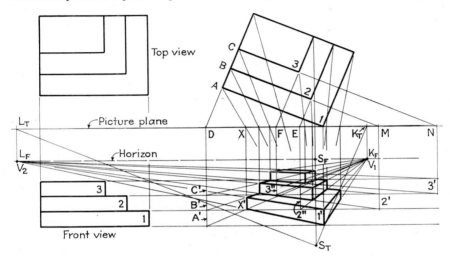

FIGURE 11. Elements of angular perspective.

and 3 are extended until they meet the picture plane at E and F, and in the two vertical lines 2'' and 3''.   The left-hand vertical faces A, B, and C of the steps, when extended, meet the picture plane at D and are shown, respectively, at A', B', and C'.

The edges 2', 3', 2'', 3'', A', B', and C' are all extensions, into the picture plane, of vertical planes of the steps.   From the upper and lower ends of the lines 1', 2'', 3'', A', B', and C', lines are drawn to meet at the vanishing point V_1.   Limited parts of these lines will represent the perspective views of the edges of the steps that are parallel to the line S K.   Similarly, from the upper and lower ends of the lines 1', 2', and 3', lines are drawn to meet at the vanishing point V_2.   Limited parts of these lines will represent the perspective view of edges of steps that are parallel to the line S L.   Any horizontal line of the object may thus be extended until it meets the picture plane; and the perspective view of the line may be determined by joining the vanishing point of the line with the point where the extended line meets the picture plane.

The vertical edge A of the steps is first located in the picture plane at X and is then transferred to X′ in the perspective view. X′ is limited by the two lines that have been drawn from the upper and lower ends of A′ to V_1. X′ is also limited by the lines that have been drawn from the upper and lower ends of 1′ to V_2. This is a check on the accuracy of the work. All the other vertical edges of the steps may be found in a similar way, and the perspective drawing may be completed by bringing out the lines of the picture.

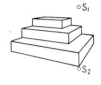

FIGURE 12. Perspective views compared.

The point of sight should be chosen so that the entire object lies within a *cone of vision* of which the angle at the vertex is not much over 30 degrees. This requires that the point of sight should not be nearer to the object than about twice the greatest dimension of the object. Even this is too close to produce a satisfactory picture.

Figure 12 shows two perspective views of the stepped block. The upper view requires a cone of vision having about a 40-degree angle, and the station point is located in front of the steps a distance about equal to the width of the steps. To make this view appear natural, the eye must be very close to the page. For the lower view, the angle of the cone of vision is about 15 degrees, and even this drawing should be viewed with the eye only 4 inches from the page. Rather large drawing boards are required for making satisfactory perspective drawings, unless specially designed equipment is used.

17. Circles in Angular Perspective. The square block on which is mounted a cylindrical boss, Figure 13, is taken as an example. The top view is drawn in any desirable position with relation to the picture plane P; the front and top views of the station point are chosen, and the horizon H is drawn. In the front view the cylindrical part of the object is enclosed in an octagonal prism. The perspective drawing of the cylinder is made by first finding the perspective view of the octagonal prism, and then inscribing the curves of the circles within the perspective views of the octagons.

The perspective view of the square block and octagonal prism is found by using the methods explained in the article on angular perspective. The vanishing points V_1 and V_2 are located. The planes of the larger vertical faces of the square block and octagonal prism are extended to meet the picture plane at A, B, and C, and from these the vertical measuring lines 1, 2, and 3 are determined in the picture plane. The elevations of the corners of the object are transferred from the front view to the respective measuring lines 1, 2, and 3, and each of these points is connected with the proper vanishing point. The vertical lines of the picture are drawn, the other lines are added, and the perspective view is completed by inscribing the perspective circles within the octagons.   The perspective view of the circle is tangent to the sides of the octagon at their middle points.   These points may be determined if desired.   The sides of the octagon give direction to the circle at these points.   It is possible to locate points on the perspective view of the circle without drawing the octagon, but the use of the octagon usually will reduce the number of points that it is necessary to find.   By determining the center of the

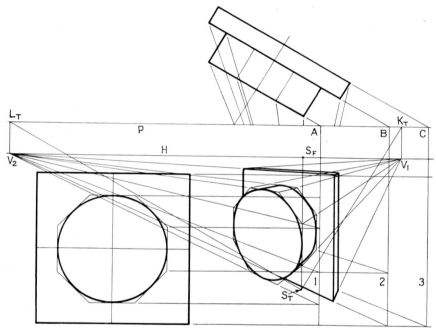

FIGURE 13. Circles in angular perspective.

octagon or circle in the perspective drawing, diagonals or diameters may be drawn to serve as a check on the location of opposing points on these lines.   The perspective view shown in Figure 13 is not very satisfactory. The station point is too close to the object.   This is necessary here so that the vanishing points may be shown in the figure.   A better picture would result if the station point were taken at least six times as far from the object.

18. Problems.

Group 91.   Angular Perspective.

19. Perspective Layouts by Photography.   Figures 14 and 15 illustrate means by which it is possible to produce any desired number of different perspective layouts of an object, with the additional advantage

that the exact appearance of each perspective picture may be determined in advance.   As shown in Figure 14, the cross sections, or frames, for each station of a fuselage are drawn on transparent plastic sheets.   These are set in a slotted base in their proper order and spacing.   The model is placed in front of a camera and is moved until the picture on the ground glass is satisfactory.   It is then photographed, and an enlargement of suitable size is made.   The enlargement is placed on the drafting board, and desired parts are traced and additions are made as required for a

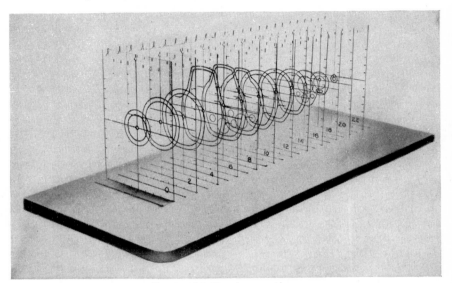

FIGURE 14. Fuselage sections.

production illustration or other use.   Figure 15 shows models of a fuselage, a wing, and a nacelle assembled and photographed as a unit.

It should be noted that the vertical lines of the models are not parallel in the perspective picture.   The three vanishing points of the three sets of parallel lines of the models are easily located.   The plan here described is useful for making basic perspective layouts of a great variety of complex objects at a considerable saving in time over the usual methods.   The complete details of this plan are explained in *Aero Digest* for October, 1943.

20. Isometric Drawings.   Figure 16 illustrates the method by which isometric views are derived.   These views are observed in the direction of the body diagonal of a cube, as is indicated by the arrow.   In the isometric view shown at A, the equal edges of the cube appear equal in length; the vertical edges are vertical; and the horizontal edges make an angle of 30 degrees with the horizontal.   When an isometric drawing of any rectangular object is made, the true lengths of the sides may be meas-

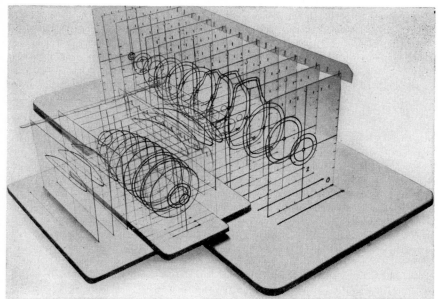

FIGURE 15. Three models assembled.

ured along the vertical and the 30-degree lines.   The appearance of an isometric view is not natural, unless the drawing is viewed at a considerable slant that approximates the slant of the body diagonal of a cube having horizontal bases.

An isometric circle for showing cylindrical parts may be enclosed in a square and drawn as shown at B.   The elliptical form is approximated by drawing circular arcs centered at the indicated points.   Methods of making isometric drawings are fully explained in engineering drawing textbooks.   Such drawings are readily made with the usual drafting instruments, but they do not afford wholly satisfactory pictorial views of objects.

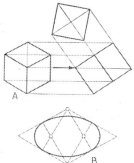

FIGURE 16. Isometric views.

21. Shades and Shadows. The effect of bright light on a structure is to produce graduated shades and shadows on the structure.   The contrast of light and shade brings the parts of the structure into relief when seen by the eye.   When a structure is seen under highly diffused light, without definite shades and shadows, it appears flat.   Shades and shadows are added to drawings when it is desired to give an appearance of depth to the structure shown in the drawing.   Such drawings frequently are used by architects, engineers, and others in order that clients and readers may more readily appreciate the appearance of the structure. They also are an aid in studying the sales appeal of a design.

Shade on the surface of an object is the darkened area caused by the exclusion of light from that area by a part of the object itself. Shadow on the surface of an object is the darkened area caused by the exclusion of light from that area by some other object. Shadow always is darker in tone than is shade.

The effect of shades and shadows on a line drawing is illustrated in Figure 17. At the left is the front view of a pergola. At the right is the

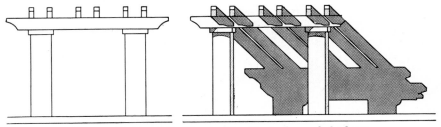

FIGURE 17. Pergola without and with shades and shadows.

same view with shades and shadows cast on parts of the pergola and on the vertical wall behind it. The shadows are indicated by a darker tone than are the shades. Outlines of shades and shadows are determined by assuming a fixed direction or source for the rays of light, and then determining the intersections of a number of rays with various surfaces of the object.

Figure 1 is an example of expert shading that gives an appearance almost equal to that of an actual photograph. Examples of freehand line shading, used to indicate the form of flat and curved surfaces, may be found in some of the illustrations of this book.

The various methods and short cuts for finding shades and shadows are not explained here, since this is a specialized art requiring many pages to explain it fully.

Chapter 14

PROJECTION METHOD AND
DIRECT METHOD

1. The older method of descriptive geometry is the *projection method* whereby objects are projected on planes of projection, as explained in the following paragraphs. The *direct method*, explained in this textbook, does not use planes of projection but deals with the object itself. The two methods require different attitudes of mind, and each has its own vocabulary.

2. Historical. Gaspard Monge (1746–1818), a French mathematician, originated the projection method of descriptive geometry when he was only nineteen years old. The story is told that, while working as a designer for the French government, he was given the job of making plans for a proposed fortress. This was a tedious process and involved long arithmetical calculations. Monge invented graphical solutions and completed the plans in such a short time that at first the commandant refused to accept them. For a long time the graphical process was kept a state secret, and the few officers who were instructed in it were forbidden to explain the method to anyone. After some years the discovery was made public.

3. Projection Method. The theory of descriptive geometry as developed by Monge is here explained so that students of the direct method may understand something of the language of the projection method. In Figure 1 are shown the two projection planes that are used in the projection method. One of the planes, H, is taken as horizontal, and the other plane, V, is vertical. The two planes intersect in the line G L that is called the *ground line*. The two projection planes divide space into four quadrants, or angles, as numbered in the illustration. Quadrants 1 and 2 are above the horizontal plane, and quadrants 3 and 4 are below the horizontal plane. Quadrants 1 and 4 are in front of the vertical plane, and quadrants 2 and 3 are behind the vertical plane. A point A is shown in the first quadrant, B in the second quadrant, C in the third quadrant, and D in the fourth quadrant.   The point A is projected onto the horizontal plane at a_h by means of a projection line that passes through A and is perpendicular to the H plane.   The V projection of A is located in a similar way at a_v by means of a projection line that passes through A and is perpendicular to the V plane.   The projections of the points in the other quadrants are found in a similar manner.   The V projection of a point corresponds to the front view of the point, and the H projection to the top view of the point.   If a side view is desired, a profile projection plane, perpendicular to the horizontal and vertical planes, is introduced. Right-angle projection is called *orthographic projection*.

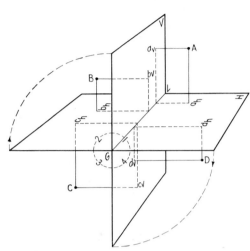

FIGURE 1. The planes of projection.

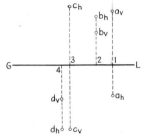

FIGURE 2. Projections of points.

In order to represent the horizontal and vertical projection planes on a flat sheet of paper, the planes are conceived as hinged along the ground line, and the two planes are brought together by closing the second and fourth quadrants.   The projections of the four points A, B, C, and D now appear as shown in Figure 2.   The point A, in the first quadrant, has its V projection above the ground line and its H projection below the ground line.   The point B, in the second quadrant, has both of its projections above the ground line.   The point C, in the third quadrant, has its H projection above the ground line and its V projection below the ground line.   The point D, in the fourth quadrant, has both of its projections below the ground line.   The two projections of a point are always in the same perpendicular.   The projection of a line is drawn through the projections of points that are on the line.

4. Relations of Views.   When a horizontal and a vertical projection plane are used, it has seemed easier to imagine an object in the first quadrant.   This started the practice of placing the V projection, or front view, above the H projection, or top view.   This custom persists in some countries and in some professions today.   Civil engineers often place the top view below the front view.   Architects place the plan below the front elevation.   The usual custom in this country is to draw objects as if they were located in the third quadrant.   This places the top view above the front view in a natural relationship.

Workmen often have great difficulty in reading a drawing when the views are arranged in an order to which they are not accustomed.   If the object represented is not symmetrical, they are likely to make a right-handed piece left-handed.   One remedy is to cut the views apart and paste them together to agree with the training of the workmen.

5. Representing Planes.   In Figure 3 the intersection of the oblique plane T with the V projection plane is the straight line T t_v.   This line is

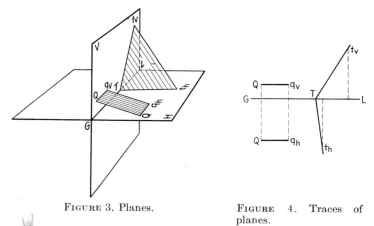

FIGURE 3. Planes.   FIGURE   4.   Traces   of
                                     planes.

called the *V trace* of the plane T.   The *H trace* is the line T t_h.   The traces of a plane always intersect on the ground line.   A plane Q, parallel to the ground line, is also shown in the illustration.   When the H and V planes are brought together, the traces of the planes T and Q appear as shown in Figure 4.   The parts of the planes here shown are in the first quadrant. Traces of planes are seldom used in practice and are not necessary for solving problems.   The plane faces of a structure are determined by the corners and edges of the structure, and these are sufficient for solving all problems relating to the surfaces of the structure.

6. Disadvantages of Projections.   In Figure 5 is shown an object of three dimensions projected on a plane.   The flat appearance of the projection clearly is noticeable.   This inherent flatness of projections is an undesirable feature, since each drawing of an object is thought of as points and lines projected and drawn on a flat sheet.   The projection idea involves an attitude of mind that requires the projection of three-dimensional objects on two-dimensional planes, and the reverse process of translating two-dimensional projections into three-dimensional objects. Also, it introduces planes of projection, quadrants, ground lines, projections, traces of planes—all of which stand in the way of thinking about the object itself. The projection method is an indirect method.

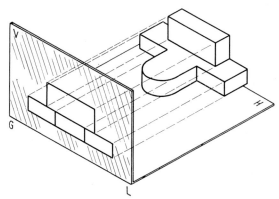

FIGURE 5. The inherent flatness of projections.

7. The Direct Method. The engineer has a practical and direct way of thinking about the drawings that he makes and reads. When the engineer designs an object, he first builds up a mental picture of the object. He then imagines that he views the visualized object in as many directions as desired, and he draws the views exactly as he sees them. And, when the engineer reads a drawing, he thinks and speaks of the object and its parts as if they actually were before him.

This natural and direct attitude of mind is a great aid in visualizing and designing structures, and in making and reading drawings. The engineer thinks in direct ways, and he makes and reads his drawings by the direct method. As the engineer thinks, the student of engineering should be taught to think.

PROBLEMS

GENERAL INSTRUCTIONS FOR DRAWING PROBLEMS

The following instructions are to be observed, unless specifically changed by the teacher of the class. The problems assigned are to be drawn in pencil on the standard printed drawing paper specified for this purpose. The solution of the problem should be limited to the 8- × 9-inch space. Only one problem is to be drawn on each sheet. Do not fold or roll the plates. Keep the paper flat and smooth. Problems not neatly and accurately drawn or not correctly lettered will be considered incorrect. A key for correcting problems is printed inside the back cover of this book.

Appearance. Every drawing must be of good quality. To make a satisfactory drawing, many details must be carefully observed. Use a correctly sharpened pencil of the proper grade, neither too hard nor too soft. Each line should be of uniform color and width from end to end. Lines should be gray in color, not black. The paper should lie on a hard, smooth surface. Draw all lines on the surface of the paper, without engraving them into the paper. Lines that may not be permanent should be very fine.

Weight of Lines. To make a drawing that is easily read, the following weights of lines should be used in every view. This applies both to required views and to any extra views that may be needed to solve the problem. All views are treated alike.

Very fine lines are used for rays that connect similar points in the different views. These lines serve to guide the eyes of the draftsman and of the reader and should never be omitted. Center lines, and the edges of reference planes from which points are measured, also should be very fine lines.

Medium lines are used for data given in the statement of the problem and for construction lines.

Broad lines are used for required data, so that the lines or object to be represented will stand out more clearly than will the lines used in obtaining the solution. Broad lines should be gray, not shiny black. When required data coincide with given data, the broad lines will cover the medium lines.

Dash lines of medium weight are used to represent the hidden lines of objects. The dashes should be closely spaced, uniform in length, and neither too long nor too short.

Drawing Lines. The student of this subject draws a multitude of lines. The method of drawing lines described below, although seemingly a trifle, produces better work, saves much time, and spares the eyes.

To draw a straight line connecting two points, place the tip of the pencil at one of the points; place the straightedge against the lead; turn the straightedge around the lead as a center until the straightedge is in line with the second point; then draw the line.   Try this method a few times and notice its advantage over attempting to aline a straightedge with two points at once.   A line cannot be determined accurately by two points that are only a short distance apart.   Another point of the line at a greater distance should be found.

Parallel and perpendicular lines should be drawn accurately parallel or perpendicular; otherwise the solution is inaccurate.   To draw parallel and perpendicular lines, slide one drawing triangle on another.

When solving problems on coordinate paper, all dimensions should be taken from the rulings on the paper, rather than from some other scale, since the dimensions of a sheet of paper change considerably with changes in humidity.

The size of a circle, and of circular objects, is specified by stating the diameter of the circle.   In general, circles are drawn first.   Rounded corners and fillets usually are specified by stating the radius of the arc. Hexagons are specified by giving the length of a principal diagonal which is the diameter of the circumscribing circle.

Visible and Invisible Lines.   In any view of an object the visible lines are those forming the outline or boundary, and those inside the outline and nearest the observer of that view.   Reference to an adjacent view usually will decide this question.

At times it is difficult to determine the visibility of some lines in a view, as is the case in the views of the pyramid, or tetrahedron, that is shown in the adjacent figure.   In each view only the line A C or B D is visible and the other is invisible.   To determine which is invisible in view X locate E_x at the apparent crossing point of A C and B D.   Since these lines do not intersect, the point E can be on one but not both lines.   In view Y, for E to be on one of the lines it must be on its ray and either at 2 on A C

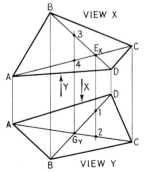

P-1. Determining visibility of lines.

or at 1 on B D.   The location 1 is nearer to the observer of view X than is location 2.   The point E is therefore taken at point 1 on the line B D. This indicates that point E and line B D are visible and line A C is hidden in view X.

The visibility of the lines A C and B D in view Y should now be determined by the student.   It is a mistake to assume that if a line is invisible in one view it also is invisible in other views.   If the lines A B and C D should intersect, the pyramid becomes a plane, and its altitude is zero.

Lettering.   Each point named in the statement of the problem and each point used in solving the problem should bear the corresponding letter or number in every view.   If required by the teacher of the class, the corners of objects also should be lettered or numbered.   Rectangular capital letters are probably better than slant letters, since they orient better with the views.   The letters should aline with the rays and reference planes in each view.   A study of the illustrations in this book will show how this may be done.   Careless lettering is a waste of time and is unsatisfactory both to the maker and to the reader of the drawing.   Adding pointing arrows often is an aid in understanding the direction in which each view is observed.

Drawing Views.   The views of a structure are drawn by locating and drawing the corners and lines of the structure.   The first view to be drawn is the one that shows the characteristic shape of the object.   This may be a principal view, an auxiliary view, or an oblique view, depending upon the position of the object.   Often it is best to start all views before completing any one view.   Details of the object are added last of all. Each detail, such as a hole, is drawn first in the view that shows its true shape.   The distance between views is immaterial, except that for ease in making and reading drawings the views should not be too far apart nor should they overlap.

Checking the Solution.   After the problem has been solved, check and review the solution.   Ask and answer questions like the following: Have the requirements of the problem been fully met?   Does each view represent the object correctly?   Does the object appear distorted in any view? What are the special points that should be checked?   Is each line of proper weight?   How could the appearance of the drawing be improved? Has the accuracy of the drawing been affected by carelessness in drawing? The engineer must check the solutions of his problems because his professional success depends upon the accuracy of his work.

PROBLEMS—CHAPTER 2

Group 1.   Drawing Simple Objects from Description.

The student should first read carefully the statement of the problem. Then he should visualize the shape, the proportions, and the position of the object that is to be drawn.   These things should be done before a single line is drawn on paper.

The position and the shape of the object determine which lines and which views should be drawn first.   It is generally undesirable, and often impossible, to complete one view without first drawing parts of other views.   After the views are completed, letter the name of each view in a convenient nearby location, and for each view show with dimension arrows the appropriate over-all width, height, and depth of the object. Before laying the problem aside, check the solution.

1. A block $2''$ deep, $3''$ wide, and $1\frac{1}{2}''$ high has a symmetrical, centrally located T-slot cut through from end to end, so as to leave the top, bottom, front, and back walls $\frac{1}{4}''$ thick.   The $\frac{1}{2}''$ opening to the slot is cut through the top face.   Two $\frac{1}{4}''$ holes, counterbored on top to a diameter of $\frac{1}{2}''$ for a distance of $\frac{1}{4}''$, are drilled centrally through the bottom part, and each hole centered $\frac{3}{4}''$ from the end of this machine part.   Draw three principal views.

2. Draw the front, top, and left-side views of a rectangular block that is $3''$ wide, $1\frac{1}{2}''$ tall, and $4''$ deep.   The corners of the block, as seen in the top view, are rounded to a radius of $\frac{1}{2}''$.   On the same centers $\frac{3}{8}''$ vertical holes are drilled through the block.   The top ends of these holes are counterbored to a diameter of $\frac{3}{4}''$ and a depth of $\frac{3}{8}''$.   A centrally located rectangular hole $1\frac{1}{2}''$ wide by $\frac{1}{2}''$ high is cut through the block from front to rear, and this hole is changed into a symmetrical T-slot by cutting a $\frac{1}{2}''$ square slot through the top face of the block.

3. A spool $3''$ tall has hexagonal ends of $3''$ diagonal and $\frac{1}{2}''$ height.   The middle part of the spool is $1\frac{1}{4}''$ in diameter.   A $\frac{1}{2}''$ hole is drilled through the length of the spool.   Show the front, top, and right-side views.

4. A right prism is $3''$ wide, $2''$ deep, and $1''$ high.   Bevel the vertical corners to an angle of $45°$ by cutting $\frac{1}{2}''$ from each corner.   The upper surface of this modified prism is the base of a right pyramid of $2''$ altitude.   Draw the front, top, and right-side views of the solid formed by the prism and pyramid.

5. A $3''$ vertical line is one diagonal of a profile hexagon and the hexagon is one base of a right prism of $2''$ length.   A rectangular groove $1''$ wide is turned in the prism so as to leave a cylindrical mid-section $2''$ in diameter.   The left end of the prism is the base of a right pyramid of $\frac{1}{2}''$ altitude and the right end of the prism is the base of a right prism of $1''$ altitude. Draw the front, top, and right-side views of this object.

6. A right prism is $3''$ wide, $2''$ deep, and $1''$ high. Bevel the vertical corners to an angle of $45°$ by cutting $\frac{1}{2}''$ from each corner. One-half inch inside the top edges of the prism is the base of a right pyramid of $2''$ altitude. Draw the front, top, and right-side views of the solid formed by the prism and pyramid.

7. A $4''$ horizontal square has the corners beveled to form a regular octagon. The octagon is the base of the frustum, $1''$ tall, of a right pyramid of $4''$ altitude. The upper base of the frustum is the lower base of a prism of $1''$ altitude. One-half inch inside of the upper base of the prism is an octagon that is the base of a pyramid of $\frac{3}{4}''$ altitude. Draw the front and top views of this solid.

8. A $3''$ horizontal square is the base of a right prism of $\frac{1}{2}''$ altitude. Centered $1\frac{1}{2}''$ directly above the upper base of the prism is a horizontal square having $2''$ diagonals parallel to the sides of the larger squares. Using straight lines, connect each corner of the upper base of the prism with the two nearest corners of the smaller square. This small square is the base of a right pyramid of $1''$ altitude. Draw the front, top, and left-side views of this solid.

9. Draw the front, top, and right-side views of a symmetrical casting having a rectangular block $1''$ tall, $4''$ wide, and $2\frac{1}{2}''$ deep, with ends rounded to a half circle of $1\frac{1}{4}''$ radius for a base. On top of the base is a rectangular column $2''$ wide, $2\frac{1}{2}''$ tall, and $1''$ deep. The column has a cap similar to the base but $\frac{1}{2}''$ high, $3''$ wide, and $1\frac{1}{2}''$ deep. Two $\frac{1}{2}''$ diameter holes, centered $3''$ apart, are drilled vertically through the base of the casting.

10. A centrally located T-shaped slot $3''$ tall and $2''$ wide is cut through from front to rear of a rectangular block that is $3''$ wide, $4''$ high, and $1''$ deep. The stem and top of the T have a $\frac{1}{2}'' \times 1''$ cross section. Two $\frac{1}{2}''$ holes, centered $1''$ to the right and left of the center of the front face, are drilled horizontally through the block. Draw the front, top, and left-side views.

11. Each face of a $2\frac{1}{2}''$ cube has a $1\frac{1}{2}''$ square recess cut into it to a depth of $\frac{1}{4}''$. A $\frac{3}{4}''$ vertical hole is drilled centrally through the cube. Draw the front, top, and left-side views.

12. A link is made from a block $4''$ deep, $2''$ wide, and $1\frac{1}{4}''$ high. The rear end as seen from the top is rounded to a half circle and a $\frac{7}{8}''$ hole is drilled vertically through the piece on the same center. Two arms are formed at the front end of the block by cutting a vertical slot $1''$ wide and $2''$ deep. The arms, as seen from the side, are rounded to half circles at the front, and a horizontal $\frac{1}{2}''$ hole is drilled through each on the same center. Draw the front, top, and right-side views of the link.

13. Show the front and top views of a symmetrical casting described as follows: To the front end of a horizontal right cylinder $2''$ in diameter $\times 2\frac{1}{4}''$ long is added a rectangular block $5''$ wide $\times 2\frac{1}{2}''$ high $\times \frac{3}{4}''$ deep. The corners of the block, as seen in the front view, are rounded to a radius of $\frac{1}{2}''$. At the right- and left-hand ends of the block centrally located slots $1''$ high and having half-circular inside ends are cut through to within $\frac{1}{4}''$ of the cylinder. There is a $1''$ axial hole drilled through the casting from front to back.

14. A rectangular block is $4''$ wide $\times \frac{3}{4}''$ high $\times 1\frac{1}{2}''$ deep. The ends of the block, as seen in the top view, are rounded to half circles, and on the same centers $\frac{3}{4}''$ vertical holes are drilled through the block. A cylindrical lug $1''$ in diameter $\times 1\frac{1}{2}''$ long is placed centrally on the top face of the block. A $\frac{3}{8}''$ vertical hole is drilled axially through the lug and block. Draw the front, top, and left-side views of the piece.

15. A casting is $3''$ square and $1\frac{1}{2}''$ deep. Cylindrical bosses $2''$ in diameter $\times \frac{1}{2}''$ long project centrally from the front and rear faces. Each boss is counterbored to a diameter of $1\frac{1}{2}'' \times \frac{1}{4}''$ deep. Trunnions $1''$ in diameter $\times \frac{3}{4}''$ long are centered on the right and left faces of the casting. A $\frac{1}{2}''$ hole is drilled axially through the trunnions and the casting from left to right. Draw the front, top, and right-side views.

16. A ring casting is $3''$ outside diameter, $1\frac{1}{2}''$ inside diameter, and $2''$ long. Two trunnions, $1\frac{1}{4}''$ in diameter, extend $\frac{1}{2}''$ from the ring. The axis of the trunnions is the perpendicular bisector of the axis of the ring. A $\frac{3}{4}''$ axial hole is drilled clear through the trunnions and ring. Draw three principal views of the casting.

Group 2.   Drawing Objects by Discarding Specified Parts.

1. A block is $3''$ square and $4''$ tall. In the top quarter discard the left two-thirds. In the next lower quarter discard the front two-thirds. In the bottom quarter discard the rear two-thirds. In the quarter just above the bottom quarter discard the right two-thirds. Draw the front, top, and side views.

2. A block is $4''$ square and $2''$ deep. Retain the following parts: The right and left one-fourths of the upper one-fourth; the lower half of the upper half; the rear half of the left two-thirds of the right three-fourths of the lower half. Draw three views.

3. Show the front, top, and right-side views of all that is left of a rectangular block, $4''$ square and $3''$ deep, after the following parts have been discarded: The lower half of the middle third that lies between the front and rear thirds; the upper half of the left half of the right half; and the upper half of the right half of the left half.

4. A block is $4''$ square and $3''$ deep. Draw its front, top, and right-side views, and then eliminate the following parts of the block: The upper three-fourths of the rear third; the lower three-fourths of the front third; and a piece, $2''$ square and $1''$ deep, out of the middle of the block.

5. In a $3''$ cube discard: The right two-thirds of the front two-thirds; the left two-thirds of the bottom third; the rear two-thirds of the top third. Draw the front, top, and right-side views.

6. A block is $4''$ wide, $2''$ deep, and $4''$ high. Discard all of the lower half of the lower half excepting the rear half of the right half. Discard all of the upper half of the lower half excepting the left half of the right half and the front of the left half. Discard all of the lower half of the upper half excepting the left half of the left half. Discard all of the upper half of the upper half excepting the rear half of the left half. Show the front, top, and right-side views of all that is left of the original block.

7. A rectangular block is $2\frac{1}{2}''$ deep, $1''$ high, and $4''$ wide. Cut a $1''$ cube from the rear left and also the rear right corner. Discard the upper half of the front half of the block. Drill a $\frac{3}{8}''$ vertical hole through the center of each quarter of the front (thinner) section. Draw the front, top, and left-side views.

8. A rectangular block is $1''$ high, $4\frac{1}{2}''$ wide, and $2\frac{1}{2}''$ deep. Draw its top, front, and right-side views. From each right-hand front and rear corner cut a block that is $\frac{3}{4}''$ deep, $1\frac{1}{4}''$ wide, and $1''$ high. From the left end, upper side, cut a block that is $\frac{1}{2}''$ high, $2''$ wide, and $2\frac{1}{2}''$ deep. Show a $\frac{3}{4}''$ hole drilled vertically through the middle of the thinner part of the block.

9. A rectangular block is $5''$ wide, $2''$ high, and $1''$ deep. Cut away the lower half of the left two-fifths of the block. Cut away the lower half of the right one-fifth of the block. Cut away the upper half of the left two-fifths of the right half of the block. Show the front, top, and right-side views of what is left of the block.

10. A block is $4''$ square and $2''$ deep. In the front, top, and left-side views, show what is left of the block when all parts excepting the following are discarded: The upper three-fourths of the right one-fourth, the upper three-fourths of the lower fourth, the front and rear one-fourths of the lower fourth of the lower fourth, and a triangular brace formed by the lower-right one-half of the rear half of the left three-fourths of the upper three-fourths.

11. Draw the front, top, and left-side views of a 3″ cube. Discard all of the upper one-fourth of the cube excepting a $\frac{3}{4}$″ cube in the rear left corner. Discard the right half, and also the front half, of the lower half of the upper half of the original cube. Discard the right one-fourth, and also the front one-fourth, of the upper half of the lower half of the original cube.

12. Discard the left half of the front half of the right half, the right half of the front half of the left half, the upper half of the upper half of the rear half, and the lower half of the lower half of the rear half of a rectangular block that is 4″ square and 2″ deep. Show a 1″ horizontal hole drilled through the center of the back. Draw the front, top, and right-side views.

13. A clamping block is made from a 3″ cube of metal by cutting away all of the block excepting: The right and left thirds of the upper one-sixth, the right and left one-sixths of the lower half of the upper third, the front and rear thirds of the lower one-sixth, the front and rear one-sixths of the upper half of the lower third, and the middle horizontal third. Show the front, top, and right-side views of the clamping block.

14. From a rectangular block that is 4″ square and 3″ deep cut away the following parts: The left three-fourths of the upper three-fourths of the front two-thirds and the right three-fourths of the lower three-fourths of the rear two-thirds. Draw the front, top, and left-side views.

COORDINATE SYSTEM FOR LOCATING POINTS

The definite assignment of a problem in the geometry of engineering drawing requires the adoption of some method of stating the exact locations of the data of the problem. The use of a simple coordinate system for locating points, together with coordinate problem paper and a coordinately ruled blackboard, provides means for quickly and exactly locating the given data of a problem.

The problem sheet, as shown to a reduced scale in Plate A, is printed with a ruled space 8 × 9 inches reserved for the solution of the problem. The cross-section lines are spaced in inches and quarters of an inch. The origin, or zero point, is taken at the lower left-hand corner of the problem grid. From the origin, both to the right and upward, the inches are numbered consecutively. A title is printed above the problem space. The title states the name of the course and reserves spaces for the problem number and group number, the name of the student, and the date. A scale of tenths of an inch and a protractor are printed on the problem sheet for use in certain problems.

The front and top views of four points are shown on Plate A. The exact locations of the front and top views of a point A, for example, are given by three figures, as A736. The capital letter preceding the figures states the name of the point. The first figure, 7, specifies that the front and top views of the point A are to be located in a vertical line 7 inches to the right of the origin or zero point. The second figure, 3, locates the front view A_F, 3 inches above the horizontal base line that passes through

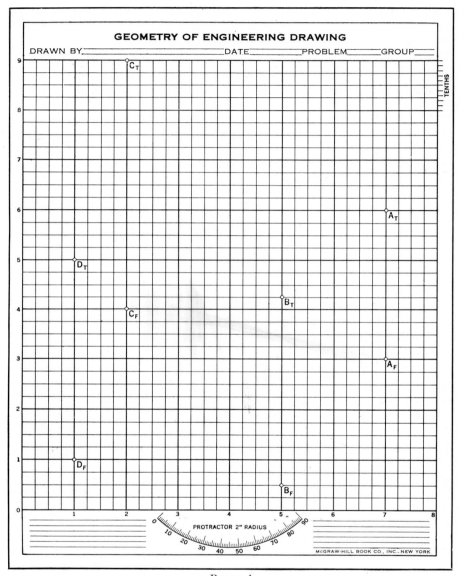

PLATE A

the origin. The third figure, 6, locates the top view A_T, 6 inches above the horizontal base line. The second figure always serves to locate the front view of the point. And, the third figure always serves to locate the top view of the point. Both are measured from the horizontal base line that passes through the origin. In stating the coordinates of some points, for example, B5,$\frac{1}{2}$,4$\frac{1}{4}$, it becomes necessary to separate the three coordinates by means of commas. The letter X when used as a coordinate indicates that the coordinate X is unknown and that the location of the missing view usually is to be determined in the solution of the problem. E24X and F7X8 are examples of unknown coordinates. When the name of a point is repeated in the statement of a problem, the coordinates of the point usually are not repeated. On Plate A the top and front views of the points A736, B5,$\frac{1}{2}$,4$\frac{1}{4}$, C249, and D115 are shown. When the views of points on the problem sheet are located, subscripts should be used to distinguish the different views of a point. Time is saved by lettering each view of a point as soon as it is located.

A study of Figure 2, Chapter 5, should aid the student if he has difficulty in drawing the side views in the following problems.

Group 3. Locating Data by Coordinates.

1. Given the triangle A018 B124 C306. Draw its front, top, and right-side views.

2. Draw three principal views of the triangle K527 L708 M634.

3. Draw three principal views of the triangle N037 P204 Q328.

4. Draw the front, top, right-side, and left-side views of triangle D227 E406 F538.

5. Draw four principal views of the triangle G517 H456 J338.

6. Draw the front, top, and left-side views of the triangle R518 S647 T706. (Note that the top view is an edge view.)

7. Draw the front, top, and left-side views of the parallelogram J504 K613 L737 M628.

8. Draw three principal views of the parallelogram Q034 R305 S418 T147.

9. Draw three principal views of the warped quadrilateral D346 E837 F605 G417.

10. Draw the front, top, and left-side views of the warped quadrilateral A447 B505 C736 D818.

11. Draw the front, top, and left-side views of the pyramid J534 K738 L824 M705.

12. Draw the front, top, and right-side views of the tetrahedron C017 D247 E425 F308.

13. Draw three principal views of the tetrahedron C134 D218 E345 F206.

14. Draw three principal views of the triangular base pyramid A027 B138 C446 D205.

Group 4. Locating Points by Measurements.

1. Locate A446. Locate B 2″ to the right of, 2″ behind, and 1″ below A. Locate C 3″ in front of, 1″ to the right of, and 3″ below B. Draw the front, top, and left-side views of the triangle A B C.

2. Locate the point A137. Locate the point B 1″ above A, 2″ in front of A, and 1″ to the right of A. Also, locate the point C 4″ below B, 2″ to the right of B, and 3″ behind B. Draw the front, top, and right-side views of the triangle A B C.

3. Locate C625. The point D is 2″ below, 3″ behind, and 2″ to the right of C. The point E is 4″ to the left of, 3″ above, and 1″ in front of D. Show the front, top, and left-side views of the triangle C D E.

4. Draw the front, top, and right-side views of the triangle R017 S T. The point S is 1″ below, 1″ in front of, and 4″ to the right of R. And the point T is 2″ to the left of, 3″ above, and 1″ in front of S.

5. Locate the point K035. The point L is 1″ to the left of M, and M is 3″ to the right of K. The point M is 4″ above L, and 3″ behind K. The point L is 2″ in front of M, and 3″ below K. Draw the front, top, and right-side views of the triangle K L M.

6. Draw the front, top, right-side, and left-side views of the triangle X Y Z328. The point X is 2″ behind, 4″ below, and 1″ to the right of the point Y. Y is 1″ to the right of, 3″ in front of, and 2″ above Z.

7. The point D is 3″ in front of, 1″ above, and 1″ to the right of the point E. And the point E is 3″ above, 1″ behind, and 3″ to the left of the point F507. Show the front, top, and right-side views of the triangle D E F.

---

8. Locate the point A104. Locate B $2\frac{1}{2}$″ to the right of, $\frac{1}{2}$″ above, and 1″ behind A. Locate C 2″ behind, $1\frac{1}{2}$″ to the left of, and $\frac{1}{2}$″ above B. Locate V 3″ above, 2″ to the right of, and 2″ behind A. V is the vertex and A B C is the base of a pyramid. Show the front, top, and right-side views of the pyramid.

9. Locate the point Q007. Locate the point R 2″ to the right of, 3″ above, and 2″ in front of Q. Locate the point S 3″ behind, 1″ to the right of, and 2″ below R. Locate the point T 1″ above, 2″ in front of, and 1″ to the right of S. Show three principal views of the pyramid Q R S T.

10. The point E is 2″ to the left of, 2″ behind, and $1\frac{1}{2}$″ below the point D645. The point K is $\frac{1}{2}$″ behind, 3″ to the right of, and 2″ below E. The point L is 2″ in front of, $\frac{1}{2}$″ to the left of, and 1″ above K. Draw the front, top, and left-side views of the tetrahedron E D K L.

11. Draw the front, top, and left-side views of the parallelogram J K L M in which the points M, K, and L are respectively 1″, 2″, and 3″ to the right of the point J535. L is 3″ below K, 1″ above M, and 2″ below J. L is 1″ in front of K, 3″ behind M, and 2″ behind J.

Group 5. Experiments in Visualization.

Article 20 of Chapter 2 should be read before the solution of these problems is attempted. The student should read the description of the object specified in the problem until he has a complete mental image of the object. He should imagine that the object itself is standing on the corner of his desk. The size and shape of the object should be completely visualized before considering the appearance of any view and before doing any drawing.

When the student is satisfied that he has a complete mental image of the object, he should imagine that he moves to positions from which he can in turn see the front, top, and right-side views of the imagined object. He visualizes the appearance of the object in each of these views and then draws the views, without again referring to the statement of the problem.

Each object described in the problems is to be regarded as a solid object without joints.

The general dimensions of the object might be noted in pencil at the bottom of the problem sheet, but no written suggestions or sketches as to the shape of the object should be made. If the student will visualize the dimensions of the object, instead of writing them down, he will have gained that much additional ability. Particular care should be taken that the statement of the problem is not memorized.

Another plan is for the teacher to place on the blackboard any general dimensions of the object, and then slowly to read to the class the description of the object, while the students visualize the object in space. After the statement of the problem is read once or twice, the students should draw the front, top, and right-side views of the object without again referring to the statement of the problem. This plan should improve the power of each student to visualize; in addition, it should train him to listen carefully.

1. In a 3″ cube discard the following parts: The middle horizontal third of the right and left thirds, and the front and rear thirds of the third between the right and left thirds.

2. A block is 2″ square and $4\frac{1}{2}″$ wide. Discard the right two-thirds of the upper three-fourths, and the upper one-half of the left one-sixth.

3. A block is 4″ square and 2″ deep. In the front half retain the right and left one-fourths. In the rear half retain the upper and lower one-fourths.

4. Given a 3″ cube, discard the lower two-thirds of the front third and the upper two-thirds of the rear third.

5. A rectangular block is 5″ wide, 4″ high, and 2″ deep. In the front half, retain the upper and lower one-fourths. In the rear half, discard the right and left one-fourths.

6. With eleven 1″ cubes build an object that appears as an inverted T in the front view, Z-shaped in the top view, and U-shaped in the side view.

7. Fasten seven 1″ cubes together so as to form an object that appears C-shaped in the top view, as an inverted L in the front view, and T-shaped in the side view.

8. With a 90° V-groove cut away one half of the volume of the upper half of a 3″ cube. Cut a similar groove in the lower half, making the grooves at right angles to each other.

9. Take fourteen 1″ cubes and pile them so that they form an object that appears U-shaped in the front view, inverted T-shaped in the side view, and a hollow square in the top view.

10. In a block that is 3″ square and 4″ deep, discard the rear three-fourths of the upper fourth, and the rear half of the fourth next above the lower fourth.

11. In a 3″ cube, retain all of the lower one-fourth. In the fourth just above the lower fourth, retain the rear and left three-fourths. In the next fourth, retain the rear and left halves. In the top fourth, retain the rear and left fourths.

12. Take sixteen $\frac{3}{4}″$ cubes and pile them so that they will form an object that appears E-shaped in the top view, L-shaped in the front view, and U-shaped in the side view.

13. Given ten 1″ cubes, fasten them together to make an object that is H-shaped in the top view, L-shaped in the front view, and I-shaped in the side view.

14. Cut away all of a 3″ cube excepting the left, right, and lower $\frac{1}{2}$″. Round the vertical upper ends to a half circle of $1\frac{1}{2}$″ radius. On the same centers, show 1″ horizontal holes drilled through.

15. In a 3″ cube retain only the upper one-fourth, the lower one-fourth, the rear one-fourth, and the left one-fourth.

16. In a 3″ cube retain only the lower fourth, and the right third of the rear third of the upper three-fourths.

17. Given a 3″ cube, discard the upper one-fourth and the lower one-half of the right and left one-fourths.

18. In a 3″ cube discard the upper two-thirds of the front half of the right and left thirds.

19. Starting with a 3″ cube, retain the right and left fourths of the front fourth, the rear fourth, and the lower fourth of the remaining fourths.

20. In a 3″ cube retain the front one-fourth. Then, in the upper half of the lower half of the cube retain the front half and the rear, right, and left one-fourths.

Group 6.　Reference Planes.

The solution of each problem of this group should show horizontal, frontal, and profile reference planes from which measurements of height, depth, and width are made. Each reference plane should be lettered.

1. Draw the front, top, right-side, and left-side views of the triangle K208 L445 M537.

2. Draw the front, top, right-side, and left-side views of the triangle A317 B456 C538.

3. Draw the front, top, right-side, and left-side views of the triangle A B427 C. A is 4″ above C, 1″ to the right of B, and 1″ behind C. C is 2″ to the left of A, 2″ below B, and 2″ in front of B.

4. In the profile triangle C D E608, the point D is 2″ above and $3\frac{1}{2}$″ in front of E, and the point C is 2″ above and $2\frac{1}{2}$″ behind D. Draw the front, top, and left-side views of the triangle.

5. Draw the front, top, and left-side views of the tetrahedron X415 Y538 Z847 W607.

6. Draw the front, top, and side views of the tetrahedron A204 B447 C128 D035.

7. Imagine that all the faces of a 3″ cube are painted and that it is then divided into 1″ cubes. Remove all 1″ cubes that are painted on more than one face. Show the front, top, and side views of what is left as a one-piece block.

PROBLEMS—CHAPTER 3

AUXILIARY VIEWS

Group 7.   Auxiliary Elevations (Horizontal-auxiliary Views).

1. Draw the following views of the tetrahedron A004 B216 C304 D225: Front, top, right-side, an auxiliary elevation 45° rear of the right, and an auxiliary elevation 30° forward of the right.

2. The following auxiliary elevation views are required of the tetrahedron K326 L427 M525 N406: 45° left of the front, 30° rear of the left, 15° rear of the right.

3. A 3″ square thin washer with a centrally located 2″ diameter hole is in a frontal plane.   Show a view taken in a direction 30° to the plane of the washer, also, a front (normal) view, and a top (edge) view.

4. A 2″ frontal circle is centered at K215.   Show auxiliary elevation taken 60° forward of the right, 15° forward of the right, and 30° rearward of the right.

5. The square A335 B425 C315 D225 is the front face of a cube.   A 1″ hole is drilled centrally through the cube from front to back.   Draw the front and top views of the cube, and an auxiliary elevation 30° to the rear of the right.

6. V626 is the vertex, and C648 F608 is one diagonal of the hexagonal base of a right pyramid.   Remove the front 1″ of the pyramid.   Draw the following views of the frustum: Front, top, left-side, and an auxiliary elevation taken 45° forward of the left.

---

7. The top view is an edge of equilateral triangle C106 D418 E.   Line C D is the base and the vertex E is above the base.   Draw normal, top, and front views of the triangle.

8. The vertical isosceles triangle with 2″ altitude has line K528 L735 for a base. The vertex M is below the base.   Draw the top (edge), normal, front, and side views of the triangle.

9. The top view is the edge view of the circle which has line P215 Q338 for a diameter.   Draw the top (edge), normal, and front views of the circle.

10. A thin metal disk is 3″ in diameter and has a 2″ round hole punched centrally through it.   The disk is bent to an angle of 90° along one of its diameters and is placed so that this diameter coincides with the line A007 X037.   One-half of the disk is in profile.   Draw the front, top, and right-side views, and an auxiliary elevation taken in a direction 30° forward of the right.

---

11. B5,3,7$\frac{1}{2}$, C6,4,5$\frac{1}{2}$ is the upper edge of a vertical rectangle.   The sides perpendicular to B C are 3″ long.   This rectangle is the left face of a right prism whose third dimension is 1″.   The left face of the prism is recessed to a depth of $\frac{1}{4}$″, and within $\frac{1}{2}$″

281

of each edge of the face.   Draw the front and top views of the block, and also an auxiliary elevation taken in a direction perpendicular to the left face.

12. A right prism that is $\frac{1}{2}''$ long has for its right-hand face a vertical hexagon, of which A245 D317 is one diagonal.   A central hexagonal hole is cut through the prism. The hexagonal ends of the hole have $2''$ diagonals that coincide with the diagonals of the larger hexagons.   Draw a front and a top view of the washer, and auxiliary elevation taken in a direction perpendicular to the right-hand face of the prism.

13. The line J307 K405 is the axis of a hollow semicylinder of $4''$ outside diameter and $3''$ inside diameter.   Draw the following views: An auxiliary elevation in the direction of the axis, the top view, and the front view.

14. A horizontal isosceles triangle, of $3''$ altitude and lying with the vertex behind and $1\frac{1}{2}''$ to the left of the middle point C605 of its $2\frac{1}{2}''$ base, is the lower face of a right square-base pyramid.   Draw the front and top views, and the necessary auxiliary view of the pyramid.

Group 8.   Frontal-auxiliary Views.

1. Draw the following views of the tetrahedron E206 F418 G506 H427: Front, top, a frontal-auxiliary taken left and $60°$ upwards, and a frontal-auxiliary right and $45°$ upwards.

2. Draw the following views of the tetrahedron A328 B415 C537 D626: Front, top, a frontal-auxiliary taken $45°$ above the horizontal and rightward, and a frontal-auxiliary taken $30°$ below the horizontal and leftward.

3. The following frontal auxiliaries are required of the tetrahedron K347 L448 M546 N427: Right and $45°$ down, right and $30°$ up, left and $60°$ down.

4. C037 D206 is the base of an isosceles triangle having $2\frac{1}{2}''$ legs.   The vertex is behind the base, and the front view is an edge view.   Draw the front, top, side, and normal views of the triangle.

5. The front view is the edge view of a square of which A035 C206 is a diagonal. Draw the following views of the square: Front, top, right-side, and a normal frontal-auxiliary.

6. C507 and F7$\frac{1}{2}$,2,6 are diagonally opposite corners of a hexagon of which the front view is an edge view.   Draw the front, top, and left-side views of the hexagon, and an auxiliary view that shows its true shape.

7. C506 E7$\frac{1}{2}$,3,5 is the diagonal of a thin square washer which appears edge view in the front view.   The washer has a $2''$ diameter centrally located hole.   Complete the front and top views and any necessary auxiliary views.

8. The edges of a thin hexagonal washer are $1\frac{1}{2}''$ long.   A $2''$ diameter hole is punched centrally through the washer.   K2,1$\frac{1}{2}$,6 is the center of this hole.   The axis is tipped $40°$ to the right of the vertical.   Two edges of the hexagon are horizontal. Draw a frontal-auxiliary taken in a direction parallel to the axis and then complete the front and top views.

9. Draw the front, top, and right-side views of a symmetrical wedge.   The horizontal base of the wedge is a rectangle $3''$ wide $\times$ $1\frac{1}{2}''$ deep, and the $1\frac{1}{2}''$ knife edge of the wedge is $3''$ above and parallel to the longer edges of the base.   The middle point of the base is at C216.   Draw also a frontal-auxiliary view of the wedge taken in the direction perpendicular to the right-hand triangular face.

10. B628 C825 is the right edge of a horizontal rectangle.   The edges perpendicular to B C are $2''$ long.   The rectangle is the upper base of a right prism that is $\frac{1}{2}''$ tall. The prism is hollowed so that the end and side walls are $\frac{1}{2}''$ thick.   Show the following views of the piece: Front, top, and frontal-auxiliary as seen at an angle of 30° above the horizontal and to the left.

11. The line B824 E828 is the diagonal of a hexagon which is the base of a right pyramid. The vertex of the pyramid is at P526. Discard the left two-thirds of the pyramid. Draw the front, top, and left-side views of the remaining frustum of the pyramid. Also, draw a frontal-auxiliary view seen in a direction left and 45° above the horizontal.

12. A306 C006 is the diagonal of a horizontal square. This square is the base of a cube. A $1\frac{3}{4}''$ vertical hole is drilled centrally through the cube. Draw the front and top views, and a frontal-auxiliary view taken in a direction to the right and 40° above the horizontal.

13. A118 B418 is the rear edge of the horizontal square base of a rectangular block that is $\frac{1}{2}''$ high. A right circular cylinder $2''$ in diameter, $1''$ long, and with the axis vertical, stands on the center of the top face of the block. Show the front and top views, and a frontal-auxiliary view at 30° above the horizontal.

Group 9. Profile-auxiliary Views.

1. Draw the following views of the tetrahedron A026 B238 C326 D247: Front, top, right-side, a profile-auxiliary taken 60° above the front, and a profile-auxiliary taken 30° below the front.

2. The following profile-auxiliary views are required of the tetrahedron K627 L728 M826 N707: Front and 45° upwards, and rear and 60° upwards. Complete top, front, and left-side views.

3. R046 T346 is the diagonal of a horizontal square which is the upper base of a cube. A $2''$ diameter vertical hole is drilled centrally through the cube. Draw a view of the lower surface of the cube as seen from the front and 15° below the horizontal, and a view of the upper surface as seen from the front and 50° above the horizontal.

------

4. The side view is an edge view of the equilateral triangle R118 S205 T. Point T is to the right of the line R S. Draw normal, right-side, front, and top views of the triangle.

5. B327 and E115 are diagonally opposite corners of a hexagon of which the side view is an edge view. Draw the front, top, and right-side views, and a profile-auxiliary view that shows the true shape of the hexagon.

6. A circular disk is $2''$ in diameter and $\frac{1}{4}''$ thick. C626 is the center of the upper face. The axis is tipped 30° forward from the vertical. Draw edge and normal views of the disk and complete the front and top views.

7. A right pyramid, having a $1\frac{1}{2}'' \times 3''$ rectangular base, lies on one of its broader triangular faces, with the vertex V$1\frac{1}{2}$,1,7 of the triangle $2\frac{1}{2}''$ directly behind the center of its base. Draw the front, top, and right-side views, and a profile-auxiliary view of the pyramid in which the upper triangular face is shown in its true shape.

Group 10. Multiple-auxiliary Views.

1. The front edge of a pyramid which has a $1'' \times 2''$ rectangular horizontal base and a $1\frac{1}{2}''$ altitude is located at K025 L125. Draw the following views of the pyramid: Front, top, side, an auxiliary elevation at 15° rear of the right, a frontal-auxiliary at 45° above the right, and a profile-auxiliary at 30° below the front.

2. C$4\frac{3}{4}$,4,6 F$6\frac{1}{4}$,4,6 is a diagonal of the horizontal upper base of a right hexagonal prism. The height is $2''$. Draw the following views: Front, top, right-side, left-side, an auxiliary elevation left and 45° rearward, a frontal-auxiliary left and 30° upward, and a profile-auxiliary forward and 60° downward.

   3. Line V7,$3\frac{1}{2}$,6 P726 is the axis of a right circular cone with a 2″ diameter base and a $1\frac{1}{2}$″ altitude.   Draw the following views: Front, top, left-side, an auxiliary elevation left and 30° rearward, a frontal-auxiliary left and 30° below, and a profile-auxiliary front and 40° upwards.

   4. A rectangular block is $1\frac{1}{2}$″ wide, 1″ high, and 2″ deep.   In the right half of the upper half remove the triangular upper and right half.   In the left half of the upper half remove the triangular upper and left half.   The remainder of the block is to represent a small house.   Show a door on the front surface, one window on the left-hand surface, and two windows on the right-hand surface.   In the problems 4*a*, 4*b*, and 4*c*, the line A E is the lower front edge of the block.   Draw the specified views.   Do not show hidden lines.

   a. (A$6\frac{1}{2}$,0,5 E805) front, top, left-side, auxiliary elevation 30° rear of the left, frontal-auxiliary left and 45° upwards, and a profile-auxiliary rear and 60° upwards.

   b. (A005 E$1\frac{1}{2}$,0,5) front, top, right-side, auxiliary elevation 30° rearward of the right, frontal-auxiliary right and 45° upwards, and a profile-auxiliary rear and 60° upwards.

   c. (A$2\frac{1}{2}$,0,6 E406) front, top, right-side, left-side, auxiliary elevation right and 30° forward, frontal auxiliary left and 60° upwards, profile auxiliary front and 30° upwards.

PROBLEMS—CHAPTER 4

OBLIQUE VIEWS

Group 11. Oblique Views Taken in Specified Directions.

1. Show the appearance of the triangle A016 B238 C325 as viewed in the direction Q115 towards P227.

2. Draw an oblique view of the triangle L517 M735 N808 taken in the direction of the arrow R838 S716.

3. A626 C825 is the diagonal of a horizontal square. Show its shape when viewed in the direction M6,1,4$\frac{1}{2}$, N7,2,5$\frac{1}{2}$.

4. E125 G315 is the diagonal of a frontal square. Draw an oblique view taken in the direction S136 T2,1$\frac{1}{2}$,5.

5. J118 M338 is the diagonal of a frontal hexagon. Show its shape when viewed in the direction C437 D228.

6. Q526 T825 is the diagonal of a horizontal hexagon. Draw an oblique view taken in the direction of the arrow G535 H6$\frac{1}{2}$,2,5$\frac{1}{2}$.

7. Draw an oblique view of the horizontal circle of 3″ diameter centered at B and viewed in the direction A513 B6$\frac{1}{2}$,0,4.

8. A 2″ diameter frontal circle is centered at point Q348. Draw a view taken in the direction P457 Q.

---

9. Draw an oblique view of the tetrahedron K727 L517 M735 N808 taken in the direction of the arrow R838 S716.

10. Show the appearance of the tetrahedron A016 B238 C325 D206 as viewed in the direction Q115 towards P227.

11. A626 C825 is the diagonal of a horizontal square which is the base of a right pyramid having its vertex at V7,0,5$\frac{1}{2}$. Show the pyramid as viewed in the direction M6,1,4$\frac{1}{2}$ N7,2,5$\frac{1}{2}$.

12. Q505 T804 is the diagonal of a horizontal hexagon which is the base of a right pyramid with V6$\frac{1}{2}$,2,4$\frac{1}{2}$ as the vertex. Draw an oblique view taken in the direction of the arrow G514 H6$\frac{1}{2}$,0,4$\frac{1}{2}$.

13. E125 G315 is the diagonal of a frontal square which is the rear base of a right prism of 1″ depth. Draw an oblique view of the prism taken in the direction S136 T2,1$\frac{1}{2}$,5.

14. J217 M437 is the diagonal of a frontal hexagon which is the forward face of a right prism 1″ deep. Show the prism when viewed in the direction C536 D327.

15. Refer to Problem 4, Group 10. Draw an oblique view (A6$\frac{1}{2}$,0,4 E804) taken in the direction M623 N714.

16. Refer to Problem 4, Group 10. Draw an oblique view (A606 E7$\frac{1}{2}$,0,6) taken in the direction P828 Q717.

17. Refer to Problem 4, Group 10. Draw an oblique view (A004 E$1\frac{1}{2}$,0,4) taken in the direction S2,$1\frac{1}{2}$,3 T114.

18. A 2″ diameter frontal circle, centered at point Q348, is the base of a right cone having its vertex at V346. Draw a view of the cone taken in the direction P457 Q.

19. Draw an oblique view taken in the direction A523 B$6\frac{1}{2}$,1,4, of the right circular cylinder having the 3″ diameter horizontal circle centered at B as the upper base and an altitude of 1″.

Group 12.   Objects in Oblique Positions.

1. E125 F317 is the axis of a right prism. The ends of the prism are $1\frac{1}{4}$″ squares, and one diagonal of each square is horizontal. Show the front, top, auxiliary, and end views of the prism.

2. C215 D3,2,$4\frac{1}{2}$ is the axis of a right prism. The diagonals of the hexagonal bases are $2\frac{1}{2}$″ long, and one diagonal of each base is horizontal. Draw the front, top, auxiliary, and end views of the prism.

3. K1,1,$4\frac{1}{2}$ L224 is the axis of a right cylinder, of which the diameter is 2″. Show the following views: Front, top, auxiliary, and oblique.

4. V706 is the vertex and C6,1,7 is the center of the base of a right hexagonal pyramid. The sides of the hexagon are 1″ long, and one diagonal is horizontal. Draw the necessary auxiliary and oblique views and then complete the top and front views of the pyramid.

5. Draw the front and top, and the necessary auxiliary and oblique views of a right hexagonal pyramid of which P308 is the vertex, M$1\frac{1}{2}$,$1\frac{1}{2}$, 6 is the center of the base, and A2,$2\frac{1}{2}$,X is one corner of the base.

6. Draw the top view, and the necessary auxiliary view and oblique view of the right pyramid of which V517 is the vertex, C706 is the middle point of the hexagonal base, and P8X7 is one corner of the base.

7. C627 is the center of the 2″ circular base and V508 is the vertex of a cone. Show the front, top, auxiliary, and oblique views of the cone.

8. C626 is the center of the 3″ base and A704 is the vertex of a right circular cone. Draw oblique and auxiliary views of the cone and then complete the top and front views.

9. V315 is the vertex and C237 is the middle point of the $1\frac{1}{2}$″ frontal base of an isosceles triangle. This triangle is the front face of a square-base pyramid. Draw the front, top, auxiliary, and oblique views of the pyramid.

10. V617 is the vertex and C725 is the middle point of the 2″ horizontal base of an isosceles triangle. This triangle is the lower face of a square-base pyramid. Draw the front, top, left-side, auxiliary, and oblique views of the pyramid.

11. A right hexagonal pyramid lies on one of its triangular faces. The vertex of the lower face is at G005 and is 2″ in front of, and an equal distance to the left of, the middle point of its 1″ base. Show the front and top views, and any necessary auxiliary and oblique views of the pyramid.

12. The horizontal line B1,0,$5\frac{1}{2}$ C206 is the lower edge of a rectangle that is $2\frac{1}{2}$″ long, and that makes an angle of 30° with the horizontal. This rectangle is the lower face of a right prism. B C is also the edge of one of the hexagonal bases of the prism. Show the following views of the prism: Front, top, right-side, auxiliary, and end.

PROBLEMS—CHAPTER 5

Group 13. Drawing Lines in Specified Directions.

Each problem of this group states that four different lines or figures are to be drawn.   Divide the problem space into four equal spaces by penciling a horizontal and a vertical dividing line.   Each of the smaller spaces is to be used for the views of one of the lines or figures.   The first line or figure specified is to be drawn in the upper left-hand space, the second in the upper right-hand space, the third in the lower left-hand space, and the fourth in the lower right-hand space.   Letter each figure, line, or point, and in each view use the proper subscript, or letter the name of each view. Just above the lower edge of each problem space letter the name of the type of line or figure drawn in that space.   Each line or figure drawn should be a general type, except when a special position is required.   For example, if a horizontal line is specified, the line should not also be frontal or profile.   An additional auxiliary view may be necessary when some of the figures are drawn.

1. Draw the front, top, and right-side views of the following lines: An oblique line A B, a horizontal line C D, a profile line E F, and a vertical line G H.

2. Draw the front, top, and right-side views of the following lines: A frontal line A B, a horizontal-profile line C D, an oblique line E F, a horizontal line G H.

3. Draw the front, top, and left-side views of the following lines: A vertical line R S, an oblique line T U, a horizontal line V W, and a frontal line X Y.

4. Draw the front, top, and left-side views of the following lines: A frontal line J K, a horizontal-frontal line L M, a horizontal-profile line N O, and an oblique line P Q.

5. Draw the front, top, and right-side views of an isosceles triangle, having a $1''$ base and a $1\frac{1}{2}''$ altitude, in the following positions: Horizontal with base profile, frontal with base vertical, profile with a leg vertical, and vertical (edge view in the top view but not frontal or profile) with base horizontal.

6. Draw the front, top, and left-side views of an equilateral triangle, with $1\frac{1}{2}''$ sides, in the following positions: Frontal with no side horizontal or vertical, horizontal with side frontal, profile with a side horizontal, and vertical (edge view in the top view but not frontal or profile) with a side vertical.

7. Draw the front, top, and right-side views of a square, having $1\frac{1}{2}''$ diagonals, in the following positions: Frontal with a diagonal vertical, horizontal with no side or diagonal profile, vertical (edge view in the top view but not frontal or profile) with a side vertical, profile with a diagonal horizontal.

8. Draw the front, top, and right-side views of a hexagon, with $1\frac{1}{2}''$ diagonals in the following positions: Horizontal with a diagonal frontal, frontal with a diagonal vertical, profile with no diagonal horizontal or vertical, and vertical (edge view in the top view but not frontal or profile) with a diagonal horizontal.

9. Draw the front, top, and right-side views of the following $1\frac{1}{2}''$ circles: A horizontal circle, a frontal circle, a profile circle, a vertical circle (edge view in the top view but not frontal or profile).

Group 14.   True Lengths of Oblique Lines.

The true length of each line in the problems of this chapter is to be found by means of a normal view of the line.   Do not use some other method.   As usual, required data should be heavy.   And, as usual, adjacent views should not overlap or join.   Letter all points and reference planes in every view.   When an answer in figures or words is required, the result should be stated in the lower right-hand corner of the problem space.   Make measurements to the nearest one-hundredth of an inch.

1. Find the true length of the line C135 D318 and check this length by means of another normal view.

2. Find the true length of the line E618 R735 and check this length by means of another normal view.

3. Find the true length of the line Q136 P417 and check this length by means of another normal view.

4. Find the true length of the lines A046 B208 and C408 D815.

5. Find the true lengths of the lines E007 F348 and H437 K805.

6. Find the true length of each of the lines E036 F317 and 0514 P628.

7. State in inches the sum of the lengths of the lines D136 E408 and E F827.

8. Show the sum of the true lengths of the lines C123 D208 and E414 F825.

9. Determine the difference, in inches, in length of the lines A045 B208 and C608 D836.

10. Of the lines D415 E627 and D F036, which one is the longer and how much?

11. Determine, in inches, the perimeter of the triangle L217 M435 N518.

12. Determine, in inches, the perimeter of the triangle C247 D115 E527.

13. State, in inches, the perimeter of the triangle R314 S547 T735.

14. How much farther is it, in inches, from D712 to E827 by way of F605 than it is from D to E in a straight line?

15. What is the total length, in inches, of the lines A225 B227, B C428, C D408, D E638?

16. What is the total length, in inches, of the straight lines A125 B317, B C435, and C D628?

Group 15.   True Lengths of Lines—Miscellaneous Problems.

1. The line B C7X7 is the same length as the line A025 B308.   Draw the front and top views of both lines.

2. Draw the front and top views of the line C A41X that is equal in length to the line C146 B208.   The point A is behind C.

3. Locate the line K407 L81X equal in length to the line K M135.

4. The lines K323 L507 and L M81X are equal in length. Draw their front and top views.

5. The lines A415 B828 and C034 D2X8 are equal in length. Draw their front and top views.

6. The lines B03X C228, C D508, and D E8X7 are equal in length. Draw their front and top views.

---

7. The end P of the line P724 Q808 remains fixed while the end Q is shifted rearward to a point Q' 1″ below and 3″ to the left of P. Show the line in its new position. Do not change its length.

8. The end C of the straight rod C538 D315 remains fixed while the end D is swung to a new position D' below C, 3″ to the right of, and 1″ in front of C. Show the rod in its new position.

9. C346 D306 represents a vertical rod of fixed length. The end C remains fixed while the end D is moved to D' 3″ to the right and 2″ to the rear of C. Show the rod in its new position.

10. The location of the end F of the straight rod E307 F615 is fixed. The end E is moved to a new position E' above and 3″ in front of, but not to the right or left of, its original position. Show the rod in its new position.

11. The rod A528 B846 is swiveled about its middle-point C as a center. The end B is moved until it is behind C, $\frac{1}{2}$″ to the right of C, and 1″ below C. Show the rod in its new position. The length of the rod does not change.

---

12. The line R025 S108 is the base of a vertical isosceles triangle having $2\frac{1}{2}$″ equal legs. The vertex T is above the base. Draw a normal auxiliary view of the triangle and complete the top, front, and right-side views.

13. Draw the front, top, side, and normal views of the equilateral triangle K025 L306 M. The front view is an edge view and point M is behind line K L.

14. The front view is the edge view of the equilateral triangle J K L. J and K are on the line E507 F835, and $1\frac{1}{2}$″ from its mid-point. L is behind E. Draw four views of this triangle.

15. The right-side view is an edge view of an isosceles triangle of which E028 F205 is the base. The equal legs are 3″ long. The vertex is to the right of E and F. Determine the front, top, and right-side views of this triangle.

16. The side view is an edge view of a square having line K538 M707 for a diagonal. Draw a normal view of the square and then complete the side, front, and top views.

---

17. V535 R606 is one of the equal legs of an isosceles triangle. The other leg is along the line V T218. Draw the front, top, and left-side views of the triangle.

18. Shorten the line V326 C458 until it is just as long as the line V A505, and then draw an isosceles triangle of which these lines are two sides.

19. In the isosceles triangle V435 C418 D, V is the vertex, and the corner D is on the line V E847. Show the front and top views of the triangle.

20. Draw the front and top views of an isosceles triangle with vertex at A338. The equal legs are 3″ long and take the direction respectively of the lines A E206 and A F727.

21. V318 is the vertex and A235 B607 is the base of a triangle. Shorten the base of this triangle by cutting 2″ from each end. Draw the front, top, and right-side views of the reduced triangle.

22. Draw the front, top, and right-side views of the line J034 K118. Locate the points B and C on the line J K and $1\frac{1}{2}$″ from its end points.

23. Locate the points K and L on the line E528 F804 and 2″ either side of its middle point M.

24. The point D is below, 3″ to the left of, 1″ behind, and 4″ from the point C635. The point E is below, 2″ behind, 1″ to the right of, and 3″ from C. Draw the front and top views of the lines C D and C E.

25. Draw the front and top views of the line G H: G is on the line R035 S307, 2″ from R. H is on the line U508 V827, and 1″ from V.

26. Locate the point K on the line E045 F307 and 3″ from E. Locate the point L on the line Q524 P618 and $1\frac{1}{2}$″ from P. Draw the front and top views of the line K L.

---

27. Draw the front, top, and right-side views of the line C226 A335 and of the sphere of which C is the center and C A is the radius.

28. C226 is the center of a sphere, and P3,$1\frac{1}{2}$,7 is a point on the surface. Show the front, top, and side views of the sphere.

29. Q226 is the center of a 3″ sphere. Where is point P337 with respect to the sphere—inside or outside, and by how much?

30. M4,$1\frac{1}{2}$,6 is the center of a sphere. Give the location of points N627, Q325, and P526 with respect to the sphere—inside, on, or outside, and by how much.

31. Three tangent 2″ spheres are placed on a horizontal surface. A fourth 2″ sphere is placed in the cup formed by the first three. What is the height of the pile of spheres?

32. A517 B717 C615 are the centers of three $1\frac{1}{2}$″ spheres. A fourth sphere is placed in the cup formed by the first three. Show the front, top, and left-side views of the spheres. Omit hidden lines.

33. B6,3,$6\frac{1}{2}$ is the center of a 5″ sphere and C625 is the center of a $1\frac{1}{2}$″ sphere. Is the small sphere entirely inside the large sphere? Show by diagram.

34. H516 is the center of a 1″ sphere that rests on a horizontal surface. Around this sphere and touching it are grouped six similar spheres. In three of the cups formed by these spheres are placed three 1″ spheres, and a single 1″ sphere is placed on top. Draw the front, top, and side views. Do not show hidden lines.

---

35. C108 D408 is one edge of the horizontal square base of an equilateral pyramid. Draw three views of the pyramid.

36. C407 D604 is the left edge of the horizontal base of an equilateral tetrahedron. Draw the front, top, and left-side views, and the necessary auxiliary view of the tetrahedron.

Group 16.   Calculating the Lengths of Lines.

The problems in this group provide a test of one's skill to make accurate drawings. For each problem of this group the required distances should first be determined graphically. The distances should be measured by using the printed inches and tenths of an inch of the problem sheet. These distances should be estimated to the nearest one-hundredth of an inch and recorded on the sheet. The required distances should then be calculated—all calculations being shown on the problem sheet. The difference between the calculated and the graphically determined distances should be stated and underscored. A difference in excess of two-hundredths of an inch indicates an error in drawing or calculating. Check your work and eliminate errors.

1. Determine the length of the line M035 N218.
2. Determine the length of the line A518 B635.
3. Find the true lengths of the lines K036 L317 and Q514 P628.
4. Find the true lengths of the lines C046 D208 and H408 K815.
5. Determine the sum of the lengths of the lines M136 N408 and N R827.
6. Determine the difference in length of the lines X045 Y208 and K608 L836.
7. Determine the perimeter of the triangle A314 B547 C735.
8. Determine the length of the diagonal of a 12″ cube.
9. In a steel brace of a transmission tower, the center of one rivet hole is 12′6″ to the left of, 15′6″ below, and 8′0″ behind the center of another rivet hole. Determine the center to center distance. (Scale: $\frac{1}{4}″ = 1′$.)
10. Several guy wires of equal length support a chimney. The top end anchor point of one guy wire is 45′ above, 28′ to the left, and 31′ in front of the lower-end anchor point. Determine the straight-line distance between the anchor points. (Scale: $1″ = 10′$.)
11. A mast 100′ tall has three guy wires fastened 35′ below the top. One of these guy wires is anchored at a spot 30′ east, 60′ south, and 20′ below the bottom of the pole. Using a scale of $1″$ equals $20′$, determine the straight-line distance between the guy-wire fastenings.
12. The center of one pulley is 95′ above, 36′ to the right of, and 48′ in front of the center of another pulley. Determine the straight-line distance between the centers. (Scale: $1″ = 20′$.)

Group 17.   Intersecting Lines.

In all intersecting line problems the lines are regarded as unlimited in length. When necessary, the lines should be extended beyond the stated points that determine the line.

1. Draw front and top views of the intersecting lines A134 B31X and C026 D434, and locate the point of intersection M.
2. Draw the front, top, and side views of the intersecting lines F334 G018 and E407 K1X6, and locate A, the point of intersection.
3. Draw the front, top, and side views of the line E02X F416 intersecting the line C114 D338 at the point P.
4. Show the location of point Q, the intersection of lines G747 H705 and E845 F61X.
5. Draw the front, top, and left-side views of the line C818 D5X7 that intersects the line A457 B406 at E.
6. Locate the points where the lines A125 B647, C327 D408, and E136 F547 intersect.
7. Show the front, top, and left-side views of the line K50X P84X that intersects the lines C447 D835 and E634 F708 at points S and T.
8. In the front, top, and left-side views of the triangle C418 D806 E634, show the horizontal line C J, the frontal line J K, and the profile line K L of the triangle.
9. Through O4X6 draw a frontal line that intersects the lines Q147 R304 and S534 T708 at A and B. Through P41X draw a horizontal line that intersects the lines Q R and S T at C and D.

10. Draw a frontal line Q526 P intersecting the line A107 B334 at P; a horizontal line, $1\frac{1}{2}''$ below B, intersecting A B and Q P at C and D; a profile line, $1''$ to the right of B, intersecting C D and Q P at K and J.

11. In the front, top, and right-side views draw the vertical line intersecting the lines E045 F208 and J008 K334 at Q and P, and the horizontal line through A0,$2\frac{1}{2}$,X intersecting the lines E F and J K at B and C.

12. In the front, top, and left-side views show a vertical line A B, a horizontal-profile line C D, and a frontal line K P, all intersecting the lines J517 K836 and L534 M708.

Group 18.   Parallel Lines.

1. Draw the lines R836 S7XX and R T5XX parallel respectively to the lines B208 C435 and A046 C.

2. Through the point P326 draw the lines P X and P Y one-half the length D F and parallel respectively to the lines A418 B534 and C646 D808.

3. Draw the front and top views of three lines that end at K707, and are parallel and equal in length to the sides of the triangle C046 D208 E325.

4. Draw the front and top views of the lines A427 B, A C, and A D, respectively parallel and equal in length to the sides of the triangle Q512 R823 S704.

5. Draw the front, top, and right-side views of the parallelogram B008 C217 D334 E.

6. F415 D827 is one diagonal of a parallelogram, and C538 is one end of the second diagonal.   Draw the front, top, and left-side views of the parallelogram.

7. Given the lines C408 D535, D E727, and E F518, begin at F and duplicate the given series of lines in the same order, direction, and length.   Draw three principal views.

8. Join the middle points of the adjacent sides of the warped quadrilateral A408 B534 C728 D815.   Draw three views.

9. Show the front, top, and side views of the warped quadrilateral A005 B148 C217 D436.   Join the middle points of the adjacent sides of the quadrilateral.

10. The point B is $1\frac{1}{2}''$ to the right of, $\frac{1}{2}''$ behind, and $1''$ above, the point A105. The point D is $\frac{1}{2}''$ behind, $\frac{3}{4}''$ to the left of, and $1\frac{1}{2}''$ above A.   The point E is $2\frac{1}{2}''$ behind, $\frac{3}{4}''$ to the right of, and $2''$ above A.   The lines A B, A D, and A E are three edges of a parallelepiped.   Draw its front, top, and side views.

11. A014 B205 C3,$1\frac{1}{2}$,$3\frac{3}{4}$ is the base of a triangular prism.   Its parallel sides are $2''$ long and parallel to the line Q535 P658.   Show the front, top, and side views of the prism.

12. A507 B625 C816 is the triangular base of a prism.   The sides of the prism are $2\frac{1}{4}''$ long and are parallel to the line Q106 P047.   Draw the front and top views of the prism.

13. The triangle A417 B505 C726 is the lower base of a prism.   The three parallel sides are $1\frac{1}{2}''$ long, and are parallel to the line R004 S226.   Show the front and top views of the prism.

14. The edges of an equilateral parallelepiped are $2''$ long, and three intersecting edges are on the lines A314 B145, A C207, and A D626.   Draw its front and top views.

Group 19.   Force Polygons.

In the following problems the arrowhead for each force is placed on the last-named point of the line that represents the force, thus indicating whether the force pushes or pulls on the point. The scale of all of these forces is here taken as 1,000 pounds per inch. In each problem the required force is to be determined by means of front and top views of a space polygon drawn to one side in the problem space. The front and top views of the required force or forces are to be shown as required arrows acting on the given point. And, the value of the force in pounds is to be marked on the normal view of the arrow where that value has been determined. Scale the force to the nearest 50 pounds by using the decimal scale that is printed on the problem sheet. Keep the force polygon separate from the front and top views of the forces acting on the given point.

1. Determine the force that will balance the forces J637 K558, J L828, and J M704.

2. Determine the force T S that, when acting on point S, will balance the forces S648 P427, S R716, and Q827 S.

3. The forces A117 K225, B204 K, and C437 K are all pushing on the point K. Determine the tension force that will balance the given forces.

4. The forces Q 235 A0,$3\frac{1}{2}$,4, Q B126, Q C317, Q D445, all pull on the point Q. Find the value and direction of the force which will balance the four given forces.

5. Three balanced forces act on the point F618, as follows: The force E535 F, a force in the direction F G826, and a force in the direction F J4X7. Determine the front and top views, and the values of the unknown forces F G and F J.

Group 20. Are the Given Lines Perpendicular?

The problems in this group are to be solved by inspection and study of the front and top views. Additional views need not be drawn. Perpendicular-line principles should be applied to each pair of lines. If a pair of lines is perpendicular, this fact should be recorded on the problem sheet. All pairs should be considered.

1. Among the following lines list those pairs which are perpendicular to each other: C145 D307, E018 F434, J516 K726, L717 M715.

2. Among the following lines list those pairs which are perpendicular to each other: A127 B337, C406 D436, E015 F315, G546 H627.

3. Among the following lines list those pairs which are perpendicular to each other: A038 B215, B C547, C D527, D E707, E F8,0,$5\frac{1}{2}$.

4. Among the following lines list those pairs which are perpendicular to each other: A028 B227, C236 D348, E515 F815, J436 K406, P547 Q727.

5. List the right angles in the tetrahedron K137 L234 M515 N745.

Group 21. Horizontal, Frontal, and Profile Lines Perpendicular to Oblique Lines.

1. Through D4X8 draw a horizontal line that is perpendicular to and intersects the line A038 B325 at M, and through P54X draw a frontal line that is perpendicular to and intersects the line C605 D847 at Q.

2. Draw the frontal line C00X D2XX that is perpendicular to and intersects the line A134 B418 at a point O. Draw also the horizontal line K71X L5XX that is perpendicular to and intersects the line E507 F834 at a point P.

3. Draw the frontal line E43X F perpendicular to and intersecting the line C135 D218 at F. Draw the horizontal line L5X6 M perpendicular to and intersecting the line J548 K806 at M.

4. At the middle point A of the line J438 K245 erect the frontal-perpendicular line A B. At the middle point E of the line J L504 erect the horizontal-perpendicular line E F.

5. Draw the frontal-perpendicular bisector A B of the line J026 K318, and draw the horizontal-perpendicular bisector CD of the line K L835.

6. Draw the perpendicular bisector A11X B3XX of the line E124 F426, and the perpendicular bisector C5X5 D6XX of the line F G716.

7. Draw the line A335 B perpendicular to and intersecting the line C056 D306 at B, and the line K745 L perpendicular to and intersecting the line A E838 at L.

8. Draw the lines C2X7 B518 and D4X5 A635 perpendicular to the line A B.

9. Draw the 3″ horizontal line A306 B and the 2″ frontal line A C perpendicular to M234 N607.

10. Draw the horizontal line R307 S 3″ long and perpendicular to the line K234 L118. Also, draw the frontal line R T 4″ long and perpendicular to the line K M706.

11. Draw the 3″ horizontal-perpendicular bisector A1XX B of the line J008 K445, and the 4″ frontal-perpendicular bisector C5XX D of the line K L828.

12. Draw the 4″ horizontal-perpendicular bisector L M3XX of the line E034 F408, and the 3″ frontal-perpendicular bisector R5XX S of the line F G825.

13. Draw the lines A314 B and E447 F perpendicular to the line C108 D145, and intersecting it respectively at B and F.

14. Draw the lines P047 Q and J406 K perpendicular to the line R334 S318 and intersecting it respectively at the points Q and K.

Group 22.   Perpendicular Oblique Lines.

1. Through the point Q748 draw the line that is perpendicular to the line S538 T705 and intersects it at a point P.

2. Through C117 draw the line that is perpendicular to and intersects the line E134 F408 at a point Q.

3. In four views show the perpendicular intersecting lines C336 D and A308 B025.

4. Locate the line L705 M that is perpendicular to the line A518 B835 and intersects it at the point M. Draw the front, top, left-side, and auxiliary views of the two lines.

5. Through the point Q435 draw the line that intersects and is perpendicular to the line J725 K308 at P.

6. The perpendicular lines A258 B306 and C014 D intersect at the point D. Draw their front, top, and auxiliary views.

7. In the front, top, left-side, and auxiliary views show the line M817 N perpendicular to and intersecting the line C508 D845.

8. Draw four views of the line K108 L perpendicular to and intersecting the line R035 S418 at L.

9. In the front and top views show the perpendicular lines J405 K047 and J L6X8.

10. Draw the line E1X8 B436 perpendicular to the line B C718.

11. Draw the line P8X4 K704 perpendicular to the line K L528.

12. Show the line A524 B805 perpendicular to the line A C30X, and the line C A perpendicular to the line C D2X7.

13. Show the lines E117 F and R5X6 B418 perpendicular to the line A035 B. F is on A B.

14. Through the point D414 draw the line that is perpendicular to the line C206 D and intersects the line A423 B135.

15. Draw the line Q P through the middle point P of the line R127 S308 perpendicular to and intersecting the line D015 E428 at Q.   Show three views of the lines.

Group 23.   Right-angled Figures.

1. M706 N538 is one leg of a right triangle.   The third corner is on the line D427 M. Show three views of the triangle.

2. A136 B528 is one leg of a right triangle.   The hypotenuse is along the line A D705.   Draw the right triangle A B C in the front and top views.

3. The hypotenuse of a right-angle triangle is T648 S50X, and the right angle is at R724.   Draw the front and top views, and the necessary auxiliary view of the triangle.

4. The hypotenuse of the right-angle triangle A208 B114 C lies along the line A D325.   Draw three views of the triangle.

5. A148 B335 is the hypotenuse of a right-angle triangle.   The third corner of the triangle is on the line A D407.   Show two principal views and an auxiliary view of the triangle.

6. J408 K815 is the hypotenuse of a right-angle triangle.   The third corner is on the line J M535.   Show the front, top, and left-side views of the triangle.

7. Show three views of the right-angle triangle of which H508 J824 is the hypotenuse, and of which the third corner is on the line H K747.

8. P025 Q306 is the hypotenuse of a right-angle triangle.   The third corner is on the line P M238.   Draw the front, top, and right-side views of the triangle.

9. A614 B306 is the base of an isosceles triangle having its vertex on the line C434 D025.   Draw the top and front views of the triangle.

10. K323 L646 is the base of an isosceles triangle.   The vertex is on the line D315 E737.   Draw the front and top views of the triangle.

11. Draw three views of the rectangle C607 D715 E64X F.

12. Draw the front and top views of the rectangle A617 B205 C1X6 D.

13. Show three views of the rectangle D247 E315 F20X G.

14. Draw the front, top, and auxiliary views of the rectangle C D707 E518 F. The long sides of the rectangle are 3″ in length and one of them is along the line M8X5 D.

15. A115 C328 is the diagonal of a square.   K0X7 is a point on the line of the second diagonal.   Draw the front, top, and auxiliary views of this square.

16. R618 T735 is the diagonal of a square.   E54X is a point on the second diagonal. Draw the front, top, and auxiliary views of the square.

17. H136 L308 is one diagonal of a square.   P3X7 is a point on the second diagonal. Draw the front, top, and right-side views of the square.

Group 24.   Distance from a Point to a Line.

When a specified distance is required in a problem, the line representing the distance is to be drawn as required data in each view.   The true length of the line is to be found, and the words True Length should be lettered along the normal view of the line followed by the length stated in inches.

1. Find the distance from the point C407 to the line K224 L147.

2. Find the distance from the point T225 to the line R148 S406.

3. Find the distance from the point C416 to the line A538 B704.

4. Find the distance from the point P228 to the line E407 F114.

5. Find the distance from the point P047 to the line J218 K235.

6. Find the distance between the parallel lines A538 B806 and C248 D516.

7. Determine the distance between the long sides of the parallelogram C207 D328 E837 F716.

8. C326 B135 is the base and V208 is the vertex of a triangle. Find the true length of the altitude of the triangle.

9. A548 is the vertex and B317 C445 is the base of a triangle. Determine the true length of the altitude of the triangle.

10. C046 D108 is the base and V427 is the vertex of a triangle. Draw the altitude and find its true length.

Group 25.   Drawing One Line Perpendicular to Two Lines.

1. Draw the line A C perpendicular to the lines A505 B317 and AD616.

2. Draw the line A K perpendicular to the lines A405 B214 and A C623.

3. Draw the line J316 M perpendicular to the lines J K428 and J L405.

4. Draw the line A425 D perpendicular to the lines A B618 and A C207.

5. Draw the line P635 Q perpendicular to, but not intersecting, the lines A323 B405 and B C716.

6. Locate the line M424 Q perpendicular to the nonintersecting lines A314 B406 and C505 D724.

7. Draw the line Q526 R that is perpendicular to, but does not intersect, the lines A324 B407 and C318 D505.

Group 26.   Rectangular Objects.

1. Draw the front and top views of the right prism having for its upper base the triangle D127 E315 F436. The altitude is 1″.

2. The triangle A525, B7,3,5$\frac{1}{2}$ C4,2$\frac{1}{2}$,6 is the upper base of a right prism of 2″ altitude. Draw the front and top views of this prism.

3. Draw the front and top views of the right prism that has the triangle A227 B414 C636 for one base and an altitude of 1″.

4. The rectangle C117 D225 E4,X,5$\frac{1}{2}$ F is the base of a right prism of 1″ altitude. Show the front and top views of the prism.

5. The diagonals of an octahedron are equal in length, and each is a perpendicular bisector of the other two. The line A827 B4,3,5$\frac{1}{2}$ is one diagonal of the octahedron. S5$\frac{1}{2}$,X,7 is a point on the second diagonal. Determine the corners of the octahedron, and then draw its front and top views.

Group 27.   Common Perpendicular to Two Nonintersecting Lines.

1. Locate A B, the common perpendicular to the two lines J417 K736 and L618 M805.

2. Find the line C D that is perpendicular to, and intersects, each of the lines R015 S148 and J207 K324.

3. Locate K L, the shortest distance between the lines D015 E128 and F206 G438, and determine its length.

4. Locate E F, the shortest distance between the lines A505 B746 and C728 D805, and determine its length.

5. Locate the line M N that is perpendicular to and intersects each of the lines J018 K305 and E005 F247.

6. Locate the shortest line Q P that intersects the lines A026 B318 and C014 D337.

7. Find C D, the line that is perpendicular to, and intersects, the lines K005 L118 and P205 Q338.

8. Locate the line E R that is perpendicular to, and intersects, the lines A048 B205 and C356 D437.

9. Draw the line A B perpendicular to, and intersecting, the frontal line K016 L436 and the horizontal line M207 N405.

10. Locate and determine the length of the line, Q S, that represents the shortest distance between the frontal line J008 K338 and the profile line L147 M105.

11. E506 F718 and G637 J714 are points on two brake cables. Locate the points at which the cables are closest together and determine this distance.

12. The lines R336 S104 and M007 N318 represent the location in space of the center lines of two pipes which are to be cut and joined with right-angle pipe fittings. Indicate the center-line distance between the pipes, the distance from R where pipe R S is cut, and the distance from N where pipe M N is cut. (Scale $1'' = 10''$.)

Group 28.   Angle between Two Lines.

1. Find the true size of the angle L026 M207 N434.

2. Determine the true size of the angle A017 V237 B304.

3. Determine the true size of the angle between the lines E736 F814 and E D604.

4. Find the true size of the angle A005 B138 C215.

5. Find the true size of the angle L415 M538 N827.

6. Determine the true size of each of the angles of the triangle R507 S736 T818.

7. Determine the true size of each of the angles of the triangle Q528 R818 S506.

8. Determine the true size of each of the angles of the triangle H008 K128 L405.

---

9. Locate the bisector of the angle Q016 R305 S423.

10. Show the bisector of the angle C417 D736 E808.

11. In the front, top, auxiliary, and normal views show the bisector of the angle B003 A226 C414.

12. Determine the bisector of the angle D137 E214 F336.

Group 29.   Straight-line Questions.

Answering these questions affords experience and training in reading carefully, in visualizing, in thinking, and in making accurate statements.

1. What is an oblique line?

2. Is a line in the rear face of an object a frontal line?

3. In what views is it possible to tell whether or not a line is horizontal?

4. How is it possible to tell if a view shows the true length of a line?

5. The top view shows the true length of what type of line?

6. In what views can it be determined whether or not a vertical line and an oblique line are perpendicular?

7. How is a frontal line limited in direction?

8. In what views will two nonparallel horizontal lines appear parallel?

9. Are all views of a line adjacent to an end view of the line true-length views?

10. Do nonparallel lines in space ever appear parallel on a drawing?

11. What are perpendicular lines?

12. What line represents the shortest distance from a point to a line?

13. Can the true length of an oblique line be shown in a principal view?

14. Are all frontal lines perpendicular to all horizontal lines?

15. What is a profile line?

16. Are all horizontal lines perpendicular to all vertical lines?

17. In what views may the end view of a horizontal-frontal line be seen?

18. What is a vertical line?

19. What views show the true length of an oblique line?

20. A view shows the end view of two lines. Are they parallel?

21. In what views may the depth of one point of a line with respect to another be observed and measured?

22. What views show the true length of a horizontal line?

23. Is an oblique view necessary to show the end view of an oblique line?

24. What is the perpendicular-line principle?

25. In what views may the true length of a profile line be seen?

26. What is a horizontal-frontal line?

27. In what views are all points of a profile line equidistant from the observer?

28. What views show the true length of a horizontal-frontal line?

29. In what views are all points of a horizontal-profile line equidistant from the observer?

30. Are all vertical lines parallel?

31. A view shows two lines true length. Are they perpendicular?

32. Is it possible to tell from any single view whether or not a line is horizontal-profile?

33. What views show the true length of a vertical line?

34. Are all frontal lines perpendicular to all profile lines?

PROBLEMS—CHAPTER 6

CURVED LINES

The curves specified in the problems are to be determined by plotting consecutive locations of the generating point. The method used in plotting the points should in each case be developed from the law that governs the motion of the generating point, except in the few problems where a different method is specified. Plot a sufficient number of points to secure a smooth, accurate curve. Approximate methods of drawing curves should not be used. The size of a circle is specified by stating its diameter.

Group 30. Circles.

1. On the center C226 draw the front, top, and right-side views of a 2″ frontal circle, a 2″ profile circle, and a 2″ horizontal circle.

2. Show the front, top, and right-side views of a 2″ horizontal circle, a 4″ frontal circle, and a 3″ profile circle all centered at point C226.

3. A425 B626 is the axis of a 3″ circle, and B is its center. Show the front, top, and normal views of the circle.

4. E536 F616 is the axis of a 2″ circle with its center at F. Draw normal, edge, left-side, and top views of the circle.

5. The top edge of a $2\frac{1}{2}$″ profile circle is tipped to the right until the axis makes an angle of 30° with the horizontal. Draw the front, top, and normal views of the circle and its axis in the new position.

6. A 3″ frontal circle is tipped by moving its lower edge 1″ to the rear. Show the circle in its new position by drawing the front, top, left-side, and normal views.

7. P626 is the center of a 3″ circle that lies on a horizontal plane. The circle is tipped by raising its front edge $1\frac{1}{2}$″ above the rear edge. Show three principal views and the normal view of the circle in its new position.

8. A026 B217 is the axis of a 2″ circle having its center at B. Draw normal, edge, front, and top views of the circle.

9. Draw the front, top, edge, and normal views of a 2″ circle with center at C426 and with the axis passing through the point K318.

10. A circle passes through the point M726, and Y637 X5,1,$5\frac{1}{2}$ is the axis of the circle. Draw its normal, edge, front, and top views.

11. D745 E617 is the axis of a circle and P7$\frac{1}{2}$,2,6 is a point on its circumference. Draw the front, top, edge, and normal views of the circle.

12. P2$\frac{1}{2}$,X,6$\frac{1}{2}$ is a point on the circumference of, A438 is a point on the axis of, and C326 is the center of, a circle. Draw the front, top, edge, and normal views of this circle.

13. C626 is the center of a 3″ circle. The point A745 is equidistant from all points on its circumference. Draw the front, top, edge, and normal views of the circle.

Group 31.   Ellipses.

In the first five problems of this group, all points are to be located on the ellipses by using the compass to locate different positions of the generating point.

1. The major axis of a frontal ellipse is C507 D567. The minor axis is 2″ long. Show the front, top, and left-side views of the ellipse.

2. The major axis of an ellipse is a horizontal-frontal line. The foci are 3″ from the center, C426, of the ellipse. P625 is a point on the ellipse. Draw its front and top views.

3. K036 L836 is the major axis of a frontal ellipse. The foci are 6″ apart. Show the front and top views of this ellipse.

4. C415 is the center, F715 is one focus, and P517 is a point on the curve of an ellipse. The minor axis of this ellipse is the major axis of a second horizontal ellipse of which the foci are 3″ apart. Show the front and top views of both ellipses.

5. C447 D417 is the minor axis of a frontal ellipse. The foci are 6″ apart. P647 is a point on a second ellipse having the same foci. Draw the front and top views of both ellipses.

6. The major axis of an ellipse is A412 B417. The horizontal minor axis is 3″ long. By means of a trammel locate points on the curve and draw the front and top views of the ellipse.

7. E126 F726 is the major axis of an ellipse, and K625 is a point on the curve. With the aid of a trammel locate points on the ellipse. Show its front and top views.

8. A178 B718 is the major axis of an ellipse, and C138 is a point on the curve. With the aid of a trammel locate points on the ellipse and draw its front and top views.

9. Use a trammel to locate points on the two following frontal ellipses, and then draw their front and top views: S758 T128 is the major axis of both, and the foci are 6″ apart for one ellipse. The minor axis of the second ellipse is 2″ long.

Group 32.   Parabolas.

In the problems of this group, show as much of the curves of the parabolas as can be drawn within the limits of the problem space.

1. F648 is the focus of three frontal parabolas. The vertical directrices of the three parabolas are, respectively, $\frac{1}{2}$″, 1″, and 2″ to the right of the focus. Draw the front and top views of the parabolas.

2. Three frontal parabolas have a common focus at F448. The horizontal directrices are, respectively, 1″, 2″, and 3″ above the focus. Show the front and top views of the three parabolas.

3. Three parabolas pass through the respective points A316, B216, and C116. D012 E812 is the common directrix. The foci are on the line Q412 P417. Show the front and top views of the three curves.

4. C238 D328, and E418 are points on three parabolas. F548 is the common focus, and F G048 the axis. Each directrix is to the right of the focus. Draw the parabolas.

Group 33. Hyperbolas.

In the problems of this group, show as much of the curves of the hyperbolas as can be drawn within the limits of the problem space.

1. Three hyperbolas have E406 and F403 as foci in common. Each of the points A502, B602, and C702 is on one of the hyperbolas. Show the top view of the curves.

2. The respective constant differences of three frontal hyperbolas, with foci at C248 and D648, are 1″, 2″, and 3″. Draw the front view of the hyperbolas.

3. E304 and F504 are the common foci, and J601 and K702 are points on two hyperbolas. Draw the normal view of the two curves.

4. The foci of two frontal hyperbolas are $\frac{1}{2}$″ to the right and to the left of the point C448. J528 and K628 are points on the curves. Show the normal view of the two hyperbolas.

Group 34. Archimedean Spirals.

In each problem of this group show as many turns of the required spirals as can be drawn within the limits of the problem space.

1. P44X is the pole of an Archimedean spiral of 2″ lead. Show two turns of a normal view of a right-hand frontal spiral.

2. The generating point of an Archimedean spiral starts at the pole P458, and in the first revolution passes through the points A348 and B278. Draw a normal view of the spiral.

3. C204 is the pole of a left-hand, and D604 is the pole of a right-hand, horizontal Archimedean spiral of 1″ lead. Show the top view of two turns of each spiral.

4. The generating point of a horizontal, right-hand Archimedean spiral starts at the pole P305, and is at A304 after revolving 90° around the pole. Show a normal view of the spiral.

Group 35. Involutes.

In the problems of this group, show as many turns of each involute as can be drawn within the limits of the problem space.

1. C505 is the center of a horizontal 1″ circle. Draw the top view of a right-hand involute of this circle. Start the involute at the front point of the circle.

2. Draw the front view of the left-hand involute of the $1\frac{1}{4}$″ frontal circle centered at C448. The initial point of the involute is the lowest point of the given circle.

3. C448 is the center of a $1\frac{1}{2}$″ frontal circle. Draw a right-hand involute of this circle, taking the left point of the circle as end point of the involute.

4. The extreme left-hand point of a 2″ horizontal circle centered at P404 is the initial point of the left-hand involute of the given circle. Draw a normal view of the involute.

5. In the top view, show three right-hand involutes of the horizontal equilateral triangle of which the vertex is directly behind E404, the middle point of one 1″ side.

6. In the front view, show four left-hand involutes of the frontal 1″ square that is centered at C458.

7. A448 is the middle point of a vertical $1\frac{1}{2}$″ line, and the line is one diagonal of a frontal hexagon. In the front view, show the six left-hand involutes of the hexagon.

Group 36.   Trochoids and Cycloids.

1. C448 is the center of a $1\frac{1}{2}''$ frontal circle that rolls, to the right and to the left, on a horizontal straight line.   Show the trochoids generated by points fixed to this circle: The top point of the circle, a point $\frac{1}{2}''$ below C, and a point $2''$ below C.

2. The point M448 is the center of a $2''$ frontal circle that rolls on a horizontal line. Show the trochoids generated by the top point of the circle, by a point $\frac{1}{2}''$ above the center, and by a point $1\frac{1}{2}''$ below the center.

3. A $1\frac{1}{2}''$ horizontal circle makes four revolutions while rolling completely around the inside of a square.   Show the square and also the cycloids that are generated by the forward point of this rolling circle in its initial position.   The initial position of the circle is in the left-front corner of the square.

4. The line A238 B638 is one side of a frontal equilateral triangle.   A frontal circle rolls on the outside of the triangle, and a point on this circle generates three cycloids that meet at the vertices of the triangle.   Show the triangle and the cycloids.

Group 37.   Epicycloids and Hypocycloids.

1. C418 is the center of the $8''$ frontal director circle of an epicycloid and a hypocycloid.   P458 is a point on both curves.   The rolling circles are $1''$ in diameter. Show a complete curve of each type.

2. K448 is the center of a $4''$ frontal director circle.   Symmetrically disposed about a vertical line draw an epicycloid and a hypocycloid generated by a point on a $2''$ rolling circle.

3. M408 is the center of a $10''$ frontal director circle.   Symmetrically disposed about a vertical line show the epicycloid and hypocycloid generated by a point on a $2''$ rolling circle.

Group 38.   Sinusoids.

1. A $2''$ frontal circle is centered at C048 and a $1\frac{1}{2}''$ frontal circle is centered at D128.   On horizontal axes, draw the sine curves of these circles.

2. J438 is the center of a frontal $2\frac{1}{2}''$ circle, and K468 is the center of a $1\frac{1}{2}''$ frontal circle.   Draw a complete sinusoid for each of these circles.

3. Show a complete sinusoid of each of the following frontal circles: A $2\frac{1}{4}''$ circle centered at A428, and a $1\frac{1}{2}''$ circle centered at B468.

Group 39.   Double-curved Lines.

1. Draw a front view and a top view of a smooth double-curved line that contains the points A B C D.   In these two views locate 10 additional points and then from these 14 known points plot the side view.   (A038, B124, C217, D345.)

2. Draw a front view and a side view of a smooth double-curved line that contains the points E F G H.   In these two views locate 10 additional points and then from these 14 known points plot the top view.   (E824, F736, G535, H618.)

3. Draw a top view and a side view of a smooth double-curved line that contains the points J K L M.   In these two views locate 10 additional points and then from these 14 known points plot the front view.   (J517, K604, L738, M846.)

Group 40.   Helices.

In each problem of this group draw the helix for the entire length of the cylinder or cone.

1. C246 D206 is the axis of a 2″ cylinder.   F646 G606 is the axis of a 3″ cylinder. On the smaller cylinder, draw a right-hand helix of 4″ lead.   On the larger cylinder, draw a left-hand helix of 2″ lead.

2. A406 B426 is the axis of a 4″ cylinder.   B C446 is the axis of a 2″ cylinder.   On each of these cylinders show a left-hand helix of 1″ lead.

3. M206 N236 is the axis of a 3″ cylinder.   On this cylinder show a right-hand helix that makes two-thirds of a turn per inch.   On the 2″ cylinder of which R607 S657 is the axis, draw a left-hand helix having two-fifths of a turn per inch.

4. V446 is the vertex and C406 is the center of the 4″ base of a right circular cone. Draw the front and top views of the cone and on the cone show two turns of a right-hand conical helix of 2″ lead.

5. A left-hand conical helix of 2″ lead is wound around the right circular cone of which V425 is the vertex and C405 is the center of its 6″ base.   Show the front and top views of the cone and of two turns of the helix.

6. V412 is the vertex and C418 is the center of the 2″ base of a right circular cone. On this cone are two turns of a right-hand helix of 3″ lead.   Draw the front and top views of the cone and helix.

––––––––––––

PROBLEMS—CHAPTER 7

PLANES

Group 41. Points and Lines in Planes.

1. Locate three views of the points A1X7 and B21X in the plane Q016 R338 S425.

2. In the plane D426 E635 F818 show the points K51X and J7X7.   Draw the front, top, and left-side views.

3. Locate the points A21X and B3X5 in the plane M034 N116 Q408.   Show three views.

4. Locate, in three views, the points R62X and S7X7 in the plane A445 B607 C836.

5. In the front, top, and left-side views show the line R6X7 S73X in the plane E508 F634 G827.   Check the solution.

6. In the plane A008 B347 C425 show the line F1X7 G43X.   Draw the front, top, and right-side views.   Check the solution.

7. Show the front, top, and left-side views of the line A4X6 B73X of the plane D538 E604 F825.   Check the solution.

8. Draw the front and top views of the triangle A11X B34X C6X8 that is in the plane D045 E308 F856.   Check the solution.

9. Draw the front and top views of the triangle C62X D3X6 E2X4 that lies in the plane Q508 R845 T034.   Check the solution.

10. Determine the front and top views of the triangle K4X7 L6X8 M7X4 that is in the plane R005 S326 T414.   Check the solution.

11. In the front, top, and right-side views of the plane K015 L208 M346, show the frontal line M C, the horizontal line K D, and the profile line L E.

12. Draw the front, top, and side views of the horizontal line T Y, frontal line R X, and the profile line S Z of the plane R056 S305 T428.

13. Show three views of the horizontal line D E, the frontal line C F, and the profile line B G of the plane C046 B318 D435.

14. Show three principal views of the plane K038 L305 M546, and the frontal line C11X D4XX and the horizontal line F0XX E3X6 of the plane.

15. In three principal views show the horizontal line J6X7 K8XX and the frontal line L5XX M80X of the plane Q545 S708 T823.

Group 42. Plane Figures.

1. The front view is the edge view of the square of which A035 C217 is one diagonal. Show the front, top, right-side, and normal views of this square.

2. A528 D736 is the diagonal of a hexagon that lies in a vertical plane.   Show the front, top, left-side, and normal views of the hexagon.

3. Draw the front, top, and normal views of the hexagon of which C645 F727 is one diagonal and the front view is the edge view.

4. C516 D735 is the diameter of a circle, the edge view of which is seen in the side view. Draw the front, top, left-side, and normal views of this circle.

5. Draw the front, top, edge, and normal views of the triangle C535 D617 F736. Indicate the strike and dip of the plane of the triangle.

6. Draw the front, top, edge, and normal views of the triangle D014 E123 F206. Indicate the strike and dip of the plane of the triangle.

7. Show the true shape of the triangle B534 C617 D826. Indicate the strike and dip of the plane of the triangle.

8. Draw the front, top, edge, and normal views of the triangle J516 K637 L803. Indicate the strike and dip of the plane of the triangle.

9. Show the front, top, edge, and normal views of the triangle A448 B735 C817.

10. Draw the front, top, edge, and normal views of the square of which $J2,0,6\frac{1}{2}$ L338 is a diagonal, and P427 is a point in the plane of the square.

11. A505 B638 is the base of an isosceles triangle having a $1\frac{1}{2}''$ altitude. The triangle is in the plane A B K817. Draw the normal, edge, top, and front views of the triangle.

12. B237 is a point in the plane of a hexagon and A125 D314 is one of its diagonals. Draw the front, top, edge, and normal views of the hexagon. Indicate the strike and dip of the plane.

13. A $2''$ circle centered at C626 lies in the plane C D508 E836. Draw the normal, edge, top, and front views of the circle.

14. A026 B324 is the strike of a plane. The dip is 30° rearward. A B is one edge of an equilateral triangle that lies in this plane, with the third vertex below A B. Draw four views of the triangle.

15. J537 K836 is the base of an equilateral triangle that dips 45° forward of the base. Show the front, top, edge, and normal views of the triangle.

16. C025 F326 is one diagonal of a hexagon that dips 60° forward. Draw the front, top, edge, and normal views of this hexagon.

17. A135 B236 is the upper edge of a hexagon which dips 60° to the southeast. Show the front, top, edge, and normal views of the hexagon.

18. Q527 T826 is one diagonal of a hexagon that dips 60° forward. Draw the front, top, edge, and normal views of this hexagon.

Group 43. Parallel Planes.

1. Through the point A108 pass the plane A B C parallel to the plane Q518 R656 S727.

2. Through the point P226 pass the plane P Q R parallel to the plane J526 K708 L845.

3. Parallel to the plane D125 E247 K306 draw the plane A537 B6X7 C43X.

4. Parallel to the plane J116 K248 L305 draw the plane D516 E43X F73X.

5. Locate the plane P406 Q1X7 R2X4 that is parallel to the plane D535 E648 F806.

6. By means of a horizontal line and a frontal line represent the plane C217 D E that is parallel to the plane T527 R646 S704.

7. Draw the plane P135 Q32X R21X parallel to the plane A036 B317 C208. What is the distance between the planes?

Group 44. Perpendicular Lines and Planes.

1. Show the front, top, and right-side views of the line T P that is perpendicular to the plane R034 S208 T426.

2. Show the line F137 GXX5 perpendicular to the plane C445 D608 E856.

3. Draw the front, top, and right-side views of the line B448 C3XX that is perpendicular to the plane R018 S235 T507.

4. In the front, top, and left-side views, show the line C546 D perpendicular to the plane Q457 R608 S836.

5. In the front, top, and right-side views show the plane A036 B204 C428, and the line E335 F2XX that is perpendicular to it.

6. Given: The triangle M036 P148 Q207. Locate the front, top, and right-side views of the line K L3XX that passes through the middle point K of the side M Q, and is perpendicular to the triangle.

7. The dip of a plane is 60° forward of the strike A025 B426. Show three views of the line B CXX4 that is perpendicular to the plane.

8. In three views show the line C503 DX2X that is perpendicular to the plane of which A223 B325 is the strike, and the dip is 30° leftward.

9. Draw the front, top, and auxiliary views of the line A537 B7XX that is perpendicular to the plane of which the strike is C524 D727 apd the dip is 40° to the leftward.

10. A plane passes through the point S436, has a strike, the bearing of which is N 52° E, and a dip of 32° in a southeasterly direction. From the point C545 draw the line C D perpendicular to this plane. D is in the plane.

11. L525 is a point in a plane. The strike of the plane has a bearing of N 32° E. The dip is 48° in a northwesterly direction. Draw the line J548 K perpendicular to the plane and terminating at K in the plane.

12. Given a point A834 in a plane that has a strike, the bearing of which is N 72° W and a dip of 26° in a southerly direction, draw the line R506 S perpendicular to the plane. Locate S in the plane.

13. The triangle D424 E505 F8,3,4$\frac{1}{2}$ is one base of a right prism of 2″ altitude. Show the front and top views.

14. Show the front and top views of the right prism of which the triangle J436 K618 L505 is one base, and the altitude is 1$\frac{1}{2}$″.

15. Draw the three views of the right prism of which the triangle M025 K1,4,5$\frac{1}{2}$ L234 is one base, and 3″ is the altitude.

16. The triangle A414 B607 C826 is the lower base of a right prism of 1″ altitude. Draw the front, top, and left-side views of the prism.

17. Pass the plane Q436 R2XX S5XX perpendicular to the line A245 B507.

18. Through the point P225 draw the plane P Q3XX R4XX perpendicular to the line M318 N735.

19. Draw the plane R117 S T perpendicular to the line C416 D045.

20. Pass the plane K514 L737 M perpendicular to the plane A317 B125 C234.

21. Pass the plane R515 S826 T6XX perpendicular to the plane D046 E307 F425.

22. Through the line R137 S315 pass the plane that is perpendicular to the given plane C436 D718 E825.

Group 45.   Three Perpendicular Lines and Planes.

1. Draw the line B528 C4X6 perpendicular to the line B A745, and draw the line B D3XX perpendicular to the plane A B C.

2. Perpendicular to the oblique plane A148 B205 C417 and to all horizontal planes pass the plane Q R635 S.

3. Find the plane P625 Q3XX R7XX that is perpendicular to the oblique plane K207 L436 M518 and to all profile planes.

4. Pass the plane C648 D8XX E4XX perpendicular to the planes P057 Q346 R428 and R S115 T207.

5. Find the plane P226 Q R that is perpendicular to the planes A446 B518 C705 and D534 E718 F825.

6. Of the mutually perpendicular lines A224 B008, A C, and A D, the line A C is perpendicular to the plane A B T415. Locate the three lines.

7. Each of the lines J335 K707, J L, and J M is perpendicular to the other two. The line J M is in the plane J K A218. Draw the front and top views of the three perpendicular lines.

8. Of the three mutually perpendicular lines Q P, Q S, and Q R, the line Q R is in the plane Q337 P008 C415. Show the front, top, and right-side views of the three lines.

9. F617 is one corner of a $1\frac{1}{2}''$ cube. One edge lies along the line F G736 and one surface is in the plane F G K535. Draw the front and top views of the cube.

10. The point A406 is the lowest corner of a $2''$ cube. The edges of the cube are on the lines A K214 and A L6,$1\frac{1}{2}$,X. Show the front and top views of the cube.

11. The line A106 B027 is one edge of a rectangular block. The edge A C is $2''$ long, and is perpendicular to the plane A B X417. The edge A D is $1\frac{1}{2}''$ long. Draw the front and top views of the block.

Group 46. Intersection of a Line and a Plane.

1. Show the front and top views of the point P where the line L248 M604 pierces the plane A126 B635 C507. Check the solution.

2. Find the point Q, where the line E105 F548 intersects the plane J046 K625 L308. Check the solution.

3. The line D216 E847 intersects the plane A045 B508 C736 at the point P. Locate P.

4. Locate the intersection M of the line A245 B717 and the plane R117 S537 T704. Check the solution.

5. Locate the point A where the line K034 L316 intersects the plane C438 D505 E846. Check the solution.

6. Locate the point C where the line A416 B847 intersects the plane J034 K257 L548. Check the solution.

7. Locate the point T where the line C217 D745 intersects the plane E056 F508 G835. Also, locate the point R where the line C B718 intersects the same plane. Check.

8. Show the point P where the line A126 B645 pierces the plane R248 S504 T637, and the point Q where the line B C407 pierces the same plane.

9. Find the point A on the line M215 N527 and in the plane C237 D314 E646. Also, find the point B on the line J308 K734 and in the given plane. Check.

10. The dip of a plane is 40° to the rearward of the strike M128 N425. Find the intersection Q of this plane with the line C317 D438.

11. Find P, the intersection of the line C425 D006 with the plane which has a strike A018 B414 and a dip of 30° forward.

12. R636 S837 is the strike of a plane having a dip 20° forward. Locate M, the intersection of line E507 F725 with the plane.

13. A plane with strike G405 H703 and dip 50° rearward is intersected by the line K614 L835. Locate the point of intersection E.

14. Two of the faces of the pyramid R116 S325 T448 U627 are intersected by the line A235 B618. Find the points of intersection K and L.

15. Find the two points M and N where the line P335 Q617 enters and leaves the pyramid V534 C226 D406 E648.

16. Show the front and top views of the two points V and W where the line K107 L736 enters and leaves the pyramid D314 E546 F707 G428.

___

Group 47.   Intersections of Several Lines and a Plane.

1. The triangle A006 B2,0,4$\frac{1}{2}$ C308 is the base of a right pyramid of 4″ altitude. Discard that part of the pyramid that is above the plane having a strike J326 K525 and a dip 40° forward.

2. Show that part of the pyramid—of which C105 E308 is one diagonal of the horizontal square base and the altitude is 4″—that is below the plane Q028 R205 S416.

3. A538 C818 is one diagonal of a frontal square.   This square is the base of a right pyramid of 3″ altitude.   Show the intersection of this pyramid with the plane of which P547 Z748 is the strike, and the dip is 60° forward.

4. V246 is the vertex, and B006 C207 D406 E205 is the base of a pyramid.   Discard that part of the pyramid that is above the plane having S116 T314 for a strike and a dip of 45° forward.   Draw three views.

5. A505 D608 is one diagonal of the horizontal hexagonal base of a right pyramid of 3″ altitude.   Show all of this pyramid that is below the plane R327 S718 T805.

6. E107 H305 is one diagonal of a horizontal hexagon.   This hexagon is the base of a right pyramid of 3$\frac{1}{2}$″ altitude.   In the front, top, and auxiliary views show the intersection of the pyramid with the plane having a strike K424 L225 and a dip of 30° rearward.

7. The axis of a 3″ right circular cylinder is A606 X646.   In the front, top, and auxiliary views draw the part of the cylinder that is below the plane that has a strike T425 K826 and a dip of 60° forward.

8. M206 N236 is the axis of a 2″ right circular cylinder.   Show the part of the cylinder below the plane having R326 S525 for a strike and a dip of 40° forward.

___

Group 48.   Distance from a Point to a Plane.

In each of the problems in this group, determine to the nearest one-hundredth of an inch the perpendicular, the vertical, and the shortest horizontal distances from the given point to the given plane.   Show the lines representing these distances in the front and top views.

1. Determine the perpendicular, the vertical, and the shortest horizontal distances from point P334 to plane J024 K137 L315.

2. Determine the perpendicular, the vertical, and the shortest horizontal distances from point A727 to plane B506 C808 D735.

3. Determine the perpendicular, the vertical, and the shortest horizontal distances from point N107 to plane K027 L238 M315.

4. Determine the perpendicular, the vertical, and the shortest horizontal distances from point Q547 to plane R838 S536 T408.

5. Determine the perpendicular, the vertical, and the shortest horizontal distances from point D716 to the plane having A426 B828 for a strike and a dip 30° rearward.

6. Determine the perpendicular, the vertical, and the shortest horizontal distances from point M134 to the plane having K003 L204 for a strike and a dip of 60° southeast.

7. Determine the perpendicular, the vertical, and the shortest horizontal distances from point R237 to the plane having S118 T216 for a strike and a dip 55° eastward.

___

Group 49. Intersection of Planes.

1. Find D E, the intersection of the plane A238 B324 C547 with the vertical plane through F115 G617.

2. Locate K L, the intersection of the planes A718 B424 C136 and D634 E308 F025.

3. Find E F, the intersection of the plane A308 B615 C145 with the horizontal plane through D026.

4. Determine P K, the intersection of the planes C017 D445 E708 and R138 S205 T846.   Check the solution.

5. Determine the intersection K L of the planes A017 B534 C806 and D204 E438 F707.   Check the solution.

6. Locate the intersection M N of the planes J038 K404 L717 and R208 S645 T016. Check the solution.

7. Find the line S T that lies in the planes D045 E534 F607 and L104 M748 N815. Check the solution.

8. Locate J K, the line of intersection of the planes C127 D404 E746 and F256 G508 H624.   Check.

9. Locate the intersection X Y of the planes A018 B135 C327 and D527 E718 F846. Check the solution.

10. Locate the line S T in the planes C046 D307 E435 and F424 G538 H815.   Check the solution.

11. Find E F, the intersection of the planes A124 B208 C446 and Q537 R828 S605. Check the solution.

12. Locate J K, the intersection of the planes M708 P534 Q427 and D037 E326 F115.   Check the solution.

13. Locate the intersection Q P, of the planes B035 C248 D404 and E507 F635 G828. Check the solution.

14. Q215 R318 is the strike of a plane with a $67\frac{1}{2}°$ leftward dip, and S337 T536 is the strike of a plane with a 60° forward dip.   Locate A B, the intersection of the planes.

15. Given: A plane with a strike C503 D704 and a dip of 60° forward, and a plane with a strike E527 F825 and a dip 40° forward.   Find S T, the intersection of the two planes.

16. Find R S, the intersection of the plane of which E515 F717 is the strike with a dip of 35° forward, and the plane of which M606 N805 is the strike with a dip 60° rearward.

17. Locate the point P where the planes A046 B308 C725, J116 K445 L808, and R235 S418 T856 intersect.

18. Locate Q, the intersection of the planes R018 S345 T807, X134 Y217 Z426, and J526 K617 L734.

Group 50. Angles between Lines and Planes.

1. Find the true size of the angles that the line A715 B847 makes with horizontal, frontal, and profile planes.

2. Find the respective angles H, F, and P that the line M036 N308 makes with all horizontal, frontal, and profile planes.

3. Show the respective angles H, F, and P that the line S436 T717 makes with all horizontal, frontal, and profile planes.

4. Find the true size of the angles that the line D127 E346 makes with horizontal, frontal, and profile planes.

5. Find the angle between the plane L206 M123 N014 and the line Q215 R036.

6. Find the angle between the plane F617 G534 H826 and the line S736 T815.

7. Find the angle that the line A136 B304 makes with the plane Q005 R238 S325.

8. Find the angle between the plane J007 K323 L516 and the line L M304.

9. Find the angle between the plane R114 S206 T535 and the line E448 F315.

10. Find the angle between the line C336 D116 and the plane having A028 B226 for a strike and a dip 30° forward.

11. Find the angle between the line E507 F825 and the plane having R536 S837 for a strike and a dip 20° forward.

12. Find the angle between the line K135 L216 and the plane having M024 N325 for a strike and a dip 45° rearward.

---

13. Show the front and top views of the lines E436 F5X4 and E G31X that each make an angle of 42° with the horizontal. Point F is below E and point G is in front of E.

14. Show the front and top views of the lines A237 B1X4 and C535 D62X that each make an angle of 28° with the horizontal. Point B is below A and point D is behind C.

15. Draw the front and top views of the line A426 B that is 3″ long and makes an angle of 15° with a horizontal plane and 30° with a frontal plane. Point B is below, to the right of, and behind point A.

16. Draw the line M448 N that makes an angle of 15° with a frontal plane and 52° with a horizontal plane. The point N is to the left of M, 2″ below M, and in front of M.

Group 51. Angles between Planes.

1. Determine the true size of the angles that the plane Q037 R108 S246 makes with horizontal, frontal, and profile planes.

2. Determine the true size of the angles that the plane K607 L816 M735 makes with horizontal, frontal, and profile planes.

3. Determine the true size of the angles the plane R047 S115 T226 makes with horizontal, frontal, and profile planes.

4. Determine the true size of the angles that the plane E027 F208 G335 makes with horizontal, frontal, and profile planes.

---

5. Determine the true size of the angle between the planes A607 B735 C726 and A B D516.

6. Determine the true size of the angle between the planes D623 E806 F834 and D E G606.

7. In the tetrahedron G304 H004 J216 K225, find the true size of the angle between planes G K H and G K J; and also planes G H J and G H K.

8. In the tetrahedron K326 L427 M525 N406, find the true size of the angle between planes K L M and K L N; and also planes K M N and L M N.

9. Two metal plates, Q434 R508 S645 and R S T826, are joined by welding along the common edge R S. Determine the angle between these plates.

10. A bracket made from sheet metal is folded along the line A538 B615. Point C714 is located in the surface to the right of the fold line and point E504 in the surface to the left. Determine the angle between the two surfaces of the bracket.

11. Two adjacent surfaces of a corner brace contain the points E137 F216 G228 and E F H037. Determine the angle between the two surfaces.

12. M028 N328 is the rear edge of a horizontal 3″ square that is the upper end of a symmetrical hopper. The 1″ square outlet is 2″ below the upper end. Determine the angle between two adjacent slanting faces of the hopper.

---

13. Locate a plane E408 F8X8 G80X that makes an angle of 70° with a frontal plane and has a dip of 30°.

14. Locate the plane A528 B4X8 C62X which makes an angle of 60° with a horizontal plane and 75° with a frontal plane.

15. Locate a plane K408 L2X8 M10X that makes an angle of 50° with all frontal planes and an angle of 70° with all horizontal planes.

Group 52. Timber Framing.

Each of the problems in this group is to be solved to the scale 3″ = 1′ (quarter size).

1. Show the face, edge, and end views of a 2″ × 4″ common rafter for a roof having a rise of 8″ in a run of 12″.

2. Show the face, edge, and end views of a 2″ × 4″ common rafter for a roof having a rise of 6″ in a run of 12″.

3. Show the face, edge, and end views of a 2″ × 6″ common rafter for a roof having a rise of 9″ in a run of 12″.

4. Show the face, edge, and end views of a 2″ × 4″ jack rafter for a roof having a rise of 8″ in a run of 12″.

5. Show the face, edge, and end views of a 2″ × 6″ jack rafter for a roof having a rise of 10″ in a run of 12″.

6. Show the face, edge, and end views of a 2″ × 4″ jack rafter for a roof having a rise of 15″ in a run of 12″.

7. Show the face, edge, and end views of a 2″ × 4″ hip rafter for a roof having a rise of 8″ in a run of 12″.

8. Show the face, edge, and end views of a 2″ × 6″ hip rafter for a roof having a rise of 6″ in a run of 12″.

9. Show the face, edge, and end views of a 3″ × 6″ hip rafter for a roof having a rise of 12″ in a run of 12″.

10. Show the top, face, edge, and end views of a 2″ × 4″ brace between two profile walls. M8X3 N5X7 is the center line of the brace and point M is 8″ above point N. The 4″ faces of the brace are vertical.

11. Show the front, top, face, edge, and end views of a 2″ × 4″ brace between point C528 in a frontal plane and point D705 in a horizontal plane. The 4″ faces of the brace are vertical and C D is the center line.

12. A right pyramidal roof of 10″ altitude is built on a horizontal square base having R004 T408 for a diagonal. The four similar hip rafters are made of 2″ × 4″ pieces. Show the top view of the four rafters in place and the face, edge, and end views of one of the rafters. The top surface of each rafter is to be beveled.

13. One vertical 4″ × 4″ post is placed 8″ in front of and 12″ to the left of another vertical 4″ × 4″ post. Two surfaces of each post are frontal. A slanting 4″ × 6″ strut, inclined at 45°, braces the posts. The 6″ faces of the strut are vertical. Show the top, face, edge, and end views of the strut.

Group 53.   Miscellaneous Problems.

1. Draw three views of the locus of a point that is equidistant from the points M036 and N208.

2. Determine the locus of a point that is equidistant from the points R628 and S805. Draw three views.

3. Find the locus of a point that is equidistant from the points E006 and F325. Draw top, front, and side views.

---

4. Find the locus of a point that is equidistant from the points C535, D617, and E736.

5. Determine the locus of a point that is equidistant from the points D014, E123, and F206.

6. Locate the locus of a point that is equidistant from the points B534, C617, and D826.

---

7. Locate the line M N that is parallel to the line C027 D315 and intersects the lines E016 F228 and G126 H307.

8. Draw the line K L that intersects the line D015 E128 at K and the line F206 G438 at L and is parallel to the line R038 T227.

9. Locate the line X Y intersecting the lines K005 L118 and P205 Q338 and parallel to the line A127 B326.

---

10. Locate H J perpendicular to the plane K624 L814 M706 and intersecting the lines A615 B424 and C505 D713.

11. Locate the line C145 M N that intersects the lines F347 G504 and S608 T834.

12. Locate the line through R526 that intersects line K208 L334 at S and line M135 N707 at T.

13. Show the part of a 2″ diameter sphere that is below the plane C225 D024 E146. The center is at point C.

14. Locate the locus of a point that is equidistant from the points J305, K426, L526, and M514.

PROBLEMS—CHAPTER 8

INTERSECTION AND DEVELOPMENT OF SURFACES

Intersection Problems

Group 54. Miscellaneous Intersections.

This group of problems is divided into subgroups of three problems each. The problems of each subgroup are chosen so that all three methods of finding intersections can be used to advantage in solving the three problems of the subgroup. Each problem requires a different method from the other two. The order of the problem in the group does not indicate the method that should be used in solving it. Each problem should be visualized, and the best method for solving it should be determined.

1. L338 N108 is the diagonal of a frontal square which is the base of a right pyramid of 3″ altitude. Determine the intersection of this pyramid with the plane Q135 R427 S007 and show the portion of the pyramid behind the plane.

2. Locate the intersection of a 4″ sphere, centered at P224, with a right circular cone having its horizontal base centered at C206 and its vertex at V2,3½,6. Draw three views.

3. A205 B208 is the diagonal of a horizontal square which is the base of a right prism of 4″ altitude. C026 D027 is the diagonal of a profile square which is the left-hand base of another right prism of 4″ altitude. Show three views of the two prisms as one solid.

---

4. Determine the intersection of a 3½″ sphere centered at P626 with a 2½″ sphere centered at Q5,3,5½. Show three views.

5. J248 K208 is one diagonal of a frontal square which is the base of a right pyramid of 3½″ altitude. B416 D437 is one diagonal of a profile square which is the right-hand base of a right prism of 4″ altitude. Show three views of the two pieces as one solid.

6. A207 D405 is a diagonal of the horizontal base of a right prism of 3″ altitude. Locate the intersection of the prism with plane K005 L327 M315 and show the part of the prism below the plane.

---

7. V646 is the vertex and A204 D208 is a diagonal of the horizontal base of an oblique pyramid. M606 and N246 are the centers of the horizontal hexagonal bases of an oblique prism. The diagonals are 3″ long, and one diagonal of each base is frontal. Show the two intersecting pieces as one solid.

8. M606 N646 is the axis of a 2½″ right circular cylinder. Locate the intersection with plane E805 F402 G738.

9. Show three views of the intersection of a 3″ sphere centered at $S2,1\frac{1}{2},6$ with a 2″ right circular cylinder having A224 B228 for an axis.

Intersection and Development Problems

Developments and views should be drawn neatly and accurately. They should neither overlap nor extend beyond the problem space. To prevent overlapping, the development may be drawn on a separate sheet.

When possible, developments should be symmetrical and should be cut so as to require the shortest seam. The complete full-scale development should be shown, unless otherwise specified in the statement of the problem. Bases and cut sections are not required unless so specified. The near side of the pattern should be the inside. The net development should be shown. Allowances for seams and wiring should not be shown. The folding lines should be drawn on the development. Time may be saved by using two compasses on many of the developments. Show the invisible parts of intersections. Lines that may be seen through the open ends of pipes should be shown as visible.

Clear visualization is necessary if problems are to be solved readily. Much ingenuity is needed in choosing the best method of solving a problem and in carrying out the details of the solution. Often, more than one method of finding intersections may be applied to advantage in a single problem.

Group 55.   Right Prisms and Pyramids.

1. The triangle A006 B108 C205 is the lower base of a right prism 3″ tall. Show the development of this prism below a receding plane through E02X F30X. Include the base and cut section.

2. E537 F738 G836 is the upper base of a right prism of 3″ altitude. Show the part of the prism above the plane having the line M516 N817 for a strike and a dip of 30° rearward. Draw the development to include the cut section.

3. The rectangle Q528 R638 S818 T is the rear base of a rectangular block 4″ long. Show a development of that part of the block behind a vertical plane through points M5X7 and N8X5. Include the base and the cut section.

4. The parallelogram K006 L107 M306 N205 is the base of a right prism of 4″ altitude. Show three views and the development of that part of the prism below plane C017 D3,1,$7\frac{1}{2}$ E135.

5. G624 H628 is the axis of a right hexagonal prism. A $2\frac{1}{2}$″ diagonal of each base is horizontal. Show the development of the prism and indicate on it the line of intersection of the prism and a vertical plane through A4X5 B8X8.

6. A right prism of 3″ altitude has a horizontal hexagonal base of which one diagonal is H207 K405. Show the part of the prism and its development below the plane P005 Q327 R315.

7. An equilateral triangle with $3\frac{1}{2}$″ sides is the base of a right pyramid of 2″ altitude. Show three views of the pyramid and a symmetrical development which includes the base.

8. C005 D305 is the front edge of a horizontal equilateral triangle. The triangle is the base of a right pyramid that is 4″ tall. Discard the upper 2″ of the pyramid and then draw a development of the lower part. Include both bases.

9. B308 C008 is the lower edge of a frontal equilateral triangle which is the base of a right pyramid of 3″ altitude. Show three views and the development of the part of the pyramid behind the vertical plane through J0X5 K3X8.

10. The parallelogram C4,0,6$\frac{1}{2}$ D608 E8,0,6$\frac{1}{2}$ F605 is the base of a right pyramid of 2″ altitude. Show three views and the development of the pyramid.

11. The parallelogram K004 L205 M404 N203 is the base of a right pyramid of 2″ altitude. Show three principal views and the development of the part of the pyramid above the plane K E107 F414.

12. The vertical square base of a right pyramid is 3″ behind the vertex V625. One diagonal of the base is vertical and 3″ long. Show the true shape of the section cut by the vertical plane R4X7 S8X5 and the development of the part of the pyramid behind the plane.

13. V526 is the vertex, C725 is the center of the square base, and D7$\frac{1}{2}$,2$\frac{1}{2}$,6 is a corner of the base of a right pyramid. Show a development of the part of the pyramid between the base and a profile plane 1″ to the right of the vertex.

14. K138 N418 is one diagonal of a frontal hexagon. This hexagon is the base of a right pyramid of 3″ altitude. Show the front and top views, and the development of the part of the pyramid between the vertex and the vertical plane through R007 S508.

15. C836 and F806 are diagonally opposite corners of a profile hexagon that is the base of a right pyramid of 4″ altitude. Show the front and left-side views, and the development of the part of the pyramid between the base and the receding plane through Q50X R73X. Show the true shape of the cut section.

16. V425 is the vertex, and A0,3$\frac{1}{2}$,5 is one corner of the profile hexagonal base of a right pyramid. Show the front, top, and right-side views and the development of the part of the pyramid to the right of plane R115 S218 T245.

17. V056 is the vertex and C236 is the center of the hexagonal base of a right pyramid. One corner of the base is M2,3,4$\frac{1}{2}$. Show the front, top, and end views, and a development of the part of the pyramid to the right of a profile plane that is 1″ to the right of V.

18. C606 is the center and J505 is one corner of a horizontal hexagon which is the base of a right pyramid of 4″ altitude. Show the true shape of the intersection of the pyramid and plane D745 E405 F748, and develop the part between the plane and the base.

Group 56. Oblique Prisms and Pyramids.

1. D025 E235 is one edge and E is the upper corner of a frontal equilateral triangle. This triangle is one base and D K137 is one edge of an oblique prism. Draw the front and top views and the development of this prism.

2. L116 N214 and D237 F335 are the respective diagonals of two horizontal squares which are the bases of an oblique prism. Show the front and top views of the prism and its development.

3. A6,2,6$\frac{1}{2}$ B8,2,6$\frac{1}{2}$ and E548 F748 are the upper edges of two 1″ × 2″ frontal rectangles. These rectangles are the open ends of a pipe connection. Draw the front, top, auxiliary, and end views, and the development of this pipe.

4. M236 N116 is the axis of an oblique prism. One diagonal of each hexagonal base is frontal. The diagonals are 2″ long. Draw the front, top, and end views, and develop the surface of the prism.

5. P648 K736 is the axis of an oblique hexagonal prism. The diagonals of the frontal bases are 2″ long and one diagonal of each base is horizontal. Draw the front, top, auxiliary, and end views, and the development of the prism.

6. The triangle A006 B208 C305 is the base of an oblique pyramid with its vertex at V337. Draw the top and front views, and the development of the entire pyramid.

7. The figure J018 K238 L418 M208 is the base and V225 is the vertex of an oblique pyramid. Draw the front and top views, and the development of the pyramid.

8. The frontal square, having A837 C617 for a diagonal, is the base and V524 is the vertex of an oblique pyramid. Draw the front and top views, and the development of the pyramid.

9. The vertex of an oblique pyramid is at M845. A738 D518 is a diagonal of the frontal hexagonal base. Draw two views and a development of the pyramid.

10. J715 M517 is one diagonal of the horizontal hexagonal base of an oblique pyramid. V445 is the vertex. Draw two views and the development of the pyramid.

Group 57. Hoppers and Transitions.

1. A hopper has a horizontal 3″ square top and a 1″ × 2″ horizontal rectangular bottom. Two sides of the hopper are vertical. The hopper is 4″ tall. To one-half size show the front and top views and the development of the hopper.

2. To a quarter-size scale draw the front and top views and the stretchout of a hopper having an 8″ horizontal square inlet and a 4″ horizontal square outlet. The diagonals of the inlet and outlet are perpendicular, and the hopper has a length of 8″.

3. Draw the front, top, and left-side views, and one-half of the development of a symmetrical hopper having a horizontal 3″ square for an inlet and a horizontal hexagon with 1″ sides for an outlet. Two sides of the hexagon are parallel to two sides of the square. The hopper is 2″ long.

4. A symmetrical hopper has an 8″ × 24″ horizontal rectangle for an inlet and a 4″ × 8″ horizontal rectangle for an outlet. The outlet is 12″ below the inlet. The longer sides of the outlet and inlet are parallel. To a one-eighth scale, draw three views of the hopper and its development.

5. Draw two views and the stretchout of a symmetrical hopper having an 8″ square inlet and a 3″ square outlet. The sides of the squares are parallel and the hopper is 12″ deep. Use one-quarter scale.

6. Design a symmetrical hopper having the outlet and inlet as horizontal hexagons. A diagonal of the inlet is perpendicular to, and twice the diagonal of, the outlet. The height equals the shorter diagonal. Draw three views and one-half of the development.

7. A horizontal hexagon with a 3″ frontal diagonal is the inlet and a 1″ horizontal square with two sides frontal is the outlet of a hopper of 3″ height. Draw three views and one-half the development of the hopper.

---

8. Design a transition piece to connect the open ends of two heat pipes of rectangular cross section. A536 C837 is the diagonal of one end and F707 H804 is the diagonal of the other. Draw three views and the development of this transition (half size).

9. M735 N835 is the upper edge of a 1″ × 3″ frontal rectangle and G5,$\frac{1}{2}$,7 H7,$\frac{1}{2}$,7 is the lower edge of a frontal square. The rectangle and square are the open ends of a transition piece. Draw two views and the development of this transition piece.

10. Two horizontal squares are the open ends of a transition piece. One square is centered 3″ directly above the other and the diagonals of one are parallel to the sides of the other. Draw two views and the development of this transition piece.

11. Draw three views and the development of a connection for two heating pipes having the rectangles K048 L248 M247 N047 and A316 B416 C414 D314 for their open ends.

12. Draw the front, top, and side views, and the development of the transition piece connecting the open ends of two pipes having A035 B237 C336 D134 and E016 F316 G315 H015 respectively as their ends.

Group 58.   Polyhedrons.

1. Draw the front, top, and auxiliary views of a regular octahedron in which the upper face is an equilateral triangle having line M527 N$3\frac{1}{2}$,2,$5\frac{1}{2}$ for its left edge.

2. Draw the front, top, and right-side views of a regular dodecahedron in which the forward face is a frontal pentagon having the line A225 B325 for a lower edge.

3. Draw three views of the regular icosahedron in which the upper end is a right pyramid having a horizontal pentagonal base of which the line R1,$3\frac{1}{2}$,6 S2,$3\frac{1}{2}$,7 is one side.

PROBLEMS—CHAPTER 9

SINGLE-CURVED SURFACES

Cylinder—Cone—Convolute

The general instructions for drawing intersections and developments should be read again at this time and should be observed when drawing the problems of this chapter.

Group 59. Calculating Bend Allowances.

Make calculations to the nearest 0.01″.

1. Calculate the length of the material needed to form a cylindrical tube of 4″ outside diameter from metal 0.172″ thick. Also, calculate the length needed if the tube were formed from metal sufficiently thin that no bend allowance is necessary. Note the difference in the two lengths.

2. Calculate the length of metal needed for a 90° bend, inside radius 1″, and metal thickness 0.14″.

3. For Figure 7, Chapter 9, calculate the allowances that must be made for the bends centered at a, b, and c if R = 1″, T = 0.220″, and angle B = 60°.

4. For Figure 7, Chapter 9, calculate the allowances that must be made for the bends centered at a, b, and c if R = 6″, T = 0.344″, and angle A = 130°.

Group 60. Cylinder and Plane Intersections and Developments.

1. Draw the development of the part of the 2″ right circular cylinder that has A227 B257 for an axis and is below the receding plane through M02X N35X. Show the true shape of the intersection.

2. Draw the development of the part of the $1\frac{1}{2}$″ right circular cylinder that has C624 D628 for an axis and is behind the vertical plane through K5X4 L7X7. Show the true shape of the intersection.

3. Draw three principal views of the $1\frac{1}{2}$″ right circular cylinder having K124 L128 for an axis. Show the intersection with the plane R034 S234 T118 and the development of the part of the cylinder that is below the plane.

4. A right circular cylinder has M757 N717 for an axis and a 2″ diameter. Show the true shape of the intersection of the cylinder with a receding plane through G51X H84X, and on the development of the cylinder show the line of intersection with the plane.

---

5. P646 Q606 is the axis of a $2\frac{1}{2}$″ right circular cylinder. In two principal views, show all of this cylinder below plane L404 M805 N637 and draw a symmetrical development.

6. The horizontal $1\frac{1}{2}''$ circle centered at E207 is the lower base of a right circular cylinder of 5″ altitude. In the front, top, and auxiliary views show the part of the cylinder that is above plane Q057 R128 S345. Also, draw a symmetrical development of this part.

7. A714 B718 is the axis of a right circular cylinder of 2″ diameter. Draw the front and top views, and develop that part of the cylinder that is behind plane D807 E517 F825.

8. The axis of a 2″ right circular cylinder is F206 G246. On the development of this cylinder draw a diagonal, and then show this diagonal in the front view of the cylinder.

9. H617 K647 is the axis of a 4″ right circular cylinder. In the front and top views, show the front half of the cylinder. On the development of this front half draw a diagonal and then show this diagonal in the front view.

10. Draw the front and top views of the $1\frac{1}{2}''$ right circular cylinder of which J624 K628 is the axis. In the center of the development of this cylinder, with the seam at the lowest element, draw a 2″ circle. Show this circle on the top view of the cylinder.

11. Q536 P516 is the axis of a 4″ right circular cylinder. Show the path of the shortest distance on the surface of this cylinder from point A41X on the front of the cylinder to B63X on the rear.

12. M6,0,$6\frac{1}{2}$ is the center of the horizontal $2\frac{1}{2}''$ circular base of a right cylinder. One inch above M a horizontal hexagon, with one diagonal frontal, is circumscribed about the cylinder. The hexagon is the base of a right pyramid of 4″ altitude. In the top, front, and left-side views show the cylinder pointed to the shape of the pyramid.

13. The 2″ horizontal circle centered at K606 is the lower base of a right cylinder $4\frac{1}{2}''$ tall. E436 F626 is the axis of a right prism, the square base of which is centered at E with one of its 2″ diagonals horizontal. In the front and top views, show the intersecting prism and cylinder. Also, show the development of the surface of the prism to fit the cylinder.

14. K306 L346 is the axis of a 3″ right circular cylinder. M126 N526 is the axis of a right prism of which each hexagonal end has one $2\frac{1}{2}''$ diagonal vertical. Show the two pieces as one solid in three principal views.

Group 61. Elbows and Branches.

1. P446 is the center of a 2″ horizontal circle and Q0,$1\frac{1}{2}$,6 is the center of a 2″ profile circle. These circles are the ends of a three-piece pipe elbow having a least radius of bend of 1″. Draw two views of the elbow and the development of the middle section.

2. M106 is the center of a horizontal 2″ circle, and N436 is the center of a profile 2″ circle. These circles are the open ends of a four-piece pipe elbow having a $1\frac{1}{2}''$ least radius of bend. Draw the front and top views of the elbow and a development of one of the middle sections.

3. K447 is the center of a 2″ profile circle, and L707 is the center of a 2″ horizontal circle. These circles are the open ends of a five-piece elbow having a 2″ least radius of bend. Draw the front and top views of the elbow and a development of one of the middle sections.

4. G2,$1\frac{1}{2}$,3 is the center of a $2\frac{1}{2}''$ frontal circle, and H5,$1\frac{1}{2}$,6 is the center of a $2\frac{1}{2}''$ profile circle. These circles are the open ends of a six-piece elbow having a $1\frac{1}{2}''$ least radius of bend. Draw the front and top views of the elbow and a development of one of the middle sections.

5. E247 and F647 are the centers of two $1\frac{1}{2}''$ circles whose axes intersect at P407. These circles are the open ends of a three-piece elbow having a $1''$ least radius of bend. Draw the front view and develop the middle section.

6. R124 and S524 are the centers of two $1\frac{1}{2}''$ frontal circles which are the open ends of a seven-piece U-shaped pipe bend. The center of bend is T325 (least radius of bend is $1\frac{1}{4}''$). Draw a top view and develop one of the middle sections.

---

7. The horizontal $2''$ circles centered at A447, B207, and C607 are the open ends of a breeching. Design a symmetrical breeching, and show the front view and the development of one of the inclined sections.

8. The horizontal $1\frac{1}{2}''$ circles centered at D557, E307, and F707 are the open ends of a breeching. Design a symmetrical breeching, and show the front view and the development of one of the inclined sections.

9. G257 and H607 are the centers of two horizontal $2''$ circles which are the open ends of an offset pipe connection. Design two similar three-piece elbows to make the connection. Show the front view and develop one of the sections.

10. K114 M417 and L616 M are the axes of two vertical $2''$ circles which are the open ends of two pipes. Design a three-piece elbow to connect these two pipes. The least radius of bend is $1''$. Show the top view of the elbow and the development of the middle section.

Group 62. Oblique Cylinder Developments.

1. A735 and B607 are the centers of the $2''$ horizontal circular bases of an oblique cylinder. Draw the front and top views and such other views as are necessary in order to make a development of the surface.

2. C126 and D307 are the centers of the $1\frac{1}{2}''$ horizontal circular bases of an oblique cylinder. Draw the front, top, auxiliary, and end views of the cylinder, and the development of the surface.

3. E558 and F747 are the centers of the $2''$ frontal circular bases of an oblique cylinder. Draw a symmetrical development of the surface. Show all necessary views.

4. G617 and H735 are the centers of the two frontal $1\frac{1}{2}''$ circular bases of an oblique cylinder. Show the front, top, auxiliary, and end views of the cylinder, and draw a symmetrical development of the surface.

---

5. A sheet-metal hood has a $1\frac{1}{2}''$ horizontal circle centered at J357 for its upper opening and a $1\frac{1}{2}'' \times 5\frac{1}{2}''$ rectangle with semicircular ends for its lower opening. The centers of the $1\frac{1}{2}''$ semicircles are at K137 L537. Show the front and top views of the hood, and draw a symmetrical development of the right half of the surface.

6. A transition piece has a horizontal $2''$ circle, centered at P635, for its upper end and a $2'' \times 4''$ rectangle with semicircular ends for its lower opening. The centers of the semicircular ends are at M505 and N705. Show the front and top views of the transition, and draw a symmetrical development of the left half of the surface.

7. Show the front and top views of two intersecting oblique cylinders having $1\frac{1}{2}''$ circular bases. Q407 R637 is the axis of one cylinder and R S707 is the axis of the other. Draw a symmetrical development of the left-hand cylinder cut to fit the right-hand cylinder.

Group 63. Intersecting Cylinders.

1. A215 B217 is the axis of a right circular 2″ cylinder. C0,$1\frac{1}{4}$,6 D4,$1\frac{1}{4}$,6 is the axis of a right circular $1\frac{1}{2}$″ cylinder. Show these intersecting cylinders in three principal views, and draw a development of the right-hand end of the smaller cylinder.

2. E426 F826 is the axis of a $1\frac{1}{2}$″ right circular cylinder. G606 H646 is the axis of a $1\frac{3}{4}$″ right circular cylinder. In three principal views show the intersecting cylinders, and draw a symmetrical development of one end of the smaller cylinder.

3. K636 L606 is the axis of a 3″ right circular cylinder. M4,$1\frac{1}{2}$,5 N8,$1\frac{1}{2}$,5 is the axis of a 1″ right circular cylinder. Show the intersection of the two cylinders in the front view and the development of the left-hand end of the smaller cylinder.

4. P304 Q308 is the axis of the upper half of a 6″ right circular cylinder. R026 S626 is the axis of a $1\frac{1}{2}$″ right circular cylinder. Show the front and top views of the two cylinders and their intersection.

---

5. T246 U206 is the axis of a 3″ right circular cylinder, and W5,3,$5\frac{1}{2}$ X2,$1\frac{1}{2}$,$5\frac{1}{2}$ is the axis of a $1\frac{1}{2}$″ right circular cylinder. Show the cylinders and their intersection in the front and top views. Draw the development of the smaller cylinder cut to fit the larger cylinder.

6. Y346 Z306 and A135 B515 are the respective axes of a 3″ and a 1″ right circular cylinder. Draw the front and top views of the cylinders and their intersection. Develop the left end of the smaller cylinder.

7. The axes of three $1\frac{1}{2}$″ pipes are 120° apart and meet at a point. Draw the front and top views of the intersection and a development of one of the pipes indicating the shape needed to make all three pipes fit together symmetrically.

---

8. The horizontal 3″ circles with centers at C205 and D636 are the bases of one cylinder, and the horizontal 2″ circles with centers at E224 and F506 are the bases of a second cylinder. Show the front and top views of these oblique cylinders and their intersection.

9. One oblique cylinder has its horizontal circular bases centered at G224 and H606, and a second cylinder at J307 and K634. The bases are respectively 3″ and 2″ in diameter. Show the front and top views of the intersecting cylinders.

Group 64. Cylindrical-faced Objects.

1. A038 B138 is the rear edge of a 1″ × 2″ horizontal rectangle. E327 F328 is the upper edge of a 1″ × 2″ profile rectangle. These rectangles are the open ends of two pipes which are to be connected by a transition elbow having plane and cylindrical surfaces. Draw three views of the elbow and the developments of its four surfaces.

2. C048 D348 is the rear edge of a 1″ × 3″ horizontal rectangle. G135 H235 is the upper edge of a 1″ × 3″ frontal rectangle. Design a transition elbow having cylindrical surfaces with these two rectangles as open ends. Draw three views of the elbow and the developments of its four surfaces.

3. Two frontal arcs of 5″ radius, centered at K106 and L706, determine the contour (edge view) of two of the six similar cylindrical faces of a hexagonal dome. Draw the front and top views of the dome and the development of one face.

Group 65.   Development of Right Circular Cones.

1. Draw the front and top views, and develop the surface of a right circular cone having its vertex at V246 and the center of its 3″ base at C216.

2. Draw the front and top views, and develop the surface of a right circular cone having its vertex at K225 and the center of its 4″ base at L227.

3. Draw the front and top views, and develop the surface of a right circular cone having its vertex at P646 and the center of its 3″ base at Q606.

4. Draw the front and top views, and develop the surface of a right circular cone having its vertex at R624 and the center of its 2″ base at S628.

---

5. Design a well-proportioned conical funnel having a 3″ circular intake and $\frac{1}{2}$″ circular outlet.   Draw two views and the developments of the upper and lower parts of the funnel.

6. Design a well-proportioned conical funnel having a $3\frac{1}{2}$″ circular intake and a 1″ circular outlet.   Draw two views and the developments of the two parts of the funnel.

7. Design a well-proportioned conical funnel having a $2\frac{1}{2}$″ circular intake and a $\frac{1}{2}$″ circular outlet.   Draw two views and the developments of the two parts of the funnel.

8. A cover, having semiconical ends, is made by placing a 1″ strip between the two halves of a right circular cone.   The cone has a 2″ base and a 1″ altitude.   Draw the front and top views and a development of the cover.

9. A cover, having semiconical ends, is made by placing a 2″ strip between the two halves of a right circular cone.   The cone has a $2\frac{1}{2}$″ base and a $1\frac{1}{2}$″ altitude.   Draw the front and top views and a development of the cover.

---

10. The vertex of a right circular cone is located at V636.   The development of this cone is a 225° sector of a 6″ circle.   Draw the development and the front and top views of the cone.

11. A 300° sector of a 4″ circle is the development of a right circular cone having a vertical axis.   Draw the development and the front and top views of the cone.

12. V646 C606 is the axis of a right circular cone having a 3″ base.   On the development of this cone draw a straight line joining the base ends of the two outside elements. Show this line in the front and top views of the cone.

Group 66.   Cone and Plane Intersections and Developments.

1. Two 3″ profile circles centered at A026 and B4$\frac{1}{2}$,2,6 are the bases of the two nappes of a right cone.   Show three views of the portion of this cone below the horizontal plane $\frac{1}{2}$″ above the axis of the cone.   Crosshatch the hyperbolic cut section.

2. Two $3\frac{1}{2}$″ horizontal circles centered at C646 and D606 are the bases of the two nappes of a right cone.   Show three views of the portion of this cone behind a frontal plane $\frac{1}{4}$″ in front of the axis of the cone.   Crosshatch the hyperbolic cut section.

3. V625 is the vertex and E628 the center of the 4″ circular base of a right cone. Show the front and top views of the portion of this cone to the right of the vertical plane through F5X8 G7X5.   Crosshatch the parabolic cut section and draw its true shape.

4. P246 is the vertex and Q206 the center of the 4″ circular base of a right cone. Show the front and top views of the portion of this cone to the left of the receding plane through H30X J14X.   Crosshatch the parabolic cut section and draw its true shape.

5. V624 is the vertex and D628 the center of the 3″ circular base of a right cone. Show the front and top views, and draw the development of the portion of this cone to the right of the vertical plane through K4X8 L7X4.   Crosshatch the elliptical cut section and draw its true shape.

6. R236 is the vertex and S206 the center of the 3″ circular base of a right cone. Show the front and top views, and draw the development of the portion of this cone to the left of the receding plane through M13X N40X.   Crosshatch the elliptical cut section and draw its true shape.

---

7. A646 B606 is the axis of a $2\frac{1}{2}$″ right circular cone.   In two principal views show all of this cone below plane C404 D805 E637.   Draw a symmetrical development and show the true shape of the cut section.

8. The horizontal $1\frac{1}{2}$″ circle centered at F207 is the base of a right cone of 5″ altitude.   In the front, top, and auxiliary views show the part of the cone that is above the plane G057 H128 K345.   Also, show the true shape of the cut section and draw a symmetrical development.

9. L714 is the vertex and M718 is the center of the 2″ circular base of a right cone. Draw the front and top views, and develop the part of the cone that is behind plane Q807 R517 S825.   Show the true shape of the cut section.

---

10. The upper end of a hexagonal right prism having a 3″ diagonal and a vertical axis is sharpened to a conical point 4″ long.   Show the top, front, and side views of the upper $4\frac{1}{2}$″ of the sharpened prism.

11. The upper end of a 2″ square right prism with a vertical axis is sharpened to a conical point 3″ long.   Show views across the corners and across the flats of the upper 4″ of the sharpened prism.

12. A204 B207 is one diagonal of a horizontal hexagon that is the base of a right pyramid of $3\frac{1}{2}$″ altitude.   The center of the hexagon is also the center of a 4″ circle which is the base of a right cone of $2\frac{1}{2}$″ altitude.   Show the front, top, and right-side views of the pyramid pointed to fit the cone.

Group 67.   Tapered Elbows.

1. The $2\frac{1}{2}$″ horizontal circle centered at A208, and the $1\frac{1}{2}$″ circle centered at B458 and having B C568 as its axis are the open ends of a tapered four-piece elbow.   The radius of bend is 3″ long.   Design the elbow and show the cuts on the cone from which the elbow is made.

2. The ends of a three-piece tapered elbow are the 1″ circle centered at D548 and the 3″ circle at E1$\frac{1}{2}$,2,8.   The axes of the circles intersect at F348.   The radius of bend is $2\frac{1}{2}$″ long.   Design the elbow and show the cuts on the cone from which the elbow is made.

3. The 2″ horizontal circle centered at G118 and the 1″ horizontal circle centered at H538 are the ends of a five-piece, 180° tapered elbow.   J3,3$\frac{1}{2}$,8 is the center of the bend.   Design the elbow and show the cuts on the cone from which the elbow is made.

Group 68.   Intersecting Cones.

1. A546 is the vertex and B506 is the center of the 4″ base of a right circular cone. C436 is the vertex and D406 is the center of the 3″ base of a second right circular cone. Show the front and top views of the intersecting cones.

2. E424 is the vertex and F428 is the center of the 3″ circular base of a right cone G535 is the vertex and H538 is the center of the 2″ circular base of a second right cone Show the front and top views of the intersecting cones.

3. J306 is the center of the 4″ horizontal circular base of a right cone of 3″ altitude. K408 is the center of the 6″ horizontal semicircular base of a right cone of 4″ altitude. Show the front and top views of the intersecting cones.

---

4. L206 is the center of the $3\frac{1}{2}$″ horizontal circular base of a right cone of $2\frac{1}{2}$″ altitude. M336 is the center of the 2″ horizontal circular base of an inverted right cone of 3″ altitude. In the front, top, and side views show the intersection of the two cones. Also, show the development of the inverted cone cut to fit the other cone.

5. V326 and P407 are the vertices of two right cones of which the 4″ circular bases are centered respectively at N306 and Q437. In the front and top views show the intersection of the two cones. Also, show the development of the V N cone cut to fit the P Q cone.

6. R346 is the vertex and S726 is the center of the 3″ circular base of a right cone. T506 is the vertex and U646 is the center of the 2″ circular base of a second right cone. In the front and top views show the intersection of the two cones.

7. V003 is the vertex and W705 is the center of the 6″ circular base of a right cone. X602 is the vertex and Y206 is the center of the 4″ circular base of a second right cone. Show the top view of the intersection of the two cones.

---

8. A325 is the vertex and B328 is the center of the $2\frac{1}{2}$″ circular base of a right cone. C2,$3\frac{1}{2}$,$6\frac{1}{2}$ is the vertex and D2,0,$6\frac{1}{2}$ is the center of the 3″ circular base of a second right cone. Show three views of the intersection of the two cones.

9. The 4″ horizontal circle centered at E606 is the base and F138 is the vertex of an oblique cone. The 3″ horizontal circle centered at G206 is the base and H548 is the vertex of a second oblique cone. Show the front and top views of the intersection of the two cones.

Group 69.   Intersecting Cylinder and Cone.

1. A506 is the center of the 6″ horizontal circular base of a right cone of 3″ altitude. B436 C406 is the axis of a $1\frac{1}{2}$″ right circular cylinder. Show the front and top views of the intersection of the two surfaces. Also, develop the external portion of the cylinder.

2. D246 is the vertex and D E206 is the axis of a 4″ right circular cone. F426 C026 is the axis of a $1\frac{1}{2}$″ right circular cylinder. Show three views of the intersecting surfaces. Also, show half the development of the cone with a hole cut to fit the cylinder.

3. H246 is the vertex and H K206 is the axis of a 4″ right circular cone. L4,2,$5\frac{1}{2}$ M0,2,$5\frac{1}{2}$ is the axis of a $1\frac{1}{2}$″ right circular cylinder. Show three views of the intersecting surfaces.

4. P246 is the vertex and Q206 is the center of the $3\frac{1}{2}$″ circular base of a right cone. R0,$1\frac{1}{2}$,$5\frac{1}{2}$ S4,$1\frac{1}{2}$,$5\frac{1}{2}$ is the axis of a 1″ right circular cylinder. Show three views of the intersecting surfaces.

5. V646 is the vertex and C606 is the center of the 3″ circular base of a right cone. T526 U$7\frac{1}{2}$,1,6 is the axis of a 1″ right circular cylinder. Show three views of the intersecting surfaces.

Group 70. Development of Oblique Cones.

1. A205 is the center of the horizontal 3″ circular base and B037 is the vertex of an oblique cone. Draw a symmetrical development of the surface.

2. C206 is the center of the horizontal $3\frac{1}{2}$″ circular base and D337 is the vertex of an oblique cone. Draw a symmetrical development of the surface.

3. E228 is the center of the frontal 3″ circular base and F406 is the vertex of an oblique cone. Draw a symmetrical development of the surface.

4. G728 is the center of the frontal 2″ circular base and H416 is the vertex of an oblique cone. Draw a symmetrical development of the surface.

5. J407 K807 is the major axis of a horizontal ellipse having a 2″ minor axis. This ellipse is the base of an oblique cone having L337 for a vertex. Draw a symmetrical development of the surface.

6. The vertex of an oblique cone is V336. The base is the crescent-shaped area formed by the left-hand parts of two horizontal $3\frac{1}{2}$″ circles centered at M206 and N306. Show the front and top views and a symmetrical development of the surface.

Group 71. Oblique Cone Transitions.

1. A symmetrical transition has a 3″ square inlet and a 2″ circular outlet. The inlet and outlet are parallel and 3″ apart. Draw a symmetrical development of one-half of the surface. Show two views of the transition.

2. P225 is the center of a frontal 2″ circle and A248 B208 is the diagonal of a frontal square. Draw two views of a symmetrical transition having the circle and square for open ends, and develop one-half of the surface.

3. D037 D437 is the center line of a horizontal $\frac{1}{2}$″ × 4″ inlet of a dust collector that has a horizontal $1\frac{1}{2}$″ circular outlet centered at E207. Show the front and top views of a design for this dust collector and a development of the front half.

4. The rear edge of a 2″ × 4″ horizontal rectangle is F408 G808. The center of a $1\frac{1}{2}$″ horizontal circle is H637. The rectangle and circle are the open ends of a transition. Show two views of the transition and a symmetrical development of the right half.

5. A sheet-metal transition has a horizontal 2″ circular upper end centered at J236. The transition straddles a roof ridge K224 L228. Each side of the roof slants at 45°. The four outside lower corners of the transition meet the roof at M004 N008 P408 Q404. Show two views of the transition and a symmetrical development of the front half.

6. The frontal square, of which R025 S205 is one diagonal, and the $1\frac{1}{2}$″ horizontal circle centered at T147 are the open ends of a transition. Draw the front, top, and side views of the transition and one-half of a symmetrical development.

7. The horizontal 2″ circle centered at U347 is the inlet and the two horizontal 1″ circles centered at V227 and W427 are the outlets of a breeching or Y. Design this breeching from parts of two intersecting oblique cones having the 2″ circle as a common base and vertices at X107 and Z507. Show the front and top views and a development of the right-hand half.

8. E$2\frac{1}{2}$,0,7 is the center of a horizontal circle and F038 G236 is the diagonal of a horizontal square. The circle and square are the open ends of a transition. Show the front and top views and a development of the front half of the transition.

9. A345 B547 is the diagonal of a horizontal square which is the inlet of a breeching or Y. The outlets are two horizontal 2″ circles centered at C216 and D616 respectively. Draw the front and top views of the breeching and the development of the right-hand half.

Group 72.   Developments by Triangulation.

1. A006 B406 is the major axis of a horizontal ellipse having a 2″ minor axis.   C236 is the center of a 2″ horizontal circle.   The ellipse and circle are the ends of a sheet-metal transition.   Draw the front and top views, and develop the front half of the surface.

2. D635 E638 and F$4\frac{1}{2}$,1,$6\frac{1}{2}$ G$7\frac{1}{2}$,1,$6\frac{1}{2}$ are the major axes of two horizontal ellipses which have minor axes $1\frac{1}{2}$″ long.   The ellipses are the ends of a sheet-metal transition. Draw the front and top views, and make a symmetrical development of half of the surface.

3. J326 K427 is the axis of a 2″ vertical circle centered at J, and H224 is the center of a 2″ frontal circle.   These circles are the ends of a transition piece.   Draw the front and top views, and make a symmetrical development of the transition.

4. The 2″ horizontal circle centered at L216 and the 3″ profile circle centered at M436 are the ends of a transition piece.   Show the front and top views, and draw a symmetrical development of the front half of the surface.

5. The open ends of a transition are the 3″ horizontal circle centered at N$6\frac{1}{2}$,0,6 and the 2″ circle centered at P626 with P Q536 as an axis.   Show the front and top views, and develop the front half of the surface.

Group 73.   Convolute Surfaces.

1. A236 is the center of a 2″ horizontal circle.   B006 C406 is the major axis of a horizontal ellipse having a 2″ minor axis.   The circle and ellipse are the end curves of a convolute.   Draw the front and top views, and develop the front half of the surface.

2. D634 E638 and F416 G816 are the major axes of two horizontal ellipses which have minor axes 2″ long.   The ellipses are the end curves of a transition to be designed as a convolute.   Show the front and top views of the transition and the development of one-quarter of the surface.

3. The 3″ frontal circle centered at H325, and the frontal ellipse of which J027 K427 is the major axis and the minor axis is 2″ long, are the end curves of a transition. Show the front and top views of the transition, the development of the upper half of the surface, and the true shape of a rib halfway between the front and rear curves.

4. A 3″ horizontal circle is centered at L636.   A horizontal ellipse has M214 N218 for a major axis and a 2″ minor axis.   The circle and ellipse are the end curves of a transition to be designed as a convolute.   Show the front and top views of the transition, the development of the front half of the surface, and the true shape of a rib halfway between the upper and lower curves.

5. A cover designed as a convolute has the upper halves of a frontal circle and a frontal ellipse as end curves.   The circle is centered at P615 and the ellipse has Q618 R638 for a minor axis and a 3″ major axis.   Draw the front and top views, develop the surface, and show the true shape of a rib halfway between the front and rear curves.

---

6. The open ends of a transition, designed as a convolute, are the 3″ horizontal circle centered at S$1\frac{1}{2}$,0,6 and the 2″ circle centered at T226 with T U336 as an axis.   Draw the front and top views of the transition and a development of the front half of the surface.

7. The 3″ horizontal circle centered at V6,3,$6\frac{1}{2}$ and the 2″ frontal circle centered at W614 are the end curves of a spout that is to be designed as a convolute.   Show three views of the spout and the development of the left-hand half of the surface.

8. A convolute surface joins the upper half of a frontal circle having A028 B428 for a diameter and the front half of a horizontal ellipse having A B for a minor axis and C225 for the front end of the major axis.　Draw the front and top views and half of a symmetrical development.

------

9. The axis of a right-hand helix of 2″ diameter and 2″ lead is M205 N225.　The front point of the helix is K214.　The helix is the directrix of a convolute.　Draw the front and top views of the helix and one turn of the convolute.

10. The axis of a left-hand helix of $1\frac{1}{2}$″ diameter and 2″ lead is G616 H636.　The front point of the helix is K6,2,$5\frac{1}{4}$.　The helix is the directrix of a convolute.　The outside edge of the convolute is limited by the 3″ right circular cylinder having G H for an axis.　Draw the front and top views of the helix and one turn of the convolute.

PROBLEMS—CHAPTER 10

WARPED SURFACES

Group 74.   Hyperbolic Paraboloids.

1. The lines A746 B124 and C128 D706 are the directrices, and A C and B D are two elements, of a hyperbolic paraboloid.   Show the front and top views.   Draw 11 other equally spaced elements.

2. E006 F528 and G636 H045 are the directrices of a hyperbolic paraboloid.   E H and F G are elements.   Show the front and top views.   Draw seven other equally spaced elements.   Using E F and G H as elements and E H and F G as directrices rule the surface in the other direction.

3. J045 K418 and L404 M837 are the directrices of a hyperbolic paraboloid.   J L and K M are elements.   Using 11 other equally spaced elements show the front and top views of the surface.

4. P404 Q418 and N045 R837 are the directrices of a hyperbolic paraboloid.   P N and Q R are elements.   Using 15 other equally spaced elements show the front and top views of the surface.

5. S728 T346 and V515 W108 are the directrices of a hyperbolic paraboloid.   S W and T V are elements.   Using 15 other equally spaced elements show the front and top views of the surface.

6. The straight lines A038 B338 and C005 D407 are respectively the upper and lower edges of the wing wall of a dam.   The surface of the wall is a hyperbolic paraboloid.   Double rule the surface using A B and C D as directrices and then A C and B D.   Show the intersection of the surface with a frontal plane halfway between A and C.

7. Show your own design for one end of a bridge pier on which the water-deflecting surfaces are hyperbolic paraboloids.   Double rule the surface and show a sufficient number of elements to adequately represent the surface in the front and top views.

Group 75.   Conoids.

1. Draw three views of the right conoid having a horizontal 3″ circular directrix centered at C606 and a straight-line directrix A6,3,4½ B6,3,7½.

2. The 3″ frontal circle centered at D228 and the line E025 F425 are the directrices, and a profile plane is the plane director of a right conoid.   Draw three views of the surface.   Show 16 equally spaced elements.

3. The center of a 4″ horizontal circle is G406.   The circle is one directrix of a right conoid.   The straight-line directrix is H434 J438.   The elements are frontal.   Show

328

the front and top views with elements spaced $\frac{1}{2}''$ apart, and the intersection of the surface with a horizontal plane halfway between the two directrices.

4. The vertical line through the point K326 and the 4″ profile circle centered at L026 are the directrices of a right conoid. Show three principal views of the conoid having the horizontal elements spaced $\frac{1}{4}''$ apart. Also, show the intersection of the surface with a profile plane midway between the two directrices.

5. The base of a right conoid is the horizontal ellipse of which M406 N806 is the major axis. The minor axis is 2″ long. The straight-line directrix is 3″ directly above M N. Show three principal views with profile elements spaced at $\frac{1}{2}''$ intervals.

6. P506 is the center of a 4″ horizontal circle. This circle and the line Q244 R248 are the directrices, and a frontal plane is the plane director of a right conoid. Show two views of the conoid with elements spaced $\frac{1}{2}''$ apart.

7. S528 is the center of a $3\frac{1}{2}''$ frontal circle. This circle and the line T147 U404 are the directrices, and a horizontal plane is the plane director of an oblique conoid. Show two views of the conoid with the elements spaced $\frac{1}{4}''$ apart.

8. V228 is the center of a 3″ frontal circle. W045 X445 is the upper edge of a frontal square. The circle and square are the ends of the inside surface of a concrete pipe. The surface consists of two conoids having profile elements and six triangles. Show three views of the surface with elements of the conoids spaced $\frac{1}{4}''$ apart.

Group 76.   Helicoids.

1. A436 B406 is the axis of a right helicoid of 3″ lead, 4″ outside diameter, and 2″ inside diameter. Show one right-hand turn of this helicoid. Use 13 elements.

2. C436 D406 is the common axis of a 1″ and a 3″ right circular cylinder. On the larger cylinder is a left-hand helix of 3″ lead. The helix and its axis are the directrices of a right helicoid that is bounded by the cylinders. Using 13 elements show one turn of the helicoid in the front and top views.

3. E646 F606 is the common axis of a $1\frac{1}{2}''$ and of a 3″ right circular cylinder. On each cylinder is a right-hand helix of 4″ lead. The helices are the limits of a right helicoid. Using 17 elements show one turn of the helicoid in the front and top views.

---

4. G436 H416 is the common axis of a 1″ and a 3″ right circular cylinder. On the larger cylinder is a right-hand helix of 2″ lead. The helix and its axis are the directrices of an oblique helicoid that is bounded by the cylinders. The elements are inclined at 30° to the horizontal. Using 17 elements show one turn of the helicoid in the front and top views.

5. In the front and top views, show one turn of the left-hand oblique helicoid that is generated by revolving the line J425 K224 about the axis J L428 at a uniform rate and at the same time moving the line in the direction of the axis at the uniform rate of 3″ in one turn.

---

6. M625 N725 is the upper edge of a 1″ × 2″ vertical rectangle which is the open end of a 180° pipe bend of uniform cross section having a least radius of 2″, and rising 2″ in a 180° turn. Show the front and top views of this bend.

7. P614 Q814 is the upper edge of a 2″ × 1″ vertical rectangle which is the open end of a 90° pipe bend of uniform cross section having a least radius of 2″, and rising 2″ in a 90° turn. Show the front and top views of this bend.

Group 77.   Screws and Springs.

1. A458 B408 is the axis of a 4″ right circular cylinder. Into this cylinder cut a single, right-hand, square thread of 2″ lead. Show the visible lines in the front view.

2. C458 D408 is the axis of a right circular cylinder of 4″ diameter. Into this cylinder cut a left-hand, double, square thread of 3″ lead. Show the visible lines in the front view.

3. E458 F408 is the axis of a 4″ right circular cylinder. Into this cylinder cut a triple, right-hand, square thread of 3″ lead. Show the visible lines in the front view.

4. G446 H406 is the axis of a right circular cylinder of 3″ diameter. Into this cylinder cut a right-hand and a left-hand, single, square thread of 1″ lead. Show the visible lines in the front view.

5. J458 K408 is the axis of a 3″ right circular cylinder. In the middle of this cylinder turn a square groove $\frac{1}{2}$″ wide. On the upper end cut a right-hand, single, square thread of 1″ lead. On the lower end cut a left-hand, single, square thread of 1″ lead. Show the visible lines in the front view.

---

6. L458 M408 is the axis of a 4″ right circular cylinder. Into this cylinder cut a single, left-hand, V-thread of 2″ lead. Show the visible lines in the front view.

7. On a 3″ right circular cylinder cut a double, right-hand, V-thread of 2″ lead. Show the visible lines in the front view.

---

8. Show two full turns of a $\frac{1}{2}$″ square steel spring coiled into a helix of 3″ outside diameter and 2″ lead. Omit hidden lines.

9. Show two full turns of a flat $\frac{1}{2}$″ × 1″ steel spring coiled into a helix of 4″ outside diameter and 2″ lead. Omit hidden lines.

Group 78.   Hyperboloids of Revolution.

1. A446, B426, and C406 are respectively the centers of horizontal circles which are the $3\frac{1}{2}$″ upper, the $1\frac{1}{2}$″ gore, and the $3\frac{1}{2}$″ lower circles of a hyperboloid of revolution. Show the front and top views. Draw 24 elements of one generation.

2. D436 and E406 are the centers of two horizontal 4″ circles which are the upper and lower ends of a hyperboloid of revolution. Each element advances 120° from upper to lower circle. Draw the front and top views of 24 elements of one generation.

3. F446 and G406 are the centers of two 3″ horizontal circles which are the ends of a hyperboloid of revolution. The middle circle has a diameter of 1″. Draw the front and top views. Show 24 elements of one generation.

4. H406 is the center of a $3\frac{1}{2}$″ horizontal circle and J446 is the center of a 2″ horizontal circle. These circles are the ends of a hyperboloid of revolution which has a 1″ gore circle. Draw the front and top views. Show 24 elements of one generation.

Group 79.   Cylindroids and Warped Cones.

1. A8,1$\frac{1}{2}$,8 B6,1$\frac{1}{2}$,6 and C803 D605 are the major axes of two vertical ellipses which have 2″ minor axes. The upper half of each ellipse is a curved directrix, and a profile plane is the plane director of a cylindroid. Show the surface in three principal views. Space the elements in profile planes $\frac{1}{4}$″ apart.

2. E224 and F207 are the centers of two vertical ellipses that appear as $2\frac{1}{2}$″ circles in the front view. The planes of these ellipses meet along the vertical line through G5,0,5$\frac{1}{2}$. The upper half of each ellipse is a curved directrix, and a profile plane is the plane director of a cylindroid.   Show the surface in three principal views.   Space the elements in profile planes $\frac{1}{4}''$ apart.

---

3. The centers of two $3''$ frontal circles are $G1\frac{1}{2},1,7$ and H314.   The upper halves of these circles are the curved directrices, and the horizontal-frontal line through $J2\frac{1}{4},1,X$ is the straight-line directrix of a warped cone.   Draw three principal views. Use 13 elements.

4. The centers of two $3\frac{1}{2}''$ frontal circles are K307 and L204. The upper halves of these circles are the curved directrices, and the horizontal-frontal line through $M2\frac{1}{2},0,X$ is the straight-line directrix of a warped cone.   Using 13 elements draw three principal views.

PROBLEMS—CHAPTER 11

DOUBLE-CURVED SURFACES

Group 80. Development of Spheres.

1. A626 is the center of a $3\frac{1}{2}''$ sphere. Design this sphere to be approximately made from 12 equal meridian sections. Show the front and top views, and develop one of the sections.

2. B226 is the center of a $3''$ sphere. Design for this sphere a close-fitting casing made of 12 equal meridian sections. Draw the front and top views, and develop one of the sections.

3. C508 is the center of a hemispherical dome of $3''$ radius. Design the dome to be made from 16 meridian sections. Show the front half of the dome in the front and top views, and the development of one of the sections.

---

4. D226 is the center of a $3''$ sphere. Develop an approximation for this sphere by the zone method. Use four pairs of cones. Show the front and top views, and the development of one of each pair of cones.

5. E626 is the center of a $3\frac{1}{2}''$ sphere. Design an approximation for this sphere by the zone method. Use a cylindrical equatorial section and three pairs of cones. Show the complete development of one of each of the smaller conical sections and half of the development of the large sections. Show the front and top views.

6. A hemispherical bowl is built up from a $1\frac{1}{2}''$ bottom disk and three zone sections each $\frac{3}{4}''$ high. Design the bowl to fit over a $4\frac{1}{2}''$ hemisphere. Show the front and top views of the bowl and half of each pattern for the zones.

Group 81. Sphere and Plane Intersections.

1. A $2''$ sphere is centered at A626. Show the intersection of this sphere with a receding plane through B53X C82X. Draw three views.

2. D426 is the center of a $3''$ sphere. In the front and top views show the intersection of the sphere with plane E347 F517 G618.

3. H426 is the center of a $3\frac{1}{2}''$ sphere. In the front and top views show the intersection of the sphere with plane J535 K447 L116.

4. M526 is the center of a $3''$ sphere. In the front and top views, show the portion of the sphere that remains after a section is removed between the vertical planes through M N624 and M P324. Crosshatch the cut section.

5. Q426 is the center of a $3''$ sphere. In the front and top views, show the portion of the sphere that remains after a section is removed between the receding planes through R64X S41X and T34X S. Crosshatch the cut section.

6. U426 is the center of a $3\frac{1}{2}''$ sphere. In the front and top views, show the portion of the sphere that is rearward of the vertical planes through V4X4 W6X6 and V Y2X8.

7. A $2''$ square right prism $3''$ tall with a vertical axis has the top end chamfered to a spherical surface of $1\frac{1}{2}''$ radius. Show a top view, a view across the flats, and a view across the corners of the chamfered prism.

8. A right hexagonal prism $3''$ across the corners and $3''$ tall has the top end chamfered to a spherical surface of $2''$ radius. Show an end view, a view across the corners, and a view across the flats of the chamfered end of the prism.

9. Show three views of the hole made through a $3''$ sphere by a right hexagonal prism having a $2''$ diagonal. The axis of the prism passes through the center of the sphere.

10. A right pyramid with a $3''$ square base and a $4''$ vertical axis has the top end chamfered to a spherical surface by a $3''$ sphere centered on the axis of the pyramid and $1''$ above its base. Show views of the chamfered pyramid across the flats and across the corners.

11. A507 is the center of a $5''$ sphere. B425 is the center of a $3''$ sphere. Show the intersection of the two spheres in the front and top views.

12. C628 is the center of a $4''$ sphere and D437 is the center of a $2''$ sphere. Show the intersection of the two spheres in the front and top views.

Group 82. Ellipsoids and Paraboloids.

1. A6,5,$6\frac{1}{2}$ B6,0,$6\frac{1}{2}$ is the major axis of a prolate ellipsoid. The minor axis is $2\frac{1}{2}''$ long. In three principal views show the ellipsoid and its intersections with frontal planes $\frac{1}{2}''$ and $1''$ in front of the major axis.

2. C246 D206 is the major axis of a prolate ellipsoid having a $2''$ minor axis. Show the portion of this ellipsoid below the plane E017 F304 G446. Crosshatch the cut section.

3. An oblate ellipsoid has a $6''$ major axis and a $4\frac{1}{4}''$ vertical axis of revolution. Design an ellipsoidal dome of 12 meridian sections approximating the upper half of the ellipsoid. Show the development of one section and the front and top views of the front half of the dome.

4. H636 J616 is the axis of revolution of an oblate ellipsoid having a $4''$ major axis. In three principal views show the intersection of this ellipsoid with plane K407 L814 M846.

5. N448 is the focus and a horizontal line $1''$ above N is the directrix of a frontal parabola that represents the front view of a paraboloid. Show the intersection of this paraboloid with a $3\frac{1}{2}''$ sphere centered at P628.

6. Q448 is the focus and a horizontal line $1''$ above Q is the directrix of a frontal parabola that represents the front view of a paraboloid. Show the intersection of this paraboloid with a right circular $3''$ cylinder having R408 S858 for an axis.

Group 83. Surfaces of Revolution.

1. A $4''$ diameter right circular cylinder has the upper end turned to an ogival point. Two inches from the tip a $1\frac{1}{2}''$ hole is drilled through the point. The axis of the hole is perpendicular to and intersects the axis of the point. Show the front view and the front half of the top view.

2. Design a vase-like ornament to be turned in a lathe. The ornament is 4″ tall and has the following diameters: At the base 2″, 1″ up 3″, 2″ up $2\frac{1}{2}$″, 3″ up $1\frac{1}{2}$″, and at the top 2″. Show the front and top views and the intersections of the ornament with frontal planes $\frac{1}{2}$″ and 1″ in front of the axis.

3. Design an ogival-pointed hydraulic needle having a length of 6″, a $1\frac{1}{2}$″ base, and a $2\frac{1}{2}$″ maximum diameter graduated along a reverse curve to a point. On the surface show meridian lines spaced every 30°. Show a front view and the front half of the top (end) view.

4. The points A208 and B608 are the centers of two frontal circular arcs of 5″ radius. These arcs extend upwards until they meet to become the contour of a circular dome. Show the front half of the top view and the front view. Include meridian curves spaced every 15°. Divide each meridian into six equal parts and join these division points by horizontal circles. Join the alternate division points by diagonals and thus cover the dome with triangular-shaped areas.

Group 84. Annular Torus.

1. An annular torus is generated by revolving the $1\frac{1}{2}$″ frontal circle, centered at A215, about a vertical axis through B415. In the front and top views show all of this torus that is below the plane B C825 D628.

2. E615 is the center of a 2″ frontal circle. This circle generates an annular torus by rotation about the axis F425 G405. In the front and top views show the intersection of the torus with the plane H426 J528 K604.

3. A frontal $1\frac{1}{4}$″ circle centered at L326 is revolved about line M436 N416 to form an annular torus. P404 Q408 is the axis of a $5\frac{1}{2}$″ right circular cylinder. In the front and top views show the intersection of the cylinder and the torus.

4. An annular torus is generated by revolving the horizontal $2\frac{1}{2}$″ circle, centered at R606, about the axis S404 T408. In the front and top views show the part of the torus that is rearward of the plane T U724 W126.

5. An annular torus is approximated by joining 12 equal cylindrical sections. The torus is formed by revolving a $1\frac{1}{2}$″ frontal circle, centered at A215, about a vertical axis through B415. Show the front and top views of the torus and the development of one of the cylindrical sections.

6. An annular torus is formed by rotating a 2″ sphere at a radius of 3″. Approximate this torus by joining 12 equal cylindrical sections. Show the development of one section, and the front and top views of the torus.

7. C408 is the center of, and D108 is a point on, a horizontal circle. The point D and two other points 120° from point D on this circle are the centers of three horizontal $1\frac{1}{2}$″ circles. These $1\frac{1}{2}$″ circles are the lower ends of parts of three annular torii that meet directly above point C. The horizontal axes of the torii pass through C. Draw the front view and the front half of the top view of this tripod.

8. E016 F416 is one diagonal of the hexagonal horizontal base of a right prism of 2″ altitude. A frontal circular arc of 1″ radius, centered at G$4\frac{1}{2}$,2,6, represents the contour of a groove turned into the prism. Draw three principal views of the grooved prism.

9. H706 J406 is one diagonal of the horizontal hexagonal upper base of a right prism of 4″ altitude. The upper end of the prism is turned to a contour represented by a frontal arc of $2\frac{1}{2}''$ radius centered at K346.   Draw three principal views of this turned prism.

10. A connecting rod of $1\frac{1}{2}''$ diameter has a stub end of $2'' \times 3''$ rectangular cross section.   The rod and stub end are joined by a turned fillet of $3''$ radius.   Show the front, top, and end views of the stub end of the rod to include the curves where the fillet joins the flats of the stub end.

Group 85.   Serpentines and Springs.

1. A spring having an inside diameter of $3''$ is wound right hand from $1''$ rod with a lead of $2''$.   Draw the front view and one-half of the top view of the portion of this spring having a vertical axis A458 B408.

2. E448 D408 is the axis and $C4,2,5\frac{1}{2}$ is a point on a left-hand helix of $4''$ lead. Three-quarter-inch spheres centered on the helix generate a serpentine.   Draw the front view and the front half of the top view of this serpentine.   Show its intersection with a horizontal plane $2''$ above C.

3. F457 G407 is the axis of a $2''$ right circular cylinder.   On the cylinder are two right-hand helices of $10''$ lead.   The upper end of one helix is $1''$ to the right of F, and the upper end of the other is $1''$ to the left of F.   One-inch spheres centered on these helices generate two serpentines.   Draw their front views.

4. H445 is a point on a helix of $3''$ lead and J408 K448 is its axis.   This helix is the center line of a steel rod $\frac{3}{4}''$ in diameter which is coiled into a right-hand helical spring. Show the front half of the top view and the front view of this spring.   The top and bottom ends of the spring are cut along horizontal planes through the ends of the axis.

Group 86.   Double-curved Surfaces.

1. Design the upper and lower and half-breadth contours of a fuselage.   Show the left-side view, and one-half of the front, rear, top, and bottom views.   Design the transversal sections at several stations, and then locate several water lines and buttock lines.   All lines should be clean-cut and fair.

2. Design the forebody of a ship.   Show the lines of the ship in the side, end, and bottom views.   Check the fairness of the surface by means of a cutting plane.

3. E426 and F626 are the middle points of the $4''$ vertical major axes of two frontal ellipses.   The minor axes are $2\frac{1}{2}''$ long.   These ellipses are the inside edges of a Pelton-wheel bucket.   The depth of each cup is $1\frac{1}{2}''$.   Design this bucket in the front, top, and side views, and show the horizontal, frontal, and profile contours of the inside, with contour planes spaced $\frac{1}{2}''$ apart.

4. Draw a design for a crane hook, $1\frac{1}{2}''$ inside diameter.   Sections are to be oval except for the eye, and all surfaces are to be double-curved.   Show several contours and sections.

5. In a horizontal ellipse, C016 D516 is the major axis and the minor axis is $2\frac{1}{2}''$ long. This ellipse is the lower edge of a smoothly curved lid.   The central frontal contour is a curved line through the points C, E236, F326, and D.   Design this lid in the front, top, and side views, and show the horizontal, frontal, and profile contours in planes spaced at $\frac{1}{2}''$ intervals.

6. Design a double-curved, nonsymmetrical, fair surface in three principal views. Draw the views as large as possible within the limits of the problem space.   Show horizontal, frontal, and profile contours of the surface spaced at $\frac{1}{2}''$ intervals.

PROBLEMS—CHAPTER 12

TOPOGRAPHICAL AND MINING PROBLEMS

Group 87. Topographical and Mining Problems.

In these problems the scale of the drawings is to be taken as 1 inch = 100 feet. The one-tenth-inch divisions in the upper right-hand corner of the problem sheet will be found convenient for this purpose. Letter the words strike, dip, shaft, tunnel, etc., in their proper places as an aid in interpreting the drawing. The bearing of the strike and the angle of the dip should be shown in degrees. A protractor is provided for this purpose on the problem sheets. The length of a tunnel, the depth of a shaft, and the thickness of a vein should be stated in feet. The edge view of the vein should be crosshatched. The foot wall and the hanging wall should be indicated. In general, Figure 3, Chapter 12, may be taken as an example of a complete drawing.

The most important views in mining problems are the top view, or map, and the auxiliary elevation taken in the direction of the strike. The front view principally is used to obtain data for the top and auxiliary views. The different views should not overlap, if this is at all possible. Frequently, it is impossible to draw a necessary auxiliary elevation in line with the strike. When this condition arises, the auxiliary elevation may be drawn right side up in any clear space in the lower half of the problem space. When drawings are complicated, certain points or data may be emphasized by the use of colored pencils. The intersection of two veins may be found by using the method of Article 30, Chapter 7.

The contour maps for the problems are printed on the last page of this textbook. These readily may be traced on the problem sheet by placing the sheet directly over the printed map. The 100-foot contours should be drawn as heavy lines, and the intermediate contours as fine lines. The 25- and 75-foot contours should be drawn on each problem sheet before the solution of the problem is attempted.

1. A127 B334 C408 are points in one wall of a vein of ore. D217 is a point in the other wall. Locate the foot and hanging walls of this vein, show the angle of dip, the strike and its bearing, and the thickness of the vein. Determine the length of a vertical shaft from point E4,3,6$\frac{1}{2}$ to the vein, and a horizontal tunnel from point F3,0,6$\frac{1}{2}$ to the vein.

2. In a thick stratum of rock, the points G024 H236 K403 are in one wall and point L124 is in the other wall. Determine the bearing of the strike, angle of dip, thickness of the stratum, and the foot and hanging walls for this stratum. From point M334 determine the length of a perpendicular passageway, the shortest horizontal tunnel, and a vertical shaft to the stratum.

3. N006 Q415 R537 are points of outcrop of one wall of a vein of ore. S2$\frac{1}{2}$,2,7 is a point in the other wall. Determine the bearing of the strike, the angle of dip, the hanging and foot walls, and the thickness of the vein. Determine the length of a horizontal tunnel and a vertical shaft from point S137 to the vein.

4. T505 U736 V818 are points in one wall of a stratum of coal. W846 is a point in the other wall. Show the strike and its bearing, the angle of dip, the thickness, the foot wall, and the hanging wall for this stratum. From point X317 locate and determine the length of the shortest tunnel having 10% upgrade to the stratum.

5. Points of outcrop in one wall of a bed of coal have been located at A818 B736 C505. Point D846 is located in the other wall. Determine the bearing of the strike, the angle of dip, and the thickness of the bed. Show the foot and hanging walls. Determine the length of the shortest tunnel on a 6% upgrade from daylight at E317 to the nearest wall of the bed. Also, determine the length of the shortest inclined passageway to the vein from F648.

6. G437 and H634 are points in a vertical cliff. Exposed on the face of this cliff is a seam of coal which measures 35′ across and is inclined at an angle of 52° with the horizontal line G H. The hanging wall of the seam passes through points G and K508. Determine the bearing of the strike, the dip, and actual thickness of this seam of coal.

7. One wall of a vein of ore outcrops along the line J336 K3$\frac{1}{2}$,2$\frac{1}{2}$,4$\frac{1}{2}$ on a flat hillside. A third point, L4,3$\frac{3}{4}$,5$\frac{1}{2}$, is found in the same wall by drilling. M2,2,5$\frac{1}{2}$ is another point on the flat hillside. The outcrop on the hillside is 40′ across. Determine the bearing of the strike, the dip, and thickness of the vein.

---

8. Show the front view of the Aspen Creek Gulch country (Plate B) by drawing vertical contours taken in five equally spaced frontal planes. Show the creek.

9. Show the front view of the Rainbow Canyon area (Plate C) by drawing vertical contours taken in five equally spaced frontal planes. Show the creek and its branch.

---

10. Plate B: At 17 is an outcrop of the hanging wall of a vein. By drilling, the same wall is located at 175′ below 8, and 115′ below 5. The vertical thickness of the vein is found to be 30′. Determine the strike through 17 and its bearing, the dip, the thickness, and the line of outcrop of the hanging wall of this vein.

11. Plate B: Points in one wall of a vein are discovered 25′ below points 10, 11, and 12. A point in the other wall is located 35′ below 1. Determine the bearing of the strike, the dip, and thickness of the vein. Locate the line of outcrop of the hanging wall. Show the overburden along a right section through point 14. How deep must a shaft be at point 14 to reach down to the vein?

12. Plate B: One wall of a vein of ore has a strike through point 18 with a bearing of N 76° E and a dip to the north of 35°. Determine the line of outcrop of this wall. Locate the intersection of this wall with the hanging wall of Problem 11.

13. Plate C: The strike in the hanging wall of a vein runs through points 17 and 19. Another point in the same wall is located 240′ below point 5. A core drill shows that the vertical thickness of the vein is 12'.   Determine the bearing of the strike, the dip, and thickness of the vein.

14. Plate C: A vein of coal has a strike of N 27° W through point 21, and a dip of 50° eastward.   Point 23 is located in the other wall.   Determine the thickness and the lines of outcrop of both walls of this vein.

15. Plate C: A vein of ore has a strike 30' below points 10 and 23.   Another point in the same wall of the vein is located 55' below point 26.   Determine the bearing of the strike and the dip of this vein.   In a right section through point 26 show the overburden of the vein.   Show the line of outcrop.

16. Plate C: Point 6 is an outcrop in one wall of a thick vein of coal.   Other points are located, by core drilling, 120' below point 1 and 85' below point 13.   A point in the other wall is discovered at point 15.   Show the strike through point 6 and its bearing, the angle of dip, the thickness, and the lines of outcrop of both walls.   Show the overburden (profile of the mountain) through point 1 and perpendicular to the strike. Show a shaft from the 9,300' level on this profile to the vein.   Show a drainage tunnel from point 13 to the vein.

17. Plate C: Outcrops of a vein of ore are discovered at points 2, 13, and 16 in one wall, and at point 15 in the other wall.   Determine the bearing of the strike, the dip, and the thickness of the vein.   Determine the line of outcrop of the foot wall.   In the edge view of the vein show the overburden in a right section through point 6.   Show a tunnel and a shaft from point 6 to the vein.   Indicate the length of each.

---

18. Plate B: Rock that has an angle of repose of 49° is to be dumped from the southern point of the 8,400' contour west of the creek.   Show the limits of this dump. Show the location of the center line of a drainage ditch on about a 5 % slope from point 8 to the creek.

19. Plate B: Rock that has an angle of repose of 49° is to be dumped from the southern point of the 8,400' contour east of the creek.   Show the limits of this dump. Show the location of the center line of a drainage ditch on about a 5 % slope from point 12 to the creek.

20. Plate C: Rock that stands up at 48° comes out of a shaft at point 8.   Show the outlines of the two dumps that would result if level circular areas of 50' and 100' were built up at the level of the shaft mouth.

---

21. Plate B: The center line of a level roadway at 8,200' elevation and 40' wide passes through points 8 and 12.   Show the cuts and fills that must be made at a slope of 1 to 1.   Show by different shadings the outlines of the cuts and fills.

22. Plate B: The center line of a level landing strip 110' wide and at the 8,200' level extends westward from point 18 through point 14.   Show the location of the cuts at a slope of 3 to 1, and of the fills at a slope of 1 to 1.   Show by different shadings the outlines of the cuts and fills.

PROBLEMS—CHAPTER 13

Group 88. Orthographic Pictorial Views.

Three principal views of the described object are first drawn, the best oblique direction for viewing the object is considered, and this direction is then represented by three views of a pointing arrow. The new positions of the principal views are next determined. The original principal views may be cut apart and pasted, or fixed to a new sheet. Or, the views may be traced on tracing paper in their new relative positions. The pictorial view is then drawn. Objects may be drawn to half-size or other appropriate scale if it appears there will be lack of space on the problem sheet.

1. Draw a pictorial view of the small house of Problem 4, Group 10.
2. Draw a pictorial view of the pyramid of Problem 11, Group 11.
3. Draw a pictorial view of the prism of Problem 13, Group 11.
4. Draw a pictorial view of the cutaway block of Problem 2, Group 2.
5. Draw a pictorial view of the cutaway block of Problem 4, Group 2.
6. Draw a pictorial view of the cutaway block of Problem 5, Group 2.
7. Draw a pictorial view of the cutaway block of Problem 9, Group 2.
8. Draw a pictorial view of the triangular brace of Problem 10, Group 2.
9. Draw a pictorial view of the cutaway cube of Problem 11, Group 2.
10. Draw a pictorial view of the cutaway cube of Problem 11, Group 5.
11. Draw a pictorial view of the cutaway cube of Problem 20, Group 5.
12. Draw a pictorial view of the V-grooved cube of Problem 8, Group 5.
13. Draw a pictorial view of the bracket of Problem 14, Group 5.
14. Draw a pictorial view of the link of Problem 12, Group 1.
15. Draw a pictorial view of the cylinder of Problem 19, Group 11.
16. Draw a pictorial view of the intersecting prisms of Problem 3, Group 54.
17. Draw a pictorial view of the intersecting prism and pyramid of Problem 5, Group 54.
18. Draw a pictorial view of the intersecting cylinders of Problem 2, Group 63.

Group 89. Freehand Perspective Sketches.

The methods described in Articles 5 to 9 of Chapter 13 should be followed in making the following sketches. Visualize what is to be drawn before sketching a single line. Make sketches of a reasonable size. Show all construction lines as fine lines.

To sketch easily, avoid all strain. Hold the pencil loosely and with the fingers several inches away from the point, so that the hand does not interfere with viewing the entire drawing. Strictly avoid watching the point of the pencil. Look always at the entire area of the sketch. Draw straight lines with a single stroke of the pencil. Keep sketches square with the paper by watching the edge of the sheet. The directions of lines and the proportions of the parts are judged by eye.

1. Sketch several different cubes by taking tangents in different directions, and then design blocks of various shapes by cutting away parts of the cubes.

2. Make a perspective sketch of the base block of Chapter 2 in any desired position.

3. Draw several perspective sketches of the angle plate in Article 6 of Chapter 13. Extend the base in different directions. Also, show the angle plate standing on its shorter end.

4. Make a perspective sketch of the bearing of Chapter 3 with the cylinder extending leftward. Also, show the bearing in some oblique position.

5. Make several perspective sketches of a hollow ring, using different ratios of the minor to the major axis. Show one ring standing on edge.

6. Make perspective sketches of the connecting rod of Chapter 3. Show it in several positions.

7. Make perspective sketches of the finger clamp of Chapter 3 in several positions.

8. Make perspective sketches of some of the objects described in Group 5, without drawing any principal views.

9. Make perspective sketches of some of the objects of Group 2, without drawing any principal views.

Perspective Drawings

When perspective drawings are being made, generally it is necessary either to separate the views rather widely on a large sheet of paper or to overlap the views. This is due to the need for locating the station point at a sufficient distance from the object. In the following problems, the top view of the station point often is taken below the front view, as is indicated by the coordinates; for example, S640. Subscripts should be used to differentiate between the front and top views of the station point. Since the perspective view of the object often overlaps the front view, it is better to draw the front view with rather fine lines. The required perspective view should be drawn in heavy lines. Hidden lines may be added when it seems desirable. When lines are drawn with straightedges, the use of vanishing points saves time and produces a better perspective drawing. Vanishing points within the limits of the problem sheet always should be located. When vanishing points fall outside the limits of the drawing, these should also be located if the necessary equipment is available. Here, as elsewhere, accurate work is essential if the results are to be satisfactory.

Group 90. Parallel Perspective.

1. A037 and C807 are diagonally opposite corners of the front face of a U-shaped block having 1″ square cross sections. Draw perspective views of this block on frontal picture planes 7″ and 4″ behind the station point S550.

2. E018 F314 and G518 H814 are diagonals of the upper surfaces of two rectangular blocks 3″ wide, 1″ high, and 4″ deep. Discard the front three-fourths of the left two-thirds of each block. Draw a perspective view of each L-shaped block as seen from station point S430 on a frontal picture plane through F.

3. Draw a perspective view of the T-slotted block of Problem 10, Group 1, as seen from a station point 2″ above, 1″ to the left, and 7″ in front of the upper left-hand corner of the front surface. The frontal picture plane is through the front surface of the block.

4. A perspective view is required of the casting described in Problem 13, Group 1. Invert the casting so that the cylinder is to the front. The picture plane passes through the rear surface of the base. The station point is 8″ forward of the picture plane, and 3″ leftward and 2″ above the axis of the cylinder.

In Problems 5 through 10 which follow, a perspective view is required of the object described in the problem referred to. The object may be placed in any suitable position on the problem sheet. A suitable scale, picture plane, and station point should be selected.

5. Object described in Problem 14, Group 1.

6. Object described in Problem 8, Group 2.

7. Object described in Problem 12, Group 2.

8. Object described in Problem 7, Group 5.

9. Object described in Problem 12, Group 5.

10. Object described in Problem 14, Group 5.

11. A025 B325 and C525 D825 are diameters of two frontal circles that form the front ends of two cylindrical tubes 3″ long and with walls $\frac{1}{4}$″ thick. The first tube is viewed from E$3\frac{1}{2}$,$2\frac{1}{2}$,0, and the second from F6,$1\frac{1}{2}$,0. Show the perspective views of these tubes on a frontal picture plane through the front end of the cylinders.

12. G225 H228 and J625 K628 are the axes of two cylindrical tubes of 3″ outside and $2\frac{1}{2}$″ inside diameter. The right half of the front two-thirds of each tube is cut away. Draw a perspective view of each tube on a frontal picture plane through the front end of the tubes. The right-hand tube is viewed from L850, and the left-hand tube from M550.

Group 91. Angular Perspective.

1. A406 B605 C707 D508 is the lower base of a right prism of 1″ altitude. The upper base of the prism is the base of a right pyramid of 1″ altitude. Draw a perspective view of the object as seen on a frontal picture plane through B from station point S6,$2\frac{1}{2}$,2. Show two vanishing points.

2. A perspective view of the small house of Problem 4, Group 10, is required. Arrange the top view to produce a suitable picture on a frontal picture plane through XX6 as seen from station point S530.

3. E605 F607 is the right edge of a 2″ × $2\frac{1}{2}$″ horizontal rectangle. Discard the left three-fifths of the front half. The L-shaped figure is the base of a prism of 1″ altitude representing a one-story house. Add a roof of 45° pitch, and a door and a window.   Show a perspective view on a vertical picture plane through E G407 when viewed from S323.   Locate two vanishing points.

4. E606 F4$\frac{1}{2}$,0,7 is the left front edge of a horizontal square which is the base of a cube.   Draw a perspective view of the cube as seen from station point S630 on a frontal picture plane through XX4.   Also, show a circle inscribed on each of the three visible square surfaces of the cube.

5. The horizontal 2″ and 3$\frac{1}{2}$″ circles centered at G516 are the boundaries of the lower face of a washer that is $\frac{1}{2}$″ thick.   From station point S630 show a perspective view of this washer on a frontal picture plane through G.

In Problems 6 through 15 which follow, a perspective view is required of the object described in the problem referred to.   The object may be placed in any suitable position on the problem sheet.   A suitable scale, picture plane, and station point should be selected.

6. Object described in Problem 4, Group 1.
7. Object described in Problem 3, Group 2.
8. Object described in Problem 5, Group 2.
9. Object described in Problem 9, Group 2.
10. Object described in Problem 10, Group 2.
11. Object described in Problem 11, Group 2.
12. Object described in Problem 1, Group 5.
13. Object described in Problem 2, Group 5.
14. Object described in Problem 3, Group 5.
15. Object described in Problem 15, Group 5.

INDEX

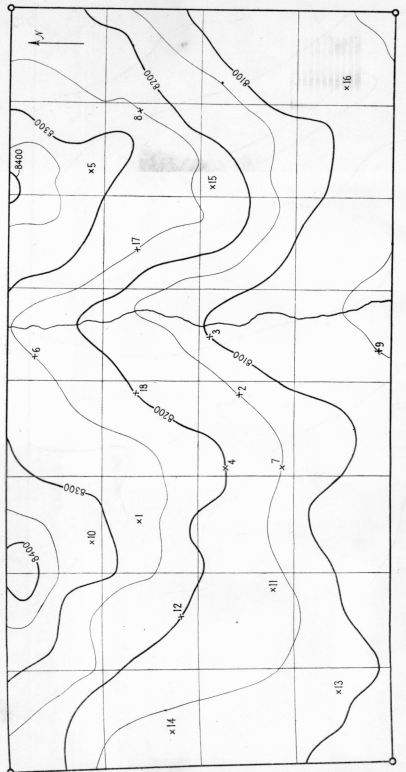

PLATE B. Contour map of Aspen Creek Gulch.

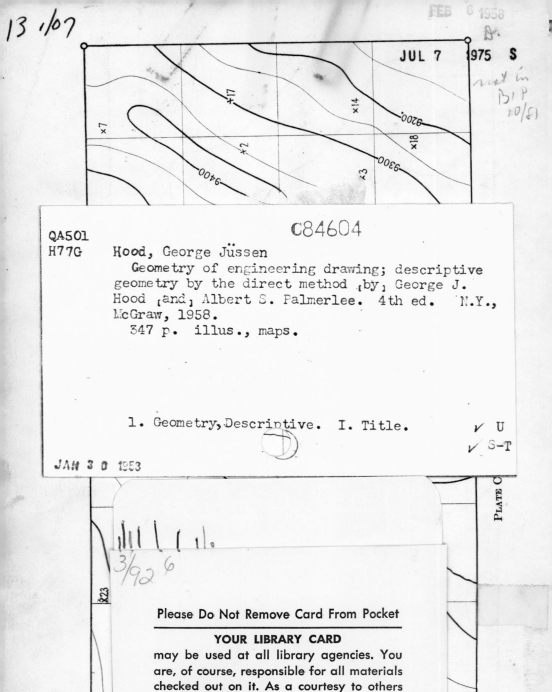